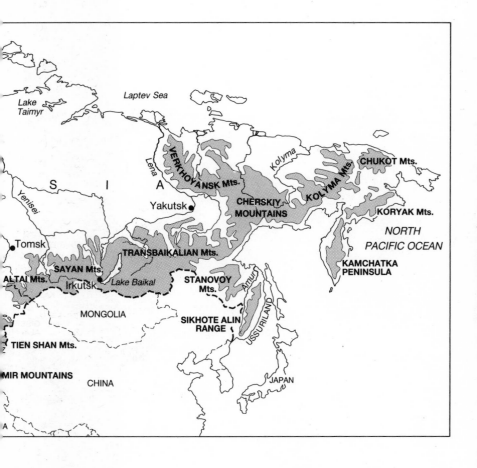

COLLINS GUIDE

BIRDS OF RUSSIA

Algirdas Knystautas

COLLINS GUIDE

BIRDS OF RUSSIA

Algirdas Knystautas

Foreword by Sir Peter Scott

A. Knystautas

HarperCollins*Publishers*

HarperCollins*Publishers*
London Glasgow Sydney Auckland
Toronto Johannesburg

ISBN 000 219913 0

Printed and bound in Hong Kong

CONTENTS

FOREWORD BY SIR PETER SCOTT

To a naturalist, the diversity of wildlife in Russia is astonishing.

Its fauna and flora are amazingly rich and varied, with about one hundred thousand kinds of plants, 140 reptile species, 30 amphibians, 1,400 fishes, and 300 mammals. Perhaps most striking is the profusion of birds, of which some 800 species occur in Russia, more than 20 being endemic – breeding only there and nowhere else.

In the north, for example, on the tundra of the Pechora river, are the breeding grounds of the west Siberian populations of Bewick's Swans, which spend the winter with us in Britain, many of them at The Wildfowl & Wetlands Trust centres at Slimbridge, Martin Mere, Welney and Caerlaverock. Those same northern regions are the home of the exquisitely patterned little Red-breasted Goose, the bird chosen as the emblem (which I was privileged to design) of the Russian Ornithological Society.

Also in Siberia, two widely separated breeding populations of the Siberian White Crane survive – one on the lower reaches of the River Ob, the other much further east in Yakutiya. This crane was until recently considered to be on the verge of extinction, but a splendid programme of international co-operation between Russian and American ornithologists has been set up to save it – with Professor Vladimir Flint and Dr George Archibald playing the leading roles.

The majority of waders (shorebirds) which occur in Western Europe on migration breed in the vast expanses of Russia's northern tundra. There are some 60 species of waders in Russia, including such rare and little-studied birds as the Ibisbill, the Spotted Greenshank, the Spoon-billed Sandpiper, and the Great Knot.

This book takes us into Russia's marvellously rich and fascinating natural world and gives a wonderful impression of its bird life. One can imagine (not without some envy!) the thousands of kilometres travelled by the author and his colleagues in order to amass this impressive body of material; their efforts have resulted in an outstanding book for which they deserve our congratulations and gratitude.

I first met Algirdas Knystautas in Moscow in 1982, when we both attended the XVIII International Ornithological Congress, together with our mutual friend Vladimir Flint. Since that time, Algirdas has visited us several times at Slimbridge and, in March 1987, came the publication of his first book to appear in Britain, *The Natural History of the USSR*.

For bird-watchers from Britain and other countries, professional and amateur alike, Russia is a country with huge potential. Many ornithologists will be eager to see its amazingly varied natural world with their own eyes, to visit the breeding grounds of birds which they perhaps know only as migrants or winter visitors. With the launch, under [former] President Gorbachev, of new policies based on "perestroika" and "glasnost", new travel possibilities may be opened up. This book should help those exciting possibilities to become a rewarding reality.

Peter Scott

Sir Peter Scott CH CBE DSC FRS
Slimbridge
February 1989

ACKNOWLEDGEMENTS

The task of this book is to review the birdlife of the former Soviet Union as it stands at present, illustrating it for the first time with original colour photographs taken in the wild together with photographs of the main habitats in which the birds occur.

Since the book has been in preparation, many changes have taken place in the Soviet Union which have resulted in its division into a number of independent countries. For the sake of simplicity, whilst it is not officially correct, we have decided to use to name Russia throughout this book when we are referring to the area of the former Soviet Union.

The book is structured in systematic order and the main part of it is the review of all the bird species currently on the checklist. Separate chapters deal with the physical geography of the world's largest country, bird migration and conservation, and ornithology and birdwatching in Russia.

Many people have helped in the preparation of this book. My particular thanks go to Dr Vladimir Flint, Mrs Elizabeth Tindle, Jeffery Boswall, Michael Wilson, Jonathan Elphick, Dr L. S. Stepanyan, Dr P. Tomkovich and the Lithuanian Society for Photographic Art.

My special thanks to those with whom I share long and exciting trips in Russia and my passion for birds and photography. They are: Henrikas Sakalauskas, Oleg Belialov, Yuri Shibnev and Aurimas Blazys.

For the provision of photographs and for other help I would like to extend my gratitude to A. Baltenas, R. R. Budrys, F. Jussi, H. Hautala, A. Karvet, V. Korkishko, N. Kuchin, A. A. Ivashchenko, A. Krechmar, A. Liutkus, V. Morozov, E. Nazarov, B. Nechaev, V. Orlov, U. Pilinkus, P. Romanov, B. Shibnev, M. Steinbakh, A. Sorokin, Yu. Vaskovsky and L. Veisman.

PHYSICAL GEOGRAPHY

A richness and diversity of natural landscapes, remote and secret places of unspoilt beauty, these give Russia a magnetic appeal and unfailing power to excite the imagination.

From west to east, from the Baltic Sea to the Pacific Ocean, the former Soviet Union extends for more than 10,000 km. When the lark rises to greet the sun near Moscow, our fellow countrymen in the Far East are already preparing for bed. In the Far North of the mainland are the Byrranga mountains of the Taimyr peninsula, while in the extreme south, the Pamir mountains form a natural boundary. The North with its Arctic and sub-Arctic zones is a world of frozen seas, lakes and boundless tundra. Further south, the forest zone stretches in a broad band from the Kodry hills in Moldavia to the magnificent Okhotsk taiga of East Asia. The forests give way to steppes and deserts and these in turn are bordered in the south by massive mountain ranges. Although the subtropics extend as a wedge into the Black Sea coastlands, the whole country lies within temperate zone of the Palearctic and there is no tropical or equatorial zone in Russia.

A large part of the former Soviet Union is occupied by plains, the two main ones being the East European and the West Siberian which are separated by the ancient Ural mountains. Breaking the monotony of flat plains are a large number of mountain ranges that vary in age: the Carpathians, Crimean mountains, Caucasus, Central Asian mountain ranges, Altai, Sayan and many others.

It is impossible to separate a bird from its habitat in any way. To see, to watch, to understand and to be delighted by birds we have to know the corresponding habitats in which they occur, and since we are dealing with the world's largest country, its by no means easy to describe all this detail. We will therefore proceed from one geographical zone to another.

THE NORTH

Vast expanses of the former Soviet Union are occupied by virtually lifeless Arctic deserts, marine islands and mainland tundras (Plate 1). In the north of the country lie two geographical zones – the Arctic and sub-Arctic. The high latitudes of the Arctic – the polar deserts – are characterised by a paucity of life forms. Islands lying within this zone in Russia include Novaya Zemlya, Franz Josef Land and Severnaya Zemlia (Northern Land).

On the islands of the northern deserts snow lies virtually throughout the year. The warmest months are July and August, when mean temperature rises to 4-5°C. The soils lie on permanently frozen ground or permafrost and there are gravelly scree fields over vast areas.

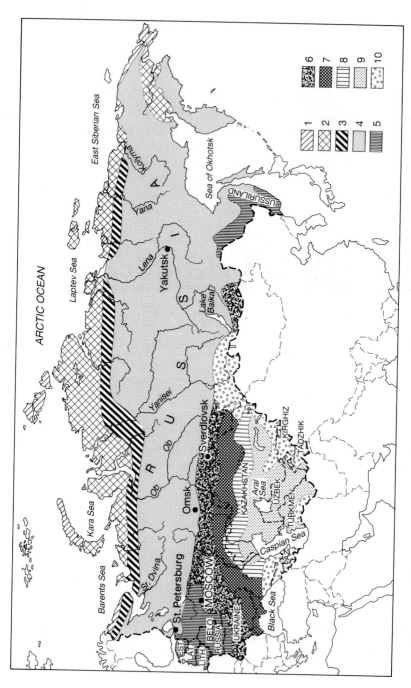

Fig. 1 *Major vegetation zones of the former USSR. 1. Polar zone; 2. Tundra; 3. Forest tundra; 4. Taiga; 5. Mixed forest; 6. Forest-steppe; 7. Steppe; 8. Semi-desert; 9. Desert; 10. Mountain regions*

Fig. 2 *Taimyr tundra. Photo H. Sakalauskas/A. Blazys*

Vegetation is extremely sparse in the Arctic deserts. There is a scanty cover of mosses and lichens, as well as a few species of algae. The plants' productivity is very low, and the mass of living vegetation above the ground is greater than that of the underground root systems.

THE TUNDRA

The vegetation of the tundra is characteristically treeless, but mosses and lichens are well developed, as are herbaceous perennials and shrubs (Plate 1). True tundras are located only in the Earth's sub-Arctic zone.

Tundra, including wooded tundra, covers about three million square kilometres, i.e. approximately 15 per cent of the area of the country. The tundra belt is 600-800 km wide. Tundra climate is harsh, with characteristically low temperatures, and these northern latitudes have a low level of solar radiation. Winter frosts reach -50°C, with strong winds up to 40 m/sec.

Characteristic of the tundra are the cloudy conditions at all times of the year, but the very long day-length during the summer means that plants get plenty of light when they are growing. A whole complex of unfavourable ecological factors means there is an impoverished flora of only 350 to 400 plant species.

It is interesting to note that many evergreens are found on the tundra. There are considerable numbers of deciduous shrubs, and prostrate forms are also represented, while the unique cushion plants are widespread. These

11

plants are less susceptible to wind and frost damage and are better protected by the snow during the winter.

Wooded tundra represents a transitional stage from tundra to taiga. The warm period there lasts for about four months. The temperatures are warmest in July and August and vary from 10 to 40°C. The snow layer in wooded tundra is much deeper than that on the tundra and quite often reaches a depth of one metre.

Conditions are mostly unfavourable to life and yet the tundra teems with birds of quite a variety of species. So what is the secret? It appears to be the birds' mobility – the vast majority use the tundra only for breeding and they are able to raise only one brood in the very short summer characteristic in this habitat. But conditions for certain groups, especially waterfowl, waders and other wetland species are ideal for breeding. It is not surprising then that these are by far the predominant groups by number of species in the tundra.

FORESTS

Now let us move down to the boundless green expanse, a carpet of forest stretching from the Baltic to the Okhotsk Sea (Plate 2). Coniferous forests occupy a huge area – they comprise 80 per cent of all the forests of Russia.

Ecologically, forest is a very complex system, but there are, of course, various types of forest of which taiga is a simpler and less rich system that the others. Layers are less well marked, the ecosystem has a lower productivity, and there are relatively few species of plants and animals. A characteristic feature of taiga is uniformity of habitat over large areas. There are several reasons for this, the main ones being the harsh climate and relatively young age of the taiga as an ecosystem – one which came into being after the recent glaciations, when the ice retreated.

An important distinguishing feature of taiga forests is the very small number of plant species represented. The taiga zone is normally divided into a northern, middle and southern belt. In Northern Europe and Western Siberia west to the Yenisei river, dense and gloomy coniferous taiga predominates – forest of spruces, firs, Siberian Stone Pine and, locally common, Siberian Larch. East of Yenisei, larch forests take over, Siberian Larch (*Laryx sibirica*) and Daurian Larch (*L. dahurica*) being the dominant species. As this vast area is entirely covered by forest, you only occasionally come across patches of steppe-type landscape. The taiga in the Far East, the Amur basin and on Sakhalin island is predominantly of the Okhotsk type. Ussuriland has this forest type only on its mountain tops. Further north, in East Siberia, it clothes only the lower and middle belts of the mountain ranges.

Composition and structure of the taiga forests are, as the examples show, subject to considerable variation, this being due mainly to the fact that this

Fig. 3 *Larch woods north of Lake Baikal. Photo L. Veisman*

ecosystem occupies such a vast area. The taiga zone extends right across the continent. It covers over 11 million square kilometres, thus constituting one third of the world's forests and 52 per cent of the territory of Russia.

A temperate climate holds sway in the taiga zone. Winters are cold, the summers relatively warm. There are considerable fluctuations in temperature, again largely owing to the great extent of the taiga, west to east and north to south. The annual amount of precipitation is 500-700 mm.

Despite a certain monotony, taiga is not a completely uniform landscape. A considerable part of the taiga forests lies within the permafrost zone, and the permanently frozen layer is as much as 116 m thick in the Yakutsk area.

Mixed forests are but one sub-zone of the country's forest zone, and represent not more than 20 per cent of the total area covered by forest. Mixed forest is a complex and distinctive system and presents a unique habitat for birds. It shows a clear division into layers or tiers, from the leaf litter to the top of mature tall trees. Only a few of its inhabitants, above all birds, are able to exploit the many different layers for foraging. However, even among the birds there is a definite choice of foraging site, and each occupies a specific ecological niche.

Mixed forests in the middle latitudes of the European part of Russia typically show, like the taiga, a certain monotony. Here we find communities composed of two to three tree species, while other species are rare and widely scattered. In the South of the Far East, in Ussuriland, on the other hand, the picture is completely different. This is a truly exotic world, full of mysteries and surprises.

As one of the world's most interesting zoogeographical and geobotanical regions, Ussuriland has long attracted the attention of naturalists. The Sikhote-Alin mountains run the whole length of Ussuriland and characteristic animals and plants of the northern taiga are distributed through these highlands. River valleys have broad-leaved forests where you will find birds which occur nowhere else in Russia. Higher up on the hills one enters the majestic but solemn world of the coniferous taiga where the eternal silence is broken only by the song of Pallas's Leaf Warbler, delivered from the tree tops. Here in the forests live tiger and bear, Paradise Flycatcher and Siberian Spruce Grouse.

The south of the Russian Far East has a simply astonishing diversity of natural, climatic, and ecological conditions, to the extent that Ussuriland can be rightly compared to a much larger area. Places here offer favourable conditions for the most varied selection of animals and birds. Bogs and marshes, seacoast, mountains, cliffs and crag, valleys and lakes, bays and inlets, huge reed-beds and a variety of forest types – all this and more can be found in Ussuriland.

The abundance of different habitats and conditions has given rise to an extremely interesting avifauna from the ornithogeographical point of view. These conditions allow ecologically closely related species to live side by side which would be unthinkable in the conditions normally prevailing in the middle latitudes. All this gives the scientist rich material to work on for the solution of evolutionary problems.

The whole territory of this region is part of the zone of the East Asian monsoons – winds which change seasonally. In winter, pressure is high over the land and low over the sea, the prevailing winds are dry and cold, blowing from a north-westerly direction. In summer, with a change in the pressure pattern, south-east winds take over and these bring warm, but misty and wet weather. The region thus enjoys dry, sunny weather in autumn and winter, while the springs and summers are dull and wet. The change in the monsoon winds takes place at the end of April and in September.

Mention of Ussuriland conjures up first and foremost a vision of the Ussuri taiga. This is a remarkable and astonishing place. There are river valleys with majestic towering White-barked Elms (*Ulmus propingua*) and Korean Willows (*Chosenia macrolepis*), dense undergrowth, and a mass of storm debris, broken-off branches and uprooted trees. Forests on the hill slopes have extraordinarily beautiful blossoming bushes (*Weigela, Diervilla, Philadelphus*), strange-looking liana thickets (*Actinidia*), and the occasional gigantic Manchurian Fir (*Abies holophylla*). Forests of the Manchurian type have the Amur Cork Tree, Walnut Trees and Korean Pines (*Pinus korainensis*). Finally, there is the dense, gloomy taiga of the Sikhote-Alin with its mighty spruces (*Picea ajanensis*). All these diverse habitats are united under the title of Ussuri taiga despite their many differences.

The very special quality and great antiquity of the Ussuri flora and vegetation, with an abundance of relict forms – this is another characteristic feature of the region.

STEPPES

Moving south of the forest we find ourselves surrounded by grass and wind in the true steppes (Plate 3). This is a type of grassland with varying thick, close cover of more or less drought-resistant vegetation. A highly productive ecosystem, steppes formerly covered a vast area of Russia in the belt lying between two transitional sub-zones – wooded or forest steppe in the north and semi-desert on the southern fringe. The steppes have always been of great importance to man as a source of food and the consequent human impact on the environment has meant that most of the unspoilt stretches of steppe now survive only under protection in nature reserves and sanctuaries.

The steppe in Russia stretches from Ukraine to Manchuria. Considerably more virgin steppe has survived in the Asian part of the country, but this is mostly as isolated fragments, primarily in inter-montane basins. The steppe zone is between 500 and 1000 km wide and the total area amounts to about 4 million square kilometres, i.e. approximately one sixth of the territory of Russia.

East of the river Ob', there are only islands of steppe vegetation, dotted over the great carpet of the Sayan and Daurian forests. Examples of such islands are the Biysk, Kuznetsk, Achinsk-Minusinsk, and further east, the Krasnoyarsk and Kansk steppes.

Steppe climate is formed under the influence of the Asian continental interior on the one hand and the Atlantic Ocean and southern seas on the other. For this reason, the climate becomes more typically continental the further east one travels. Typical here are dry, hot summers and fairly cold winters with frequent blizzards and thaws.

Though there are many different types of steppes, we can nevertheless recognise a number of features shared by all types, and also divide the steppes into northern and southern belts by their geographical location. Steppes are very rich in plant life and typically have a great number of different kinds in a small area. In some northern steppes one can find as many as 80 plant species in one square metre, a figure not exceeded by any of the other plant communities in the country.

DESERTS

Semideserts typically have areas clothed in drought-resistant grasses, semi-shrubs and shrubs, alternating with other areas devoid of plant cover. In Russia, there are semideserts in the northern part of Crimea, in the area between the Don and Volga rivers, and east of the Volga River. They stretch in a band 200-400 km wide to the border with Western China, continuing from there into Dzungaria. Semidesert is a transitional zone between steppe and desert and has no species of birds which are found there and nowhere else.

Deserts are the southernmost geographical belt in Russia and extend from the north-eastern shore of the Caspian Sea to the foothills of the Tien-Shan mountains, covering a vast area in Central Asia (Plates 4, 5). In the European part of the country there is desert around the lower reaches of the Ural, Volga, and Terek rivers. Deserts occupy in total about 2 million square kilometres, i.e. about 11 per cent of the country.

There are, of course, different types of deserts, but the climate can be characterised for all types as follows: annual rainfall is less than 200 mm, mean daytime summer temperatures are very high, around 40°C, while winter temperatures are around 0°C. Russian deserts are further subdivided into clay, sand, gravel or stone, and solonchak (pale salty soils). Clay deserts cover about one-third of the whole territory of Central Asia, and extend from the Caspian Sea south-east to the Chinese border. Trees are found here in the form of Black Saxaul (*Arthrophytum aphyllum*) thickets, while Wormwood (*Artemisia*) species are predominant in the grass cover.

Fig. 4 *Desert in Repetek Nature Reserve, Turkmenistan. Photo H. Sakalauskas*

The sand desert massif is not monolithic: in the northern sub-zone lie the Northern Kara Kum, Great and Little Barsuk sands, Muyunkum and others, while the most extensive in the southern sub-zone are the Kara Kum (Black Sands) and Kyzyl Kum (Red Sands) deserts. Characteristic of the sand deserts are so-called psamophytes – plants specially adapted to survive in the extreme desert conditions. A relatively high level of soil and ground moisture and diversity of relief types ensure a considerable variety of flora and fauna. In these conditions, not only are unique herbaceous plant communities well represented, but also shrubs and trees which quite often form dense thickets. The main plants here are the White Saxaul (*Haloxylon persicum*) and desert Acacia (*Ammodendron connolyi*).

Like sand deserts, stone deserts are found in both northern and southern desert sub-zones. Their total area amounts to about 35,000 square kilometres. The main areas of stone desert are the Ustyurt and Betpak Dala, also the north-west extensions of the Kyzyl Kum. Succulents, especially those with stems, are a quite common feature of the plant cover in stone deserts, but the predominant life form there is the xerophytic semi-shrub *Artemisia*.

Fig. 5 *Sary Ishikotrau desert south of Lake Balkhash.*
Photo O. Belialov

The flora comprises fewer than 1,000 species, and for some stone-desert plateaux the total is even more modest: 250 species in Ustyurt and 500 species in Betpak Dala.

Solonchak deserts cover an area of about 116,000 square kilometres. Within the general desert zone, they have developed primarily on the river terraces of the Syr Darja and Amu Darja rivers, also the Murgab and Tedzhen.

Desert birds are not so much varied as specific to this particular habitat. True desert species – and these are the majority – are specially adapted to desert conditions and are rarely found in other habitats. Alongside these are others which show a wider ecological range and breed in mountains, plains, forest and scrub, and finally in desert. One such is the Whitethroat (*Syvia communis*). As the climate in most of the country's deserts is strictly continental, and it is only in the extreme south that there is no permanent snow cover, most desert birds are migratory.

The small number of passerine species found in the deserts form a compact and highly specialised group which are ecologically very closely associated with this particular habitat. The majority of these birds live in sand deserts and only a few in stone deserts.

MOUNTAINS

It is probably not well known that about 37 per cent of the land area of the former Soviet Union is occupied by various mountain ranges and other uplands. Many mountain areas are renowned for their unrivalled beauty and grandeur (Plates 5-8).

"Once you have caught the resinous aroma of Turkestanic Juniper and wandered along a path in the Tien Shan mountains, you'll be enslaved for life and will gladly wear your chains to the grave". Thus wrote Professor D. Kashkarov, well known for the natural history studies he carried out many years ago in the Tien Shan mountains.

The beauty and splendour of mountain scenery, snow-capped peaks wreathed in clouds, towering Schrenk's Spruces, the courtship calls of snowcocks and agitated whistle of the Ibisbill – these all have the power to move and excite any who are not indifferent to the true beauty of the natural world. Among the delights are dwarf plants, Apollo butterflies floating drowsily over the carpet of alpine meadows, the clear, ringing song of the Blue Whistling Thrush, the piercing call of the marmot, and the majestic flight of the Golden Eagle.

Probably the most characteristic feature of mountains is the so-called vertical zonation, i.e. the distribution of animals and plants by altitudinal belts or zones. This phenomenon is, of course, best seen in high mountain ranges such as the Caucasus, Tien Shan, and Pamirs. Low, ancient mountains like the

Fig. 6 *Peaks of the Great Caucasus Range. Photo A. Sokolov*

Carpathians are clothed in forests right up to their summits, while the sharp, rocky peaks of the Caucasus or Gissaro Alay are covered in snow and mighty glaciers. Vertical zonation is also determined by temperature which in turn is influenced by altitude and the geographical latitude in which the given mountain region is situated. In the mountains of the north, which are covered in tundra or snow from top to bottom, there is little temperature difference between the foot of the mountain and its summit. In southern latitudes, by contrast, the temperature differs very considerably at different altitudes.

In mountains with clear vertical zonation, one or another plant species is predominant in each zone and the zone is inhabited by the specific animals. Apart from altitude, the exposure of slopes is of enormous importance for the distribution of mountain plants and animals. As most of Russia's mountain ranges run west to east, the exposure of slopes plays decisive role in the formation of the natural communities at different altitudes.

The northern Tien Shan mountains will serve as a classic example of vertical zonation. There, at about 1,200 m altitude, treeless foothills pass into deciduous forest which is replaced at 1,400-1,600 m by spruce forests extending up to 2,700-2,800 m. Above the spruce forest there is a zone of creeping juniper and subalpine meadows, these changing, at around 3,000 m to the meadows and cliffs of the alpine zone. Higher still lies the world of eternal snow and glaciers.

Having used the Tien Shan as an example, we may perhaps begin our journey through Russia's mountain ranges here. The Tien Shan is a vast mountainous land in Central Asia and extends for some 2,450 km, 1,200 km of which lie in Russia, the remaining part in China. There is a range connecting the Tien Shan to the system of the Dzunghar Alatau and the Pamir-Alai. The Tien Shan's ranges run mainly west to east, and the highest peaks lie in the Central Tien Shan, on the border with China: these are Peak Pobeda (7,439 m) and Khan Tengri. The most important of the Tien Shan's ranges lying within the CIS are Zailiyskiy, Kungey, Terskey, Kirgiz, Talass and the Chatkal ranges.

Another great mountainous land of Central Asia is the Pamir-Alai, which comprises the greatest mountain elevation in Russia – the Pamirs. Parts of it are also the Tadzhik depression and the Gissaro Alay, which is 900 km west to east and 80-150 km north to south. The main ranges here – Zaravshan, Gissar, Alay and Turkestan – rise to more than 5,000 m. Animal and plant life is rich and varied.

The Pamirs are Russia's highest mountains. This great massif measures 250 km north to south and 275 km west to east. The tallest peak here is Mt Communism at 7,495 m. The Pamirs also holds the country's largest glacier – Fedchenko glacier, which is 77 km long. The Pamirs are divided into separate eastern and western sections. The predominant relief in the eastern Pamirs is soft, rounded mountain ranges with absolute altitudes from 4,000 to 6,000 m. In the western Pamirs, the mountains are fragmented; here we find ranges of alpine type, with snow and glaciers, alternating with deep, narrow gorges in the bottom of which flow rushing mountain torrents. Here, relative differs from absolute altitude by 2,000 to 3,500 m. Bare rocks and screes are the predominate landscape. There is a gradual transition from the western to the eastern Pamirs.

More accessible and better known, more thoroughly explored and studied are the Caucasus mountains, whose Main Range serves as a conventional border between Europe and Asia. The Caucasus lies between the Black and Caspian seas and stretches from the Kumo-Manych depression to the border with Turkey and Iran. It covers an area of 440,000 square kilometres and is a predominately highland region.

The Great Caucasus, or Great Caucasus Range extends from the Taman to Apsheron peninsulas. In the south-east of the region lie the folded Talysh mountains which rise to 2,477 m and in the central and western parts of the Caucasus lie the Little Caucausus mountains and the volcanic Armenia Highlands. The Great Caucasus system is divided into a western, a central and an eastern section. The two mightiest ranges, with sharp, jagged peaks, are the Main and Side Ranges. The highest point in all the Caucasus is Mt Elbrus (5642 m). Many fascinating plants and animals are found in the Caucasus and the mountains are rich in relict plants, endemics and rare animal species.

The Altai, an extensive mountain region lying in the south of West Siberia, is also outstandingly beautiful. The limits of this great mountain massif are clearest in the north and west where the mountains border on plains which lie at much lower altitude. In the south and east, the Altai adjoins other mountain regions.

Adjoining the Russian Altai in the south-east is the Gobian Altai, a system of mountain ranges which extends into Mongolia and China. In the north-east, the Altai borders on the Sayan mountains. The highest point of the Altai is Mt Belukha in the Katun Range (4,506 m).

Being situated relatively far to the north, the Altai has much more obvious alpine elements at lower altitudes than the country's southern mountains. At 3,000 m altitude, a true alpine world reigns supreme – snow and glaciers, rocks and scree. Nevertheless, a visitor there will feel no lack of oxygen unlike in similar landscapes in the Pamirs or Tien Shan.

If we consider the birds of the mountain regions of Russia, especially those inhabiting the ranges in the south, it becomes clear that they can be divided into a number of groups according to their distribution. These groups are as follows: 1) species intimately associated with the high-mountain alpine and subalpine belts; 2) species occurring in both montane and lowland tundra; 3) species restricted to the montane forest zone; 4) species nesting in the piedmont, forest and subalpine mountain belts and in more or less similar habitats in lowland plains.

WETLANDS

Marshes and bogs, river valleys and lakes are found in all the geographical zones of Russia (Plates 9-11). A number of birds which inhabit them tend to be more or less confined to the various wetland habitats and cause many a headache for ornithogeographers who are attempting to allocate them to one faunal type or another.

It is well known that a special fauna and flora develops around bodies of water, a natural world different from that of adjoining areas, and this is especially true of birds. In the various geographical zones, beginning with the tundra and ending with the deserts, wetlands play an enormously important role in the life of waterfowl and other wetland species. The majority of such birds nest in a wide range of different zones, provided that the necessary habitat conditions – reedbeds and suchlike – are available locally. Such places sometimes support huge colonies of waterbirds, reaching hundreds of thousands of nesting pairs. The southern lakes and seas such as the Caspian are additionally of very great importance for wintering wildfowl which migrate there from the vast expanses of tundra and taiga.

Fig. 7 *Kyzyl Agach Nature Reserve, Azerbaidjan. Photo L. Veisman*

The world's biggest lake (the Caspian Sea) and the deepest (Lake Baikal) both lie in Russia. Here too flow mighty rivers whose catchment areas are of almost unimaginable size; there are myriads of bubbling springs and small streams, while waves break on the shores of innumerable lakes.

More than 80 per cent of the river water flows north or east into the Arctic and Pacific Oceans. The total number of rivers in the country is about 3 million, most of them being less than 100 km long. The greatest rivers – the Yenisey, Lena, Ob'-Irtysh, Amur – are over 4,000 km long. The Ob'-Irtysh system is Russia's mightiest river and has total length of 5,410 km. In the European part of Russia, the Volga river is the longest at 3,530 km. In the volume of water carried Yenisey occupies the first place, with a mean annual flow of 19,400 cubic meters of water per second. This puts it at fifth place in the world. In the greatest part of the country, the rivers freeze over in winter for a period of 2 to 7 months.

There are more than 2,800,000 lakes in the former USSR, occupying a total surface area of about 490,000 square kilometres. This figure does not include the Caspian and the Aral which are usually regarded as inland seas. Fourteen lakes, each with a surface area of more than 1,000 square kilometres are among the worlds largest. All the lakes of Russia combined hold 27,200 cubic kilometres of water, 85 per cent of this being in Lake Baikal.

Marshes and bogs occupy a total of about 2 million square kilometres or 10 per cent of the country. Most marshes and bogs are located in the forest zone owing to damp climate and other conditions. Areas with most marshes and bogs are the European north of the country and Western Siberia.

GENERAL REVIEW OF RUSSIA'S BIRD FAUNA

A SHORT HISTORY OF FORMATION

The bird fauna of Russia is relatively young, having evolved as a result of changes to the earth's surface and climate that took place after the Pliocene epoch. Some faunal elements originated in an earlier period, but the nucleus was undoubtedly formed after this fundamental change in the general climate.

Conditions for the existence of animals and in particular of birds in the Tertiary period were markedly different from those of today. Excavated fossil remains reveal the sub-tropical nature of Europe's flora and fauna in the Eocene and Oligocene epochs. A temperate climate held sway over great expanses of Siberia in the Tertiary period, while in the East the climate was colder.

This significant difference between the climate of the Western and Eastern parts of Siberia undoubtedly left its mark on the composition of the fauna, and this is indeed apparent today. Even now, cold loving species are seen to be associated with the eastern extremity of Asia, the north-west of North America, and to some extent with Pacific islands. This link finds expression in the relative abundance and variety of Arctic and taiga faunal elements in East Siberia and Alaska. The boundary between the cold-loving faunas of the western and eastern parts of the Eurasian continent is roughly marked by the course of the Siberian river Yenisey.

The maximum extent of glaciation in Europe involved the expansion of glacials in the continent's northern and middle zones, but glaciation was not synchronous on different meridians (at different lines of longitude), the advance of ice sheets in one place coinciding with the retreat in another. As a result there were now some regions with a climate that was cold but nevertheless suitable for animals.

Unevenness and lack of synchrony in the development of the glaciers were important factors not only in preserving certain bird species of northern Europe and Asia but also in promoting their expansion both latitudinally and longitudinally. This probably explains the preservation in the Arctic fauna of such very distinctive and ancient species as the Snowy Owl and Ross's Gull, these sole representatives of the genera *Nyctea* and *Rhodostethia* which we now know as characteristic birds of the Arctic. It may further explain the link of some Arctic species with the high mountain regions of Central Asia where the Shore Lark, Rock Ptarmigan and others are found.

Longitudinal shifts in range were less significant than latitudinal ones, but they too had marked influence on Russia's avifauna as we see it today. The effect of the Quaternary glaciations on the Eurasian fauna may be described as follows. Warm-loving Tertiary species were forced out by the advancing glaciers, died out but survived in the south. Some researchers see traces of this phenomenon in the present distribution of certain bird species, including the Azure-winged Magpie which has a curiously disjunct range, being found only in Iberia and the Far East (see p. 180). However, other authors tend rather to the view that the Azure-winged Magpie was originally introduced into Europe. A number of bird species re-expanded their ranges once the ice sheets had retreated.

There is a significant concentration of distinctive and for the most part ancient species in south-east Siberia, Manchuria and northern China. These are close to the fauna of south-east Asia, a region which was not affected by glaciation. Examples of such species are the Pied Harrier, Eastern Broad-billed Roller, Grey-headed Pygmy Woodpecker, and a number of passerines.

The glacial period radically changed the composition of the fauna of Europe and northern Asia. The maximum development of ice sheets in some places completely wiped out certain thermophilic species or created for them extremely harsh and hostile conditions. Only a few managed to survive as relicts of a once flourishing sub-tropical fauna. At the same time as the thermophilic species were dying out, cold-loving species were developing and, as the ice-sheets expanded, so these shifted their ranges southwards. Examples of such species are the Willow Grouse, Rock Ptarmigan, Dotterel, and a number of species found in montane coniferous forests.

A further highly significant factor involved in the formation of fauna after the glacials retreated was the arid period that followed in their wake. This aridity encouraged the development of desert and steppe landscapes and left its mark in the form of penetration by typical steppe elements into the forest zone. However, the main arid region – the great desert belt of North Africa, the Middle East and Central Asia – dates back to at least the middle of the Tertiary period and was not affected by glaciation.

Excavated fossil birds from Russia and North Africa indicated how very similar the Pleistocene fauna was to that of the present day. Nevertheless, range limits were different from now, though the avifaunas were broadly the same as in the geographical zones existing today. River valley sites have yielded fossil remains of wildfowl and other living species and this makes it seem likely that the pattern of seasonal movements in Russia during the Pleistocene was similar to that observed today.

Among the other events, apart from the glacial period, that helped to fashion the modern fauna of Russia, mention must be made of the considerable changes in relief that took place at the end of the Tertiary and in the Quaternary period. We refer to the formation of the mountain systems in Central Asia within and outside Russia. These not only made it difficult for species forced out by the ice-sheets to retreat south, but also prevented southern forms from advancing north, forms whose distribution in Central Asia is a geologically recent phenomenon.

The phenomena of a general kind discussed above changed the conditions for the existence of animals in Europe and Northern Asia and this is the reason why the Russian fauna has the features of one young and recently formed. It is relatively uniform and not rich in species, this being particularly clear in the areas once affected by glaciation. In the northern hemisphere we get a marked increase in species richness from north to south. The Arctic faunas of Eurasia and North America are essentially the same, and the taiga fauna of the two continents is also very similar, though there are clear differences. The further south we go, the greater the diversity of species, and the avifauna of the broad-leaved forests, steppe and desert landscapes of North America only vaguely recalls that found in corresponding land-scapes in Russia.

THE SPECIFIC COMPOSITION OF RUSSIA'S BIRD FAUNA

As has already been noted, the number of bird species in Russia is, considering the immense size of the country, not so great: there are 816 species including vagrants. This is about 8 per cent of all the world's species.

The proportion of passerines in the total (366 out of 816 or 44 per cent) is lower than in the world as a whole, this being mainly due to the northerly position of the country. Among the well represented orders are waders (129 breeding species), for which group suitable habitats are widespread in Russia: these are chiefly tundra and marshes or bogs in the temperate zone and for some species water bodies in desert and steppe.

The tables on pp. 26-27 show the status of species in the Russian avifauna by order and for the passerines by family. As the tables show, the orders with most species (after the passerines, of course), are the Charadriiformes (waders and allies – 129 breeding species), Anseriformes (swans, geese and ducks – 52 breeding species), and Falconiformes (raptors – 48 breeding species). Poorly represented are the Coraciiformes (rollers, kingfishers and allies – 6 breeders), Cuculiformes (cuckoos – 5 breeders) and Procellariiformes (tubenoses – 5 breeding species). The only order in which the number of vagrant species exceeds those breeding is the tubenoses – 13 as against 5. In the non-Passeriformes, vagrant species make up a total of 58 out of 450, while 5 species have become extinct in the relatively recent past. Nine species have not yet been proved to breed, 378 are breeding species.

Composition of the Russian avifauna – Non-Passeriformes

Order	Breeding species	Extinct species	Breeding not proved	Vagrants	Total
1. Gaviiformes	4	-	-	1	5
2. Podicipediformes	5	-	-	-	5
3. Procellariiformes	5	-	-	13	18
4. Pelecaniformes	8	1	-	3	12
5. Ciconiiformes	17	1	3	4	25
6. Phoenicopteriformes	1	-	-	-	1
7. Anseriformes	52	1	-	9	62
8. Falconiformes	48	-	2	4	54
9. Galliformes	21	-	-	-	21
10. Gruiformes	23	-	-	1	24
10a. Turnices	1	-	-	-	1
10b. Grues	7	-	-	-	7
10c. Ralli	12	-	-	1	13
10d. Otides	3	-	-	-	3
11. Charadriiformes	129	1	2	15	147
11a. Limicolae	79	1	2	11	93
11b. Lari	32	-	-	2	34
11c. Alcae	18	-	-	2	20
12. Columbiformes	14	-	1	2	17
12a. Pterocletes	4	-	-	-	4
12b. Columbae	10	-	1	2	13
13. Cuculiformes	5	-	-	1	6
14. Strigiformes	18	-	-	-	18
15. Caprimulgiformes	3	-	-	-	3
16. Apodiformes	5	-	-	1	6
17. Coraciiformes	6	-	-	4	10
17a. Coracii	2	-	-	-	2
17b. Alcedines	2	-	-	4	6
17c. Meropes	2	-	-	-	2
18. Upupiformes	1	-	-	-	1
19. Piciformes	13	1	1	-	15
TOTAL	378	5	9	58	450

Passeriformes

Family	Breeding species	Extinct species	Breeding not proved	Vagrants	Total
1. Hirundinidae	8	-	-	2	10
2. Alaudidae	16	-	-	-	16
3. Motacillidae	20	-	-	1	21
4. Laniidae	11	-	-	1	12
5. Dicruridae	-	-	-	2	2
6. Oriolidae	2	-	-	-	2
7. Sturnidae	6	-	1	1	8
8. Corvidae	16	-	1	-	17
9. Bombycillidae	3	-	-	-	3
10. Campephagidae	1	-	-	-	1
11. Pycnonotidae	-	-	1	1	2
12. Cinclidae	2	-	-	-	2
13. Troglodytidae	1	-	-	-	1
14. Prunellidae	8	-	-	-	8
15. Sylviidae	57	-	1	4	62
16. Regulidae	3	-	-	1	4
17. Muscicapidae	66	-	-	5	71
17a. Monarchinae	1	-	-	1	2
17b. Muscicapinae	12	-	-	-	12
17c. Turdinae	52	-	-	4	56
17d. Enicurinae	1	-	-	-	1
18. Timaliidae	1	-	-	-	1
19. Paradoxonithidae	3	-	-	-	3
20. Aegithalidae	1	-	-	-	1
21. Paridae	19	-	-	-	19
21a. Remizinae	2	-	-	-	2
21b. Parinae	17	-	-	-	17
22. Sittidae	5	-	-	-	5
23. Certhiidae	4	-	-	-	4
24. Zosteropidae	2	-	-	-	2
25. Parulidae	-	-	-	2	2
26. Passeridae	10	-	1	1	12
27. Icteridae	-	-	-	1	1
28. Fringillidae	39	-	-	-	39
29. Emberizidae	26	1(?)	1	7	35
TOTAL	330	1	6	29	366
TOTAL AVES	708	6	15	87	816

As for the passerines, the families best represented in Russia are the Muscicapidae (flycatchers – 66 breeding species), Sylviidae (warblers – 57 breeding species), Fringillidae (finches – 39 breeders) and Emberizidae (buntings – 26 breeders). Poorly represented are two tropical families – the Campephagidae (minivets – 1 species out of the world total of 72) and the Zosteropidae (white-eyes – 2 out of 79). Only one species of wren (Troglodytidae – world total 59) nests in the whole country, one species of laughing thrush (Timaliidae) and 2 out of 28 orioles. Seen as a percentage of the world total, the accentors (Prunellidae – 8 species out of 13, or 61.5 per cent) are especially well represented; Russia also has 3 out of the world's 8 waxwings (Bombycillidae – 37 per cent) and 2 out of the 4 dippers (Cinclidae – 50 per cent).

Of 366 passerines, 29 are classed as vagrants, one has become extinct in the recent past, while breeding has not yet been confirmed for six species; the remaining 330 species breed.

The total number of species recorded in Russia, can be broken down as follows: breeding (708), vagrants (87), recently extinct in Russia (6) and not yet proved to breed (15).

THE DEGREE OF AVIAN ENDEMISM IN RUSSIA

Bird Species Endemic to Russia

1. *Rufibrenta ruficollis* – Red-breasted Goose
2. *Cygnus bewickii* – Bewick's Swan
3. *Anas formosa* – Baikal Teal
4. *Falcipennis falcipennis* – Siberian Spruce Grouse
5. *Tetraogallus caucasicus* – Caucasian Snowcock
6. *Grus leucogeranus* – Siberian White Crane
7. *Chettusia gregaria* – Sociable Plover
8. *Tringa guttifer* – Spotted Greenshank
9. *Heteroscelus brevipes* – Grey-tailed Tattler
10. *Eurynorhynchus pygmeus* – Spoon-billed Sandpiper
11. *Calidris subminuta* – Long-toed Stint
12. *C. ferruginea* – Curlew Sandpiper
13. *C. acuminata* – Sharp-tailed Sandpiper
14. *C. tenuirostris* – Great Knot
15. *Numenius minutus* – Little Curlew
16. *N. tenuirostris* – Slender-billed Curlew
17. *Melanocorypha leucoptera* – White-winged Lark
18. *M. yeltoniensis* – Black Lark
19. *Motacilla taivana* – Yellow Wagtail
20. *Podoces panderi* – Pander's Ground Jay

21. *Bombycilla japonica* – Japanese Waxwing
22. *Prunella montanella* – Siberian Accentor
23. *Turdus naumanni* – Naumann's Thrush
24. *T. eunomus* – Dusky Thrush
25. *Carpodacus roseus* – Pallas's Rosefinch
26. *Emberiza chrysophrys* – Yellow-browed Bunting

Near-endemic Species
(only an insignificant part of their breeding range lies outside Russia)

1. *Mergus squamatus* – Chinese Merganser
2. *Circus macrourus* – Pallid Harrier
3. *Haliaeetus pelagicus* – Steller's Sea Eagle
4. *Lyrurus mlokosiewiczi* – Caucasian Black Grouse
5. *Tetrao parvirostris* – Black-billed Capercaillie
6. *Grus monacha* – Hooded Crane
7. *Charadrius asiaticus* – Caspian Plover
8. *Xenus cinereus* – Terek Sandpiper
9. *Glareola nordmanni* – Black-winged Pratincole
10. *Larus relictus* – Relict Gull
11. *Rhodostethia rosea* –Ross's Gull
12. *Anthus gustavi* – Pechora Pipit
13. *Hippolais caligata* – Booted Warbler
14. *Phylloscopus lorenzii* – Mountain Chiffchaff
15. *Luscinia sibilans* – Swinhoe's Robin
16. *Turdus atrogullaris* – Black-throated Thrush
17. *Loxia leucoptera* – White-winged Crossbill
18. *Emberiza tristrami* – Tristram's Bunting
19. *E. rutila* →Chestnut Bunting

The list shows that the proportion of species breeding only in Russia is not high – there are 26 true endemics out of a total of 708 breeding species (3.67 per cent). A further 19 species (the second list) are those with only an insignificant breeding population outside Russia.

The low degree of endemism in a country as huge as Russia is explained by a number of factors, primarily the geological past and peculiarities of the physical relief as it is today. The fact that a large part of the country is made up of plains, the relative newness of the avifauna as a result of the last glaciations, also the location of the centres of origin of some groups have all played key roles. Important too is the immense length of the country's land borders and the uniformity of habitat (taiga) over vast expanses.

If we look at the list from the point of view of systematics, we see that waders and passerines predominate; this is indeed just as would be expected, as the waders and allies (Charadriiformes) in the Russian avifauna number 129 breeding species and the passerines 330 breeding species. Ten species of waders breed only in Russia, as do ten passerine species (3 per cent). The group with the highest percentage of endemic species in Russia are the waders and allies.

THE SPECIES PROBLEM

Ornithologists outside Russia are well aware that Western and Russian taxonomists differ considerably in their classification of certain Russian bird species and subspecies. The concept of "species delimitation" is a highly specialised one, used primarily by the systematist, yet this technical term conceals many aspects of one of the most fundamental problems in biology – the species problem. The essence of the species problem is after all to a large extent clarifying how a species can be defined. Various species of birds which are familiar to all of us are at different stages of their evolutionary development and while some are clearly monotypic – i.e. not divisible into subspecies – the complete opposite (polytypy) is true of other species. As some are represented in the world avifauna by many subspecies, scientists are often faced with the problem determining the limits between subspecies and species.

By using museum collections and field studies Russian scientists are in a better position to reach a decision about contentious Russian species than many foreign colleagues who, in many cases, will find it impossible to undertake biological breeding studies of the birds in question.

Species whose taxonomic status is complex and difficult to define are divided into superspecies and sibling species. The sibling species phenomenon is widespread in the animal world. In most cases sibling species are morphologically extremely similar but are separated by stable reproductive isolation. Sibling species are biologically equal to any other species that have completed their formation process. They have all the features of true species and manifest clear ecological initiative, but the morphological differences are minimal. It was indeed material on sibling species which led to confirmation of the view that the actual existence of a species has nothing to do with how morphologically distinct it is. Below is a list of the sibling species groupings in the Russian avifauna as compiled by L. S. Stepanyan. It does not include those instances in which only one species in the grouping is represented in Russia.

Sibling Species in the Russian avifauna

Gavia arctica – *G. pacifica**
Gyps fulvus – *G. himalayensis**

Falco tinnunculus – *F. naumanni*
Porzana parva – *P. pusilla*
Rissa tridactyla – *R. brevirostris*
Cuculus canorus – *C. saturatus*
Delichon urbica – *D. dasypus**
Calandrella cinerea – *C. acutirostris*
Calandrella rufescens – *C. cheleensis**
Melanocorypha calandra – *M. bimaculata*
Alauda arvensis – *A. gulgula* – *A. japonica**
Anthus campestris – *A. richardii* – *A. godlewskii**
Anthus spinoletta – *A. rubescens**
Lanius cristatus – *L. isabellinus**
Acrocephalus arundinaceus – *A. stentoreus**
Regulus regulus – *R. ignicapillus*
Muscicapa sibirica – *M. griseisticta*
Luscinia luscinia – *L. megarhynchos*
Parus palustris – *P. montanus*
Sitta neumayer – *S. tephronota**
Certhia familiaris – *C. brachydactyla*
Passer domesticus – *P. indicus**
Acanthis flammea – *A. hornemanni*
Leucosticte arctoa – *L. brandtii**
Bucanetes githagineus – *B. mongolicus**
Carpodacus rhodochlamys – *C. grandis**
Loxia curvirostra – *L. pytyopsittacus*

The above list includes 56 species, forming 27 groupings. On 12 of these groupings there is nearly unanimous agreement that the forms within them should be treated as full and independent species. Others in the list, whose status is still in doubt at least for some taxonomists, are marked with an asterisk.

List of Superspecific Groupings in the Russian Avifauna

Ciconia ciconia – *C. boyciana**
Branta bernicla – *B. nigricans*
Cygnus cygnus – *C. columbianus* – *C. bewickii*
Pernis apivorus – *P. ptilorhynchus*
Accipiter badius – *A. brevipes*
Buteo lagopus – *B. rufinus* – *B. hemilasius**
Falco rusticolus – *F. cherrug**
Falco peregrinus – *F. pelegrinoides*
Falco vespertinus – *F. amurensis**

Perdix perdix – P. dauuricae
Coturnix coturnix – C. japonica*
Charadrius dubius – C. placidus*
Charadrius asiaticus – C. veredus*
Heterscelus incanus – H. brevipes
Calidris maritima – C. ptilocnemys*
Numenius arquata – N. madagascariensis*
Larus ridibundus – L. brunnicephalus*
Larus fuscus – L. argentatus – L. schistisagus
Dendrocopos major – D. leucopterus*
Corvus corax – C. ruficollis
Prunella modularis – P. rubida*
Locustella fasciolata – L. amnicola*
Locustella naevia – L. lanceolata
Hippolais caligata – H. rama
Sylvia curruca – S. althaea
Phylloscopus collybita – P. lorenzii
Phylloscopus trochiloides – P. nitidus*
Phylloscopus occipitalis – P. coronatus*
Ficedula narcissina – F. zanthopygia*
Oenanthe hispanica – O. pleshanka
Turdus pallidus – T. obscurus – T. chrysolaus
Parus montanus – P. songarus*
Parus lugubris – P. hyrcanus*
Parus major – P. cinereus – P. bokharensis – P. minor
Pyrrhula pyrrhula – P. griseiventris*
Emberiza cia – E. godlewskii*
Emberiza melanocephala – E. bruniceps

All the grouping can be neatly divided into two categories, the first concerning cases in which the breeding ranges are disjunct, and the second those groupings whose species are in geographical contact. Species in the first category are marked with an asterisk.

Sibling species and superspecies are the object of a separate, comprehensive investigation so that detailed discussion of each grouping in these two categories is inappropriate here. None the less, we feel that the propositions concerning these extremely interesting, one might say crucial, problems of modern ornithology will shed light on some questions on which different taxonomists continue to hold different views.

THE INFLUENCE OF FAUNAL TYPES ON RUSSIA'S AVIFAUNA

A comprehensive analytical study of Russia's ornithogeography was undertaken by Dr B. K. Stegman who published his conclusions in 1938. His work is considered classic in Russia and the fundamental points from Stegman's study may be summarised here as follows.

The Arctic is presented as a separate and independent region, while the forest zone of the temperate belt is far from uniform. A large part of Siberia and to some extent of northern Europe is occupied by the sub-zone of the boreal forest, or taiga, the bird fauna of which is distinctly different from the more strictly European fauna of mixed and broad-leaved woods. Nevertheless, a certain number of species inhabit the whole zone. Typical forms of different sub-zones are extremely characteristic and clearly linked with the history of the corresponding landscapes so that it is essential to divide the bird fauna of these formations into two different zoogeographical units of primary importance.

The Mediterranean sub-region has an extremely distinctive bird fauna, united by its origin and by the ecological conditions characteristic of deserts, steppes and bushy habitat. This sub-region can therefore can be taken as an area which should not be divided and in which a distinctive faunal type predominates. It is quite a different matter with the sub-region of Central Asia where extremely different elements are found. The great variety of landscapes in this sub-region make it easy to imagine how varied its birdlife is. China and Japan make up the region of East Asian mixed and broad-leaved forests, while Tibet represents the world's greatest alpine highland massif, and Mongolia is occupied by steppes and deserts. Each of these three immense regions has a completely different bird fauna.

For the northern part of the Old World we need to recognise seven main faunal types. The Arctic is, as already noted, completely separate from the other regions. Just as the taiga is linked through a number of common forms with the European mixed and broad-leaved forests, so it is also linked, and in the same way, with the Chinese faunal type. In addition, there are forms that are present in Europe and China, but absent from the taiga. The European broad-leaved forests are clearly linked with the Mediterranean faunal region. As a result, we have (excluding the Arctic) six faunal types in the Palearctic: the Siberian, European, Chinese, Mediterranean, Mongolian, and Tibetan.

Analysing the lists of Arctic species and their areas of distribution, two groups of birds may be distinguished, although there are no fundamental differences between them. The first group (of about 50 species) are those which nest exclusively north of the tree line, while the second – of about 35 species – is essentially Arctic, but in places extends to a greater or lesser degree beyond the limits of that zone. It is thus evident that the main bird population of the Arctic is composed almost entirely of endemic forms and is distinctly different from that of all the other zones. Many Eurasian Arctic species occur in the American Arctic as well.

Adjoining the Arctic is the Siberian faunal type which predominates in the taiga. Particularly well developed in Siberia where its influence spreads far to the south, it occupies in Europe only a relatively narrow belt in the north. It is obvious that any zoogeographical analysis of what constitutes the Siberian faunal type must be based on a consideration of tree-loving forms. The fullest development of the Siberian faunal type is found in East Siberia where about 50 species (out of about 200 breeders) are tree-loving forms closely associated with the taiga. Eight species are endemic to East Siberia.

Siberian faunal elements are also representitive of mountain regions of Europe, the Caucasus and Central Asia where the taiga reappears.

Taiga birds can be considered as a single and coherent ornithological complex which has its distribution centre in East Siberia.

The European broad-leaved forest zone is the centre for the development of the European faunal type, whose most typical representatives are tree-loving forms, in some cases linked not with the forest itself but with forest edge and bushy habitats. There are about 50 such species. Several more species, ecologically not linked with forests, none the less come close to this group in their distribution.

The Mediterranean faunal type basically occupies the southern fringe of Europe, North Africa and the Middle East. Characteristic of such places is the predominance of open landscapes, and the main feature of the Mediterranean avifauna is its adaptation to dry conditions. In Russia the Mediterranean faunal type is represented to some extent in Central Asia (chiefly in its lowland parts). A general analysis of the bird fauna in Central Asia shows that it is a mixture and neither on its own nor by breeding in the adjoining regions of Iran and Afghanistan can it be accepted as a separate zoogeographical unit. Characteristically even more adapted to the dry conditions than the Mediterranean is the Mongolian faunal type. While there are many forms among the typical Mediterranean species linked with shrub vegetation, all the Mongolian endemics are birds of steppes and deserts, apart from some associated with water. The Mongolian type of avifauna is distinguished by being poor in number of species, a direct consequence of the need to adapt to the harsh conditions prevailing in high-altitude, cold desert. There are about 20 species characteristic of the Mongolian faunal type.

The Tibetan faunal type is easily distinguished as being ecologically linked with an area lying above the tree line; the open alpine landscape bears some similarity to steppes and the Arctic. The bird fauna of Tibet is extremely distinctive and contains a large number of elements exclusive to this faunal type.

Finally, we come to the Chinese or Oriental faunal type which is distinguished from the previous three by its ecological link with forest, namely the mixed and broad-leaved forests of East Asia. In some respects, this zone can be seen as the sister zone of broad-leaved forests of Europe, and its avifauna does indeed have some links with those of Europe. In addition, the Chinese faunal type clearly has some kind of link with the Siberian and Himalayan fauna and can thus be seen as the connecting link between that fauna and the Palearctic. Characteristic of the Chinese faunal type is the large number of species among which are many endemics.

The most characteristic breeding birds of the various faunal types represented in Russia are listed below.

1. ARCTIC

1. *Gavia adamsii* – White-billed Diver
2. *Somateria spectabilis* – King Eider
3. *S. fischeri* – Spectacled Eider
4. *Polysticta stelleri* – Steller's Eider
5. *Clangula hyemalis* – Long-tailed Duck
6. *Anser albifrons* – Greater White-fronted Goose
7. *A. erythropus* – Lesser White-fronted Goose
8. *Chen hyperboreus* – Snow Goose
9. *Philacte canagica* – Emperor Goose
10. *Branta bernicla* – Brent Goose
11. *B. nigricans* – Pacific Brent Goose
12. *B. leucopsis* – Barnacle Goose
13. *Rufibrenta ruficollis* – Red-breasted Goose
14. *Cygnus bewickii* – Bewick's Swan
15. *Pluvialis squatarola* – Grey Plover
16. *Limosa lapponica* – Bar-tailed Godwit
17. *Limnodromus scolopaceus* – Long-billed Dowitcher
18. *Eurynorhynchus pygmeus* – Spoon-billed Sandpiper
19. *Phalaropus fulicarius* – Grey Phalarope
20. *Calidris bairdii* – Baird's Sandpiper
21. *C. acuminata* – Sharp-tailed Sandpiper
22. *C. ferruginea* – Curlew Sandpiper
23. *C. maritima* – Purple Sandpiper
24. *C. canutus* – Red Knot
25. *Tryngites subruficollis* – Buff-breasted Sandpiper
26. *Stercorarius longicaudus* – Long-tailed Skua

27. *Pagophila eburnea* – Ivory Gull
28. *Larus hyperboreus* – Glaucous Gull
29. *Xema sabini* – Sabine's Gull
30. *Rhodostethia rosea* – Ross's Gull
31. *Alle alle* – Little Auk
32. *Aethia cristatella* – Crested Auklet
33. *A. pygmaea* – Whiskered Auklet
34. *A. pusilla* – Least Auklet
35. *Nyctea scandiaca* – Snowy Owl
36. *Anthus cervinus* – Red-throated Pipit
37. *Calcarius lapponicus* – Lapland Bunting
38. *Plectrophenax nivalis* – Snow Bunting

2. SIBERIAN

1. *Tetrao urogallus* – Western Capercaillie
2. *T. parvirostris* – Black-billed Capercaillie
3. *Tetrastes bonasia* – Hazel Grouse
4. *Falcipennis falcipennis* – Siberian Spruce Grouse
5. *Cuculus saturatus* – Oriental Cuckoo
6. *Surnia ulula* – Hawk Owl
7. *Glaucidium passerinum* – Eurasian Pygmy Owl
8. *Aegolius funereus* – Tengmalm's Owl
9. *Strix uralensis* – Ural Owl
10. *S. nebulosa* – Great Grey Owl
11. *Dryocopus martius* – Black Woodpecker
12. *Picoides tridactylus* – Three-toed Woodpecker
13. *Perisoreus infaustus* – Siberian Jay
14. *Nucifraga caryocatactes* – Spotted Nutcracker
15. *Bombycilla garrulus* – Bohemian Waxwing
16. *B. japonica* – Japanese Waxwing
17. *Locustella lanceolata* – Lanceolated Warbler
18. *L. ochotensis* – Middendorff's Grasshopper Warbler
19. *Phylloscopus fuscatus* – Dusky Warbler
20. *P. proregulus* – Pallas's Leaf Warbler
21. *P. inornatus* – Yellow-browed Warbler
22. *P. borealis* – Arctic Warbler
23. *Muscicapa sibirica* – Siberian Flycatcher
24. *Ficedula parva* – Red-breasted Flycatcher
25. *F. mugimaki* – Mugimaki Flycatcher
26. *Zoothera sibirica* – Siberian Ground Thrush
27. *Turdus pallidus* – Pale Thrush
28. *T. obscurus* – Eye-browed Thrush
29. *T. iliacus* – Redwing
30. *T. eunomus* – Dusky Thrush
31. *T. naumanni* – Naumann's Thrush

32. *T. atrogullaris* – Black-throated Thrush
33. *T. ruficollis* – Red-throated Thrush
34. *Luscinia sibilans* – Swinhoe's Robin
35. *L. calliope* – Siberian Rubythroat
36. *Tarsiger cyanurus* – Red-flanked Bluetail
37. *Parus montanus* – Willow Tit
38. *P. cinctus* – Siberian Tit
39. *Sitta europaea* – Eurasian Nuthatch
40. *Fringilla montifringilla* – Brambling
41. *Acanthis flammea* – Redpoll
42. *Pyrrhula pyrrhula* – Northern Bullfinch
43. *Pinicola enucleator* – Pine Grosbeak
44. *Loxia curvirostra* – Red Crossbill
45. *L. leucoptera* – White-winged Crossbill
46. *Carpodacus roseus* – Pallas's Rosefinch
47. *Emberiza leucocephala* – Pine Bunting
48. *E. chrysophrys* – Yellow-browed Bunting
49. *E. aureola* – Yellow-breasted Bunting
50. *E. rustica* – Rustic Bunting
51. *E. pusilla* – Little Bunting
52. *E. rutila* – Chestnut Bunting

3. EUROPEAN

1. *Aquila pomarina* – Lesser Spotted Eagle
2. *Milvus milvus* – Red Kite
3. *Hieraaetus pennatus* – Booted Eagle
4. *Columba palumbus* – Wood Pigeon
5. *C. oenas* – Stock Dove
6. *Streptopelia turtur* – Turtle Dove
7. *Coracias garrulus* – European Roller
8. *Strix aluco* – Eurasian Tawny Owl
9. *Tyto alba* – Barn Owl
10. *Picus viridis* – Green Woodpecker
11. *Dendrocopos medius* – Middle Spotted Woodpecker
12. *Lullula arborea* – Wood Lark
13. *Lanius senator* – Red-headed Shrike
14. *L. minor* – Lesser Grey Shrike
15. *Oriolus oriolus* – Golden Oriole
16. *Sturnus vulgaris* – European Starling
17. *Locustella fluviatilis* – River Warbler
18. *L. naevia* – Grasshopper Warbler
19. *Acrocephalus schoenobaenus* – Sedge Warbler
20. *A. palustris* – Marsh Warbler
21. *A. scirpaceus* – Reed Warbler
22. *A. arundinaceus* – Great Reed Warbler

23. *Hippolais icterina* – Icterine Warbler
24. *Sylvia nisoria* – Barred Warbler
25. *S. atricapilla* – Blackcap
26. *S. borin* – Garden Warbler
27. *S. communis* – Whitethroat
28. *S. curruca* – Lesser Whitethroat
29. *Phylloscopus sibilatrix* – Wood Warbler
30. *Regulus ignicapillus* – Firecrest
31. *Muscicapa striata* – Spotted Flycatcher
32. *Saxicola rubetra* – Whinchat
33. *Phoenicurus phoenicurus* – Common Redstart
34. *Luscinia megarhynchos* – Nightingale
35. *L. luscinia* – Thrush Nightingale
36. *Turdus merula* – Blackbird
37. *T. philomelos* – Song Thrush
38. *T. viscivorus* – Mistle Thrush
39. *Parus cristatus* – Crested Tit
40. *P. caeruleus* – Blue Tit
41. *Certhia brachydactyla* – Short-toed Treecreeper
42. *Fringilla coelebs* – Chaffinch
43. *Carduelis carduelis* – European Goldfinch
44. *Acanthis cannabina* – Linnet
45. *Emberiza calandra* – Corn Bunting
46. *E. citrinella* – Yellowhammer
47. *E. hortulana* – Ortolan Bunting

4. MEDITERRANEAN

1. *Ammoperdix griseogularis* – See-see Partridge
2. *Chlamydotis undulata* – Houbara Bustard
3. *Tetrax tetrax* – Little Bustard
4. *Pterocles alchata* – Pintailed Sandgrouse
5. *P. orientalis* – Black-bellied Sandgrouse
6. *Merops apiaster* – European Bee-eater
7. *Caprimulgus aegyptius* – Egyptian Nightjar
8. *Dendrocopos syriacus* – Syrian Woodpecker
9. *Sturnus roseus* – Rose-coloured Starling
10. *Ammomanes deserti* – Desert Lark
11. *Melanocorypha calandra* – Calandra Lark
12. *Cettia cetti* – Cetti's Warbler
13. *Lusciniola melanopogon* – Moustached Warbler
14. *Hippolais pallida* – Olivaceous Warbler
15. *H. languida* – Upcher's Warbler
16. *Sylvia mystacea* – Ménétrie's Warbler
17. *S. hortensis* – Orphaen Warbler
18. *S. nana* – Desert Warbler

19. *Scotocerca inquieta* – Streaked Scrub Warbler
20. *Oenanthe hispanica* – Black-eared Wheatear
21. *O. picata* – Variable Wheatear
22. *O. xanthoprymna* – Red-tailed Wheatear
23. *Cercotrichas galactotes* – Rufous Bush Chat
24. *Irania gutturalis* – White-throated Robin
25. *Sitta neumayer* – Rock Nuthatch
26. *S. krueperi* – Krüper's Nuthatch
27. *Passer hispaniolensis* – Spanish Sparrow
28. *Serinus pusillus* – Red-fronted Serin
29. *Rhodopechys sanguinea* – Crimson-winged Finch
30. *Bucanetes githagineus* – Trumpeter Finch
31. *Rhodospiza obsoleta* – Black-billed Desert Finch
32. *Emberiza cia* – Rock Bunting
33. *E. melanocephala* – Black-headed Bunting

5. MONGOLIAN

1. *Anser cygnoides* – Swan Goose
2. *Buteo rufinus* – Long-legged Buzzard
3. *Grus vipio* – Japanese White-naped Crane
4. *Charadrius leschenaultii* – Greater Sand Plover
5. *C. veredus* – Eastern Sand Plover
6. *Syrrhaptes paradoxus* – Pallas's Sandgrouse
7. *Melanocorypha mongolica* – Mongolian Lark
8. *Anthus richardii* – Richard's Pipit
9. *Prunella fulvescens* – Brown Accentor
10. *Saxicola insignis* – Hodgson's Bushchat
11. *Oenanthe isabellina* – Isabelline Wheatear
12. *Phoenicurus erythronotus* – Eversmann's Redstart
13. *Emberiza godlewskii* – Godlewski's Rock Bunting

6. TIBETAN

1. *Gypaetus barbatus* – Lammergeier
2. *Gyps himalaeyensis* – Himalayan Griffon Vulture
3. *Tetraogallus himalayensis* – Himalayan Snowcock
4. *T. tibetanus* – Tibetan Snowcock
5. *Charadrius mongolus* – Lesser Sand Plover
6. *Gallinago solitaria* – Solitary Snipe
7. *Ibidorhyncha struthersii* – Ibisbill
8. *Syrrhaptes tibetanus* – Tibetan Sandgrouse
9. *Calandrella acutirostris* – Hume's Short-toed Lark
10. *Anthus spinoletta* – Water Pipit
11. *Pyrrhocorax graculus* – Alpine Chough
12. *Prunella collaris* – Alpine Accentor
13. *P. himalayana* – Himalayan Accentor

14. *Phoenicurus erythrogaster* – Güldenstädt's Redstart
15. *Chaimarrornis leucocephalus* – River Chat
16. *Tichodroma muraria* – Wallcreeper
17. *Montifringilla nivalis* – White-winged Snow Finch
18. *Leucosticte nemoricola* – Hodgson's Rosy Finch
19. *L. brandti* – Brandt's Rosy Finch
20. *Carpodacus rubicilla* – Caucasian Great Rosefinch
21. *C. rhodochlamys* – Red-mantled Rosefinch
22. *Pyrrospiza punicea* – Red-breasted Rosefinch

7. CHINESE

As this faunal type contains a large number of endemic species, it is sub-divided into two groups.

A. Species of the Chinese fauna proper:

1. *Ixobrychus eurythmus* – Schrenk's Bittern
2. *Anas poecilorhyncha* – Spotbill Duck
3. *Aix galericulata* – Mandarin Duck
4. *Circus melanoleucus* – Pied Harrier
5. *Accipiter soloensis* – Horsfield's Sparrowhawk
6. *Coturnix japonica* – Japanese Quail
7. *Phasianus colchicus* – Common Pheasant
8. *Grus japonensis* – Red-crowned Crane
9. *Porzana paykullii* – Band-bellied Crake
10. *P. exquisita* – Swinhoe's Yellow Rail
11. *Charadrius placidus* – Long-billed Ringed Plover
12. *Streptopelia orientalis* – Rufous Turtle Dove
13. *Apus pacificus* – Pacific Swift
14. *Dendrocopos kizuki* – Japanese Pygmy Woodpecker
15. *Hirundo daurica* – Red-rumped Swallow
16. *Dendronanthus indicus* – Forest Wagtail
17. *Lanius bucephalus* – Bull-headed Shrike
18. *L. tigrinus* – Tiger Shrike
19. *L. cristatus* – Brown Shrike
20. *L. sphenocercus* – Chinese Great Grey Shrike
21. *Oriolus chinensis* – Black-naped Oriole
22. *Sturnia sturnina* – Daurian Starling
23. *Sturnus cineraceus* – Grey Starling
24. *Cyanopica cyana* – Azure-winged Magpie
25. *Corvus macrorhynchos* – Jungle Crow
26. *Urosphena squameiceps* – Short-tailed Bush Warbler
27. *Horeites diphone* – Japanese Bush Warbler
28. *Locustella fasciolata* – Gray's Grasshopper Warbler
29. *Acrocephalus bistrigiceps* – Black-browed Reed Warbler

30. *Phylloscopus tenellipes* – Pale-legged Leaf Warbler
31. *P. coronatus* – Crowned Leaf Warbler
32. *Ficedula zanthopygia* – Yellow-rumped Flycatcher
33. *Cyanoptila cyanomelana* – Blue-and-White Flycatcher
34. *Petrophila gularis* – White-throated Rock Thrush
35. *Phoenicurus auroreus* – Daurian Redstart
36. *Luscinia cyane* – Siberian Blue Robin
37. *Turdus hortulorum* – Grey-backed Thrush
38. *Paradoxornis polivanovi* – Polivanov's Parrotbill
39. *Sitta villosa* – Chinese Nuthatch
40. *Chloris sinica* – Chinese Greenfinch
41. *Eophona migratoria* – Chinese Grosbeak
42. *E. personata* – Japanese Grosbeak
43. *Emberiza fucata* – Grey-hooded Bunting
44. *E. elegans* – Yellow-throated Bunting
45. *E. tristrami* – Tristram's Bunting
46. *E. spodocephala* – Black-faced Bunting

B. The second group is in its origin linked with the Indo-Malayan region
1. *Butorides striatus* – Green-backed Heron
2. *Accipiter gularis* – Besra Sparrowhawk
3. *Butastur indicus* – Grey-faced Buzzard Eagle
4. *Turnix tanki* – Yellow-legged Buttonquail
5. *Hierrococyx fugax* – Fugitive Hawk Cuckoo
6. *Cuculus micropterus* – Indian Cuckoo
7. *C. poliocephalus* – Little Cuckoo
8. *Ketupa blakistoni* – Blakiston's Fish Owl
9. *Otus bakkamoena* – Collared Scops Owl
10. *Ninox scutulata* – Brown Hawk Owl
11. *Caprimulgus indicus* – Jungle Nightjar
12. *Hirundapus caudacuta* – White-throated Needle-tailed Swift
13. *Eurystomus orientalis* – Eastern Broad-billed Roller
14. *Dendrocopos canicapillus* – Grey-headed Pygmy Woodpecker
15. *Pericrocotus divaricatus* – Ashy Minivet
16. *Terpsiphone paradisi* – Asiatic Paradise Flycatcher
17. *Suthora webbiana* – Vinous-throated Parrotbill
18. *Zosterops erythropleura* – Chesnut-flanked White-eye

MOVEMENTS

Each year, in spring and autumn, thousands upon thousands of birds migrate across the vast expanses of the former USSR from their northern breeding grounds to their winter quarters and back. Large numbers head for favourable wintering areas in the south of Russia, others continue their journey to southern Europe, Africa, and various countries of Asia. Over a long evolutionary process, certain main directions and migration routes (or flyways) used by birds have become established. For example, most species of passerines, including crows, also waders, ducks, geese, and other bird populations from northern and eastern Europe as well as west Siberia migrate south-west and spend the winter in regions which benefit from the warm influence of the Gulf Stream. East Siberian breeding species fly south-east to winter in the countries of South-East Asia. Some birds from Europe and east Siberia (especially wetland species) head either west or east, the choice of direction depending on which is the shortest route to favourable wintering grounds. Central Siberia can thus be seen as an intermediate zone, a sort of "migratory divide" from which birds disperse in an easterly or westerly direction. Only very few birds choose to fly direct to peninsular India, thus crossing the mountains and deserts of Central Asia (the Bar-headed Goose (*Anser indicus*) is remarkable in that it flies over the Himalayas).

Migration is a complex phenomenon and many details have been clarified only in recent years. The over-simplified view prevalent about 25-30 years ago imagined birds moving relatively slowly and steadily between their breeding and wintering areas; they were not thought to fly at any great height nor to undertake long unbroken flights, and it was believed that their routes were strictly determined by local topography. It has now been shown that this is true only in certain instances. Most birds in fact migrate at a considerable height (mainly under 1,500 m above the surface of the earth, less commonly at up to 4,500 m, and in exceptional cases, such as the Bar-headed Goose's flight over the Himalayas, at an altitude of up to 9,100 m) and mostly at night. Migrating birds take a direct route as far as possible, largely ignoring landscape features, and completing uninterrupted flights of hundreds or even thousands of kilometres. Migration also tends to be on a broad front, though local geography sometimes narrows this down to a belt just a few kilometres wide. This is well illustrated by the migration of White Storks (*Ciconia ciconia*) from Western Europe as they pass through Gibraltar: they cross the straits (a distance of about 15 kilometres) by soaring in a thermal to gain height, moving to another such thermal, and so on. The same picture is seen at the Bosporus which separates Europe from Asia; here the wildlife spectacular of soaring White Storks is provided by birds from Eastern Europe.

The chief method of studying bird migration still remains ringing (banding), which is also widely practised in Russia. About 8 million birds have been ringed in Russia to date (approximately 500,000 annually, producing about 5,000 recoveries). The most important centres for ringing are located in Kazakhstan (120,000 birds annually), Estonia (120,000), the Kaliningrad region (80-100,000), Lithuania (up to 80,000), Latvia (30,000), Astrakhan Reserve (20,000), Black Sea Reserve, Oka Reserve, and the St Petersburg region (about 10,000 each). The Kaliningrad region deserves a special mention because it was there that Europe's first bird ringing station (Vogelwarte Rossitten) was founded in 1901 by J. Thienemann; the site chosen was on the so-called Kurische Nehrung (Kurshskaya kosa in Russian), a spit nearly 100 km long, but only 0.7-3.7 km wide, flanked on one side by the Baltic Sea and on the other by a vast "haff" or lagoon. The observatory continues to operate, but is now called Rybachiy; its contribution to migration studies is truly immense. Data gathered over many years have, for example, allowed the conclusion that many bird species (e.g. the Great Reed Warbler (*Acrocephalus arundinaceus*) and Reed Warbler (*A. scirpaceus*), Western Greenfinch (*Chloris chloris*), Scarlet Rosefinch (*Carpodacus erythrinus*), Chaffinch (*Fringilla coelebs*), and Icterine Warbler (*Hippolais icterina*), demonstrate an amazing constancy in the timing of their migrations. Particular ringed birds have been recorded passing through the same place on the same day (or within the same 7 days) in different years; often, their passage time differs by only a matter of hours between years.

For most Russian birds, spring and autumn migration patterns have been studied in some detail and the winter quarters of different populations are also fairly well known. This means that attention can be focused on the protection of migratory birds at important refuelling sites and at places where they concentrate while actively migrating.

Divers (Gaviiformes)

These birds mostly winter along sea coasts and on various waters in the middle latitudes of the Northern Hemisphere. The Red-throated Diver (*Gavia stellata*) migrates south to the Black and Caspian Seas; the White-billed Diver (*G. adamsii*) winters off sea coasts south to the British Isles and the Sea of Japan, and the Black-throated Diver (*G. arctica*) spends the winter on the Black Sea and the Caspian, as well as off Kamchatka and the Kuril Islands. Divers migrate singly or in pairs, at an altitude of 300-500 m, but concentrations do occur on certain waters. Migration is nocturnal, though some movement – on a fairly broad front – takes place during the day. Black-throated Divers may be found on suitable waters practically anywhere in the country, though they occur only irregularly in the central European part of Russia.

Grebes (Podicipediformes)

Most grebe species move south to spend the winter on the Caspian Sea, Black Sea and waters of Central Asia. Movements of the Little Grebe (*Podiceps ruficollis*) are practically confined to its breeding range. Some birds of this species spend the winter on unfrozen waters throughout the breeding range or even north of it. Large winter concentrations of Little Grebes are unknown, birds tending to occur singly or in pairs.

Great Crested Grebes (*Podiceps cristatus*) differ in forming large concentrations (up to several thousand) in their winter quarters on the Black Sea and Caspian. They depart fairly late for their wintering areas, when water bodies are starting to freeze over, in October or November. All grebes migrate exclusively at night.

Tubenoses (Procellariiformes)

Tubenoses spend a great part of their lives on various kinds of movements and migrations. They are found from the Arctic seas to the shores of Antarctica, but mainly in the Pacific and Indian Oceans. Some species (Royal Albatross (*Diomedea epomophora*), Wandering Albatross (*D. exulans*), Southern Giant Petrel (*Macronectes giganteus*) and others) may actually circumnavigate the globe during their wanderings over the southern oceans. Species breeding in Russia such as the Northern Fulmar (*Fulmarus glacialis*), White-faced Shearwater (*Calonectris leucomelas*), Fork-tailed Storm Petrel (*Oceanodroma furcata*), Swinhoe's Storm-Petrel (*O. monorhis*) and Leach's Storm Petrel (*O. leucorhoa*) generally keep to the northern Pacific during their movements and only the Northern Fulmar is also distributed in the Atlantic.

Pelicans and allies (Pelicaniformes)

The main migration route of the Volga Delta Dalmatian Pelicans (*Pelecanus crispus*) takes them along the west coast of the Caspian Sea into the northern part of the Indian subcontinent, Iraq and Iran. Passage is quite protracted in both autumn (October-December) and spring (March-April). White Pelicans (*P. onocrotalus*) spend the winter in either India or Africa. They similarly migrate along the west coast of the Caspian.

Great Cormorants (*Phalacrocorax carbo*) disperse from their breeding grounds as soon as the breeding season is over. Adults and fledged juveniles move to the nearest sea coast, lakes near the coast, or large inland waters, where they remain until the late autumn, almost until the waters freeze over. Autumn migration of Great Cormorants tends to be a rather slow process, undertaken in stages. Different migration routes and winter quarters are used by different populations. In Russia, Great Cormorants spend the winter on large waters in Central Asia as well as on the Caspian Sea.

Most Pygmy Cormorants (*Phalacrocorax pygmaeus*) from Russia winter in southern Azerbaydzhan, this involving only a short journey from their breeding grounds, though some migrate to the southern (Iranian) shore of the Caspian Sea or to south-east Iran.

Herons, Bitterns and Storks (Ciconiiformes)

Most herons and egrets (Ardeidae) spend the winter in various countries of Asia and Africa, some also in southern parts of Russia (for example, the Great Egret (*Egretta alba*), Grey Heron (*Ardea cinerea*) and Purple Heron (*A. purpurea*)).

Once their young are fully grown, herons begin a period of post-breeding dispersal, movements which may take the birds tens or hundreds of kilometres from their breeding grounds, and often in the opposite direction to their autumn migration.

Ringing recoveries have shown that White Spoonbills (*Platalea leucorodia*) breeding on the Sea of Azov and in Ciscaucasia travel to wintering areas in Pakistan and Iran, while breeding birds from the Caspian Sea migrate to India. Both populations migrate south along the Caspian.

The migration route of White Storks (*Ciconia ciconia*) heading for their winter quarters in Africa runs through the eastern part of the Balkan Peninsula and Asia Minor (Turkey), that is around the western shore of the Black Sea and the eastern Mediterranean, then along the Nile Valley and on to southern Africa. It is curious that some White Storks, mainly immature birds, remain behind on their wintering grounds or at stopover sites during the northern summer.

Ducks, Geese and Swans (Anseriformes)

All four swan species which nest in Russia spend the winter in temperate latitudes – on inland waters which remain unfrozen, also along sea coasts. In recent years, the East-Baltic Mute Swan (*Cygnus olor*) population has shown a tendency to become more sedentary, this being a result of milder winters and the appearance of "warm" water bodies, perhaps also owing to a general increase in numbers. Nevertheless, Mute Swans are known to undertake longer movements, especially in hard winters, and they then fly south to parts of Central Asia, the Black Sea, and the Caspian Sea.

Spring migration of the north-European Greater White-fronted Goose (*Anser albifrons*) is on a broad front and birds tend to stop off at inland lakes and at other wetland sites. In autumn, migration is mainly coastal and birds use the White Sea-Baltic flyway. Whitefronts winter in Western Europe, Asia, the Indian subcontinent, China, and Japan.

Snow Geese (*Chen hyperboreus*) from Russia (Wrangel Island) fly to the USA for the winter. There are also rare, probably accidental, records on the Pacific coast of Russia. Since 1974, within the framework of the Soviet-American Agreement on Co-operation in the Protection of the Environment, special studies have been carried out on Snow Goose movements, with attention being concentrated on a programme involving individual marking of the geese with numbered (digits legible in the field) and coloured neck-collars; sightings of geese marked in this way have, for example, shown where the different populations of this species spend the winter.

Bar-headed Geese (*Anser indicus*) from the Pamir Mountains all follow the same migration route across the Pamir lakes to a fairly restricted wintering area in the Indus valley.

Red-breasted Geese (*Rufibrenta ruficollis*) may be seen in winter in Iran, Azerbaydzhan, Romania, and various other countries. It is most interesting that this species is depicted in some very beautiful Ancient Egyptian wall-paintings. Presumably Red-breasted Goose numbers were far higher in that distant age and the birds found favourable wintering areas in the Nile Valley.

Most duck species from Russia spend the winter in Africa, Asia or southern Europe. Large concentrations of wintering ducks occur in Africa, locally up to several tens of thousands. In the Sénégal delta, up to 300,000 ducks sometimes congregate, including the Garganey (*Anas querquedula*), Northern Pintail (*A. acuta*), and Northern Shoveller (*A. clypeata*). Such gatherings are also frequent in various Asian countries and in southern Europe. Studies carried out on three duck species (Mallard (*A. platyrhynchos*), Garganey, and Green-winged Teal (*A. crecca*)) have shown the existence of individual variations in the autumn migration pattern of these species. It has been established that adult ducks embark on their autumn migration earlier than young birds; juvenile Mallards show the slowest migration speed, Garganey the fastest. European populations of all three species migrate south-west, though the widest dispersal is typical of the Garganey. The main wintering grounds of the Mallard and Green-winged Teal are located on the west coasts of the Black Sea and the Mediterranean, while Garganey undertake longer flights to winter quarters lying further south. Many Mallard remain throughout the winter on unfrozen waters, including in the north of their range. Eastern populations of the Northern Pintail, Garganey, Green-winged Teal, Mallard, Eurasian Wigeon (*A. penelope*), Northern Shoveller, Tufted Duck (*Aythya fuligula*), and Ruddy Shelduck (*Tadorna ferruginea*) winter in various parts of Central Asia. Garganey from the European part of Russia have been recorded wintering in India together with birds of the Asiatic population. The Baikal Teal (*Anas formosa*) and Falcated Duck (*A. falcata*) breed in north-east Siberia and spend the winter in southern Siberia, China and Japan. In some years, flocks of up to ten thousand Baikal Teal occur in Japan. Long-tailed Ducks (*Clangula hyemalis*) from northern Siberia migrate to the Atlantic Ocean, Baltic Sea, Black Sea, Caspian Sea and the Pacific Ocean. They spend the winter on open water, quite far from the coast. The Smew (*Mergus albellus*), Goosander (*M. merganser*) and Red-breasted Merganser (*M. serrator*) migrate to various countries of Asia, but are also found within Russia during the winter, on the Black Sea and Caspian. The Goosander is known to have two disjunct wintering areas: the western includes the whole of Europe and western Asia, the eastern covers an area from the Eastern Himalayas and northern India through China to Japan. It has been discovered that most ducks show marked fidelity to their breeding areas, though some, mainly young, birds shift to a new site and an exchange between individuals of different populations takes place in the winter quarters.

Birds of Prey (Falconiformes)

Most European populations of raptors winter within Europe, and move only from northern regions into southern or central Europe. Species in this category include the Northern Sparrowhawk (*Accipiter nisus*), Rough-legged Buzzard (*Buteo lagopus*), Greater Spotted Eagle (*Aquila clanga*), Hen Harrier (*Circus cyaneus*), Marsh Harrier (*C. aeruginosus*), Merlin (*Falco columbarius*), and Common Kestrel (*F. tinnunculus*). Some, such as the Golden Eagle (*Aquila chrysaetos*) and Northern Goshawk (*Accipiter gentilis*), lead a more or less sedentary existence, only occasionally moving a little way south of their breeding range. Others, like the Osprey (*Pandion haliaetus*), Eurasian Buzzard (*Buteo buteo*), Western Honey Buzzard (*Pernis apivorus*), Short-toed Eagle (*Circaetus gallicus*), Black Kite (*Milvus migrans*), Lesser Spotted Eagle (*Aquila pomarina*), and Montagu's Harrier (*Circus pygargus*) migrate to Africa or to the countries of Central Asia. The Lammergeier (*Gypaetus barbatus*), Black Vulture (*Aegypius monachus*), Griffon Vulture (*Gyps fulvus*), and Himalayan Griffon Vulture (*G. himalayensis*) remain within the breeding range and only rarely undertake insignificant dispersive movements. The Egyptian Vulture (*Neophron percnopterus*) is the only one to depart for wintering grounds lying further south. Several falcons are long-distance migrants and most (Lesser Kestrel (*Falco naumanni*), Common Kestrel, Merlin, Western Red-footed Falcon (*F. vespertinus*), Northern Hobby (*F. subbuteo*), and Saker Falcon (*F. cherrug*)) migrate to Africa, some reaching the southernmost parts of that continent. The Gyrfalcon (*F. rusticolus*) and the Peregrine Falcon (*F. peregrinus*) mostly winter in southern regions of Russia. Amur Falcons (*F. amurensis*) have been recorded

47

migrating in huge flocks (up to several thousand birds) from the Transbaikal region of Russia across the whole of Asia to wintering grounds in Africa. Study of Northern Sparrowhawk movements has revealed that passage continues throughout the day, but peaks during the morning.

Pheasants, Grouse and allies (Galliformes)

Most birds in this order are sedentary, but some (Chukar Partridge (*Alectoris chukar*), Willow Grouse (*Lagopus lagopus*), and Grey Partridge (*Perdix perdix*)) sometimes undertake considerable seasonal movements, while the quails *Coturnix* are true migrants.

Common Quails (*Coturnix coturnix*) from breeding areas in Central Europe and Asia migrate to Africa where they winter in savannah south of the Sahara. The easternmost wintering grounds of the Common Quail lie in India, and some birds move no further than southern parts of Russia. Long-distance flights are obviously a great physical strain for this species and on reaching, for example, the northern shore after crossing the Black Sea, the birds are utterly exhausted.

Grey Partridges, though in general completely sedentary, not infrequently move quite considerable distances on the fringes, in central, and even in southern parts of their range. There are two reasons for such movements: the first is an increase in numbers following a successful breeding season, the second is harsh winter conditions. It seems that only a small number of older birds remain in northern parts of the breeding range, though there are no regular and pronounced seasonal movements, and only small flocks or single birds are noted. In the eastern part of the range, small flocks and single birds appear in deserts and foothills, including the Karakum. Chukar Partridges regularly undertake altitudinal migration, moving down to the lower parts of mountains for the winter. In Tadzhikistan, both such vertical displacement and longer-distance (over several tens of kilometres) movements have been recorded, though nothing similar has been observed in other parts of the range.

The Western Capercaillie (*Tetrao urogallus*) is strictly sedentary, never straying far from its breeding area. Young birds especially have been recorded moving for short distances, though this was always within a home range of at most 6-8 square kilometres.

In winters with heavy snowfalls and deep snow cover, Common Pheasants (*Phasianus colchicus*) sometimes make quite long-distance movements (up to 200 km). Such cases are rather frequent in the northern parts of the species' range (Balkash, Amur region). The birds shift to areas where there is little or no snow.

All five snowcocks – the Himalayan (*Tetraogallus himalayensis*), Caspian

(*T. caspius*), Caucasian (*T. caucasicus*), Tibetan (*T. tibetanus*), and Altai Snowcock (*T. altaicus*) – move only altitudinally in the mountains.

Rails, Cranes and allies (Gruiformes)

Crakes and rails (Rallidae) tend to occur in groups or small gatherings outside the breeding season, though the Black Coot (*Fulica atra*) forms much larger assemblages; for example, up to 30,000 birds congregate in the Black Sea reserve. Members of this family migrate singly or in pairs, less commonly in small parties (Black Coots in flocks of up to 500-800), and predominantly at night. The Corncrake (*Crex crex*) migrates to Africa, reaching even the south of the continent. Water Rails (*Rallus aquaticus*) winter throughout continental Western Europe and also regularly in southern regions of Russia. During their migrations, they concentrate at large lakes and in southern river deltas, but are sometimes encountered in completely unsuitable habitats, including mountains and desert. Both the Spotted Crake (*Porzana porzana*) and Baillon's Crake (*P. pusilla*) fly to various Asian countries for the winter. Over much of its breeding range, the Purple Gallinule (*Porphyrio porphyrio*) is sedentary and makes only insignificant movements. Common Moorhens (*Gallinula chloropus*) migrate on quite a broad front to Western Europe and the Indian subcontinent, and there appear to be no places where they occur in any numbers.

As the breeding range of the Common Crane (*Grus grus*) extends virtually across the whole of the former Soviet Union, there are not unexpectedly several important migration routes. The seven now in existence include the West European, the Baltic-East European, the Transvolgan-Iranian, and the

Fig. 8 *Main localities of the Common Crane* (Grus grus) *observed during migration. 1. During spring migration; 2. during autumn migration; 3. during spring and autumn migration; 4. boundary of the breeding range*

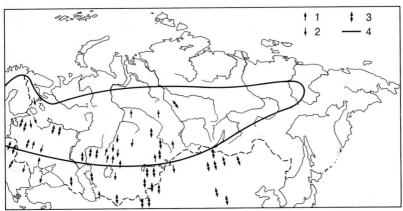

Chinese. Cranes travel at quite a height (600-1,000 m and higher), covering about 400 km per day. Serious losses are sustained by migrating cranes in Pakistan and Afghanistan, where the centuries-old practice of trapping them using decoy birds still persists. Common Cranes spend the winter in Africa and South Asia.

The Red-crowned Crane (*Grus japonensis*) migrates from its breeding grounds in Russia to winter quarters in China and Korea; the Hooded Crane (*G. monacha*) winters in Japan, and the Japanese White-naped Crane (*G. vipio*) in Korea and Japan.

Sandhill Cranes (*Grus canadensis*) breeding in north-east Siberia cross the Bering Straits, then follow the Pacific coast of America to wintering grounds in the southern states of the USA.

Siberian White Cranes (*Grus leucogeranus*) (of both the Ob' river and Yakut populations) are often seen in flocks of Common Cranes, as the two species use the same migration routes over a considerable distance. The winter quarters of the rare Siberian White Crane lie (for the smaller Ob' river population) in the Keoladeo Ghana Reserve at Bharatpur (northern India) and (for the Yakut birds) in the extensive marshlands surrounding Lake Poyang, on the lower Yangtse (Jiangxi) river; these Chinese wintering grounds were discovered as recently as 1981.

Bustards (Otidae)

Great Bustards (*Otis tarda*) winter in the Crimea, Transcaucasia, and valleys with steppe-type vegetation in the mountains of Central Asia. Southern populations undertake short-distance movements, but only in hard winters. Eastern populations also spend the winter basically within the breeding range, tending to favour valleys where there is no snow cover. Migrating Great Bustards fly relatively low and in small flocks. Several such flocks may gather at stopover sites, but they generally do not coalesce into one large assemblage. In the Crimea on the other hand, large concentrations of this species do occur - up to 1,200 birds and, in some years, as many as 2,500 to 3,000 have been seen together.

Little Bustards (*Tetrax tetrax*) are regular migrants, though there is some variation between populations; those of Western Europe and North Africa are resident. The winter quarters are located in Iran, Afghanistan, and in the steppes of Transcaucasia and the Crimea. Rather large flocks are a regular feature of the post-breeding period.

Houbara Bustards (*Chlamydotis undulata*) migrate south-west (in eastern parts of the range) and south (in other parts of the range). The species is not known to winter in Russia, apart from a few odd birds in various parts of Central Asia. Houbaras spend the winter in Iran, the Euphrates valley, and on the north-east shores of the Persian Gulf.

Waders, Shorebirds and allies (Charadriiformes)

Most waders from northern breeding areas migrate to warmer regions for the winter, mainly to tropical Africa or Asia. Wader populations from East Asia fly to southern parts of Asia, including the Indian subcontinent, and even as far as Australia, while the European breeding species head for southern regions of Europe, and Africa. Species involved include Ringed Plover (*Charadrius hiaticula*), Little Ringed Plover (*C. dubius*), Kentish Plover (*C. alexandrinus*), Greater Sand Plover (*C. leschenaultii*), Caspian Plover (*C. asiaticus*), Eurasian Dotterel (*Eudromias morinellus*), Pacific Golden Plover (*Pluvialis fulva*), Northern Lapwing (*Vanellus vanellus*), Palearctic Oystercatcher (*Haematopus ostralegus*), Pied Avocet (*Recurvirostra avosetta*), Common Snipe (*Gallinago gallinago*), Great Snipe (*G. media*), Jack Snipe (*Lymnocryptes minimua*), Curlew Sandpiper (*Calidris ferruginea*), Dunlin (*C. alpina*), Little Stint (*C. minuta*), Temminck's Stint (*C. temminckii*), Red Knot (*C. canutus*), Wood Sandpiper (*Tringa glareola*), Green Sandpiper (*T. ochropus*), Common Sandpiper (*Actitis hypoleucos*), Common Greenshank (*T. nebularia*), Black-tailed Godwit (*Limosa limosa*), Bar-tailed Godwit (*L. lapponica*), Western Curlew (*Numenius arquata*), Whimbrel (*N. phaeopus*), and Common Pratincole (*Glareola pratincola*). Quite a large number of species (Grey Plover (*Pluvialis squatarola*), Curlew Sandpiper, Red Knot, Sanderling (*Calidris alba*), Ruddy Turnstone (*Arenaria interpres*), Bar-tailed Godwit, Red-necked Phalarope (*Phalaropus lobatus*), Grey Phalarope (*P. fulicarius*) and Whimbrel), which are basically northern breeders – in the tundra and forest tundra zones, also on the shores of the arctic seas – disperse immediately after breeding and are found during their migrations along virtually all coasts and at other suitable sites throughout the tropics and subtropics of Asia and Africa. Waders typically migrate in flocks, often several species together, and are rarely seen singly. In winter quarters and at refuelling sites, the huge mixed assemblages sometimes number up to several hundred thousand birds.

Skuas (Stercorariidae)

Skuas come to land only to breed, otherwise they are more or less constantly on the move, their migrations taking them mainly across the Arctic, Atlantic, and Pacific Oceans. They not infrequently reach the coast of Africa (Pomarine Skua (*Stercorarius pomarinus*)) and Australia (Arctic Skua (*S. parasiticus*) and Long-tailed Skua (*S. longicaudus*)). Skuas normally migrate singly or in small parties of four to five birds, though quite large gatherings of Pomarine Skuas have been recorded where there is an abundance of food.

Gulls and Terns (Laridae)

Gulls are typically migratory or dispersive. Many disperse from the breeding grounds as soon as the young have fledged. Ecological plasticity is a characteristic of most gull species and in recent years they have shown an impressive ability to adapt to man-made changes in the environment. Several species (Black-headed (*Larus ridibundus*), Herring (*L. argentatus*), and Common Gull (*L. canus*)) have become regular visitors to towns outside the breeding season and their not always welcome habit of nesting on the roofs of buildings is now quite widespread. During dispersal, large numbers of gulls also congregate on urban rubbish tips and exploit the vast quantity of waste food deposited there.

Northern populations of the Black-headed Gull are migratory and depart south at the onset of winter (when lakes and rivers freeze over). The wintering area of this species includes almost all the countries of Europe, the Black Sea and Caspian littorals, and various seas lying within the Pacific and Indian Oceans. There have been more recent reports of Black-headed Gulls wintering on the west coast of Africa. The general pattern of migration is similar in both the Herring Gull and the Common Gull, which winter over vast areas of the Atlantic and Pacific Oceans. In warm winters, they quite often also occur on the coasts of the White Sea and the Barents Sea, and in large numbers along the Baltic coast. Both species also regularly spend the winter all along the Black Sea and Caspian coasts.

Little is known about where the Relict Gull (*Larus relictus*) spends the winter, though birds have been recorded in South-East Asia; on the Yellow Sea and in Vietnam. The species migrates in small parties of up to nine birds.

Both the Little Gull (*Larus minutus*) and Sabine's Gull (*Xema sabini*) undertake quite long migrations – from breeding grounds in northern Russia south as far as the African continent.

Ross's Gull (*Rhodostethia rosea*) may be called a true arctic species. From its breeding grounds on the tundra of Yakutia, this species disperses north to winter along virtually all the seas of the Arctic Ocean, and only occasionally migrates south as far as the South Kuril Islands. In the Atlantic, it is a rare visitor to the British Isles, and vagrants have also occurred in West Germany, France, and even as far south as Italy. A small number spend the winter regularly in the North Atlantic – in the waters off Greenland and Spitzbergen.

Most species of terns migrate for longer distances, mainly south to Africa and this includes the greatest migrant of them all – the "record-holding"

Arctic Tern (*Sterna paradisaea*), which migrates each year from its northern breeding grounds to seas of the Southern Hemisphere, even as far as Antarctica (a journey of 16-19,000 kilometres). Post-breeding dispersal is less well marked in the terns, but such movements do take place. Terns mostly migrate in small flocks.

Caspian Terns (*Hydroprogne caspia*) usually spend the winter in Africa and South Asia, but are occasionally recorded in winter on the south-west Caspian in Russia. Most Caspian Terns migrate overland, cutting right across the continent and thus flying over huge areas where there is no water. Post-breeding dispersal is characteristic of this species and birds will fly for tens and hundreds of kilometres from their breeding areas, not infrequently in the opposite direction to their normal migration route. Vagrant Caspian Terns have been recorded in Britain, Norway, on the Seven Islands, and on Sakhalin Island.

Auks (Alcidae)

Auk migrations show a rather varied pattern. Some species are relatively sedentary, spending the winter within their breeding range and shifting according to the state of the ice. This group includes the Black Guillemot (*Cepphus grylle*), Spectacled Guillemot (*C. carbo*), Tufted Puffin (*Lunda cirrhata*), and to some extent also the Common Guillemot (*Uria aalge*), Whiskered Auklet (*Aethia pygmaea*), and Atlantic Puffin (*Fratercula arctica*). The winter quarters of the last three species extend beyond the breeding range, mainly in a southerly direction. Brünnich's Guillemot (*Uria lomvia*) has a very extensive breeding range and occurs in winter both in the northern seas of the Atlantic Ocean (with a few recorded south to the British Isles), and in the seas of the Pacific (off the coasts of Japan, the Kuril Islands, and the USA). The Little Auk (*Alle alle*) is also found in the North Atlantic during the winter, while Razorbills (*Alca torda*) winter further south, to the western limits of the Mediterranean. Species such as Ancient Murrelet (*Synthliboramphus antiquus*), Crested Auklet (*Aethia cristatella*), Parakeet Auklet (*Cyclorrhynchus psittacula*), Marbled Murrelet (*Brachyramphus marmoratus*), and Horned Puffin (*Fratercula corniculata*) winter at sea, mainly in the southern Pacific, some of them along the coast of North America. Several different auk species often winter together, forming quite large concentrations.

Pigeons and allies (Columbiformes)

Many species of pigeons and doves exhibit marked fidelity to their breeding locality and this attachment was, of course, once widely exploited by man, specially trained pigeons being used to carry messages. Wild pigeons tend not to make long-distance movements and in places where the climate permits, most species are generally more or less sedentary. Examples are the Rock Dove (*Columba livia*), Eastern Rock Dove (*C. rupestris*), Collared Dove (*Streptopelia decaocto*), and Laughing Dove (*S. senegalensis*). Both the Stock Dove (*Columba oenas*) and the Wood Pigeon (*C. palumbus*) are partial migrants, some populations of the first moving to southern Europe and South Asia and of the second to southern Europe, Iran, and peninsular India. Eversmann's Dove (*C. eversmanni*), the Rufous Turtle Dove (*Streptopelia orientalis*) and Turtle Dove (*S. turtur*) (which also winters in Africa) fly to various countries of South Asia. Pigeons and doves are usually encountered in small flocks on passage and in winter quarters, but huge gatherings are sometimes reported, especially from the wintering grounds (in Sénégal, for example, there are areas where Turtle Dove flocks number up to 450,000 birds).

Sandgrouse (Pteroclidae)

Both Black-bellied (*Pterocles orientalis*) and Pintailed Sandgrouse (*P. alchata*) migrate to south-west Asia, though some Pintailed Sandgrouse move to Africa for the winter. Pallas's Sandgrouse (*Syrrhaptes paradoxus*) and the Tibetan Sandgrouse (*S. tibetanus*) are basically sedentary and make only insignificant movements within the breeding range.

Cuckoos (Cuculiformes)

The Eurasian Cuckoo (*Cuculus canorus*) is quite a long-distance migrant, spending the winter in Africa (European populations) and South Asia (eastern European and Asiatic populations). The Indian Cuckoo (*C. micropterus*) and Little Cuckoo (*C. poliocephalus*) from the Russian Far East migrate to wintering areas in South-East Asia, the Oriental Cuckoo (*C. saturatus*) to Indonesia, New Guinea, and Australia.

Owls (Strigiformes)

Many owl species undertake only insignificant, in some cases irregular, movements within their breeding range. There are, however, some true migrants among the owls – the Eurasian Scops Owl (*Otus scops*), Long-eared Owl (*Asio otus*), and Short-eared Owl (*A. flammeus*), which migrate to southern Europe and Africa. Others, such as the Snowy Owl (*Nyctea scandiaca*), Hawk Owl (*Surnia ulula*), Brown Hawk Owl (*Ninox scutulata*), Great Grey Owl (*Strix nebulosa*) and Tengmalm's Owl (*Aegolius funereus*), disperse to some extent, but their typically irregular movements normally take them no further than the southern limit of the breeding range. Only the Snowy Owl has been recorded further south, in Iran, Mongolia, Korea and Japan. Owls normally migrate at night. A characteristic feature of their migrations is the great variation in the timing of the movements, this being mainly due to the state of the food supply. Knowing, for example, the level of the lemming population (these animals are the owl's main prey), Snowy Owl movements may be predicted.

Nightjars (Caprimulgiformes)

Both the European Nightjar (*Caprimulgus europaeus*) and Egyptian Nightjar (*C. aegyptius*) spend the winter in Africa, the European in tropical Africa south of the Sahara, the Egyptian in the west of the continent. The Jungle Nightjar (*C. indicus*) breeds in the Russian Far East and migrates to South Asia for the winter.

Swifts (Apodidae)

There are five species of swift in Russia and all are long-distance migrants. White-throated Needle-tailed Swifts (*Hirundapus caudacuta*) and Pacific Swifts (*Apus pacificus*) migrate to Australia from breeding grounds in the Far East. The others – Alpine Swift (*A. melba*), Eurasian Swift (*A. apus*), and House Swift (*A. affinis*) – winter in the countries of South Asia or in Africa. Moreover, eastern populations of the Alpine Swift spend the winter exclusively in Asia, while western populations migrate to Africa; this is not so in the Eurasian Swift, whose eastern and western populations both migrate to Africa.

Kingfishers (Alcedinidae)

In winter, the European Kingfisher (*Alcedo atthis*) is often seen by unfrozen streams and rivers, and it is only in really severe winter weather, when all the rivers and lakes are ice-bound, that birds move to regions further south.

Bee-eaters (Meropidae), Rollers (Coraciidae), Hoopoes (Upupidae)

Species in these families migrate to Africa and, apart from the European Roller (*Coracias garrulus*), also to South Asia. The Hoopoe (*Upupa epops*) occasionally winters in the south of Russia, in Turkmenistan and Tadzhikistan. All these species migrate singly, or in small flocks, and larger assemblages are known only from the winter quarters.

Woodpeckers (Piciformes)

Woodpeckers are basically sedentary, making only irregular short-distance movements in winter. The Northern Wryneck (*Jynx torquilla*) is, however, a true migrant and spends the winter in Africa or (eastern populations) in South Asia.

PASSERIFORMES

Larks (Alaudidae)

This family contains few long-distance migrants, but both the Bimaculated Lark (*Melanocorypha bimaculata*) and Short-toed Lark (*Calandrella cinerea*) do migrate to Africa and spend the winter south of the equator. In the European part of Russia, populations of Shore Lark (*Eremophila alpestris*), Wood Lark (*Lullula arborea*), and Skylark (*Alauda arvensis*) disperse for only short distances, moving from northern breeding grounds to wintering areas further south in the country. The Crested Lark (*Galerida cristata*), Mongolian Lark (*Melanocorypha mongolica*), Calandra Lark (*M. calandra*) and Desert Lark (*Ammomanes deserti*) may be considered basically sedentary, though some irregular and only short-distance movements do take place. Two Russian endemics, the White-winged Lark (*Melanocorypha leucoptera*) and the Black Lark (*M. yeltoniensis*), also wander mainly within the breeding range or beyond it to the south. In winter, these two species occur in the Crimea, northern Caucasus, the White-winged Lark also in Turkey and Iran, the Black Lark in northern China. Larks are rarely solitary on migration, they usually move about in flocks of varying size, the very large gatherings being seen especially in winter quarters. In the Voronezh region, lark flocks usually number up to ten birds at the start of migration, but at the time of peak passage there may be as many as 200 in a flock. Larks migrate at an average height of 40-60 (20-120) m.

Swallows (Hirundinidae)

All the swallows found in Russia are summer visitors to the country and spend the winter mainly in Africa or South Asia. They migrate in flocks of several dozen or up to several hundred thousand. Flocks totalling about a million Barn Swallows (*Hirundo rustica*) have been reported from their African wintering grounds.

Pipits and Wagtails (Motacillidae)

Almost all the species of this family winter mainly in either Africa or South Asia. The Forest Wagtail (*Dendronanthus indicus*) and the Pechora Pipit (*Anthus gustavi (?) menzbieri*) migrate from their breeding grounds in the Russian Far East to South-East Asia, the Philippines, and Indonesia. White Wagtails (*Motacilla alba*), Yellow Wagtail (*M. flava*) and Tree Pipit (*Anthus trivialis*) in particular are typically gregarious in winter, flocks sometimes numbering up to several tens of thousands of birds. These three species are abundant throughout Africa (except the Sahara) during the winter.

Shrikes (Laniidae)

The breeding shrikes of the Russian Far East – Tiger Shrike (*Lanius tigrinus*), Bull-headed Shrike (*L. bucephalus*), Brown Shrike (*L. cristatus*) and Chinese Great Grey Shrike (*L. sphenocercus*) – migrate to South-East Asia for the winter, and only certain populations of the Brown Shrike move to Africa, where the Red-backed Shrike (*L. collurio*), Lesser Grey Shrike (*L. minor*) and Red-headed Shrike (*L. senator*) also spend the winter. The wintering grounds of the other species – Long-tailed Shrike (*L. schach*), Bay-backed Shrike (*L. vittatus*), and Great Grey Shrike (*L. excubitor*) – lie in southern parts of Asia.

Weavers (Ploceidae)

The few sparrows of Russia which make quite long-distance movements include the Indian Sparrow (*Passer indicus*) which migrates to South Asia, the Spanish Sparrow (*P. hispaniolensis*) (also to South Asia), the Cinnamon Sparrow (*P. rutilans*) (to Japan), and Pale Rock Sparrow (*Petronia brachydactyla*) (to Africa). The other species typically move for only short distances within the breeding range. The Streaked Rock Sparrow (*Petronia petronia*) and White-winged Snow Finch (*Montifringilla nivalis*) undertake only altitudinal movements.

Starlings (Sturnidae)

In this family, only the Indian (*Acridotheres tristis*) is sedentary, not straying far from its breeding grounds in winter. The other species migrate south – to Western Europe, Indochina, and South Asia. Starlings are diurnal migrants: movements start at dawn and continue throughout the daylight hours, peaks alternating with brief interruptions. Visible migration of the European Starling (*Sturnus vulgaris*) rarely takes place above 100 m, and most birds in fact fly no higher than 50 m above the surface. European Starlings migrate in quite large flocks – up to several hundred birds in each.

Orioles (Oriolidae)

Both oriole species breeding in Russia are long-distance migrants: the Golden Oriole (*Oriolus oriolus*) migrates to Africa, Asia and India, the Black-naped Oriole (*O. chinensis*) to India and south-east China.

Crows (Corvidae)

Many crow species typically disperse for only short distances, and some are completely sedentary. Nevertheless, there is some variation between years and quite long-distance movements by these birds occur in some years. For example, Rooks (*Corvus frugilegus*) breeding in south-east Kazakhstan have been recorded moving distances up to 2,040 km. Rook migration is generally on a broad front. When migrating through Central Asia, Rooks avoid the high mountain ranges and fly over the passes. Alpine Choughs (*Pyrrhocorax graculus*) and Red-billed Choughs (*P. pyrrhocorax*) move only altitudinally, but they do not descend below 1,200 m above sea level even in cold winters with heavy and prolonged snowfalls. Choughs characteristically move up and down the mountain each day and use a set route. Carrion Crows (*Corvus corone*) and Hooded Crows (*C. cornix*), Western Jackdaws (*C. monedula*) and Rooks are now almost always associated with man. Outside the breeding season, huge flocks (up to several thousand birds) tend to stay near towns and villages and the birds regularly forage on rubbish tips.

Waxwings (Bombycillidae)

The Bohemian Waxwing (*Bombycilla garrulus*) migrates from its northern breeding grounds in Russia to regions further south, but movements by this species are irregular. In some winters, especially the more severe ones, Waxwings may cover quite considerable distances, moving as far as the southern borders. In milder winters, they tend to stay in temperate latitudes. Migration is almost always in quite large flocks and single birds are rarely recorded. The Japanese Waxwing (*B. japonica*) migrates to Japan and Taiwan, though some birds remain in Ussuriland.

Dippers (Cinclidae) and Wrens (Troglodytidae)

Any movements undertaken by dippers are very much dependent on the weather conditions; as the rivers and streams become iced up, birds migrate south. The Brown Dipper (*Cinclus pallasii*) and the White-throated Dipper (*C. cinclus*) both descend from their high-altitude breeding grounds to winter by unfrozen water bodies. Dippers are typically solitary and are only rarely seen in pairs or in small flocks. Northern Wrens (*Troglodytes troglodytes*) lead much the same kind of existence, though they are even less likely to make any significant movements than dippers; in lowland areas, they are basically sedentary. Only the high-mountain wrens regularly migrate, i.e. descend to lower altitudes.

Accentors (Prunellidae)

The high-altitude breeders in this family – Alpine Accentor (*Prunella collaris*), Himalayan Accentor (*P. himalayana*), Brown Accentor (*P. fulvescens*) and, to some extent, the Black-throated Accentor (*P. atrogularis*) – move down to winter in the foothills, and only occasionally migrate south.

Northern populations of the Dunnock (*P. modularis*) migrate to southern Europe, south-west Asia, and North Africa. The Black-throated Accentor, Japanese Accentor (*P. rubida*), and Radde's Accentor (*P. ocularis*) all migrate south to winter quarters in Asia.

Thrushes and allies (Turdidae)

Most thrushes breeding in Russia migrate south to winter in Africa, South and east Asia: these include the nightingales *Luscinia*, redstarts *Phoenicurus*, chats *Saxicola*, wheatears *Oenanthe*, and thrushes *Turdus*, *Zoothera*. Some species make only vertical movements (Little Forktail (*Microcichla scouleri*), Güldenstädt's Redstart (*Phoenicurus erythrogaster*), and Blue Whistling Thrush (*Myiophoneus caeruleus*)) or insignificant ones within the breeding range (Blackbird (*Turdus merula*), Robin (*Erithacus rubecula*)). The Grey-cheeked Thrush (*Catharus minimus*), breeding in north-east Siberia, migrates to South America for the winter.

Parrotbills (Panuridae)

These birds remain within their breeding range during the winter and disperse only locally. The Bearded Tit (*Panurus biarmicus*) has, however, been recorded north of its breeding range, in Tyumen' region. The typically small flocks or pairs are restless, constantly on the move in search of food.

Warblers (Sylviidae)

All the warbler species breeding in Russia migrate south and spend the winter in Africa and South Asia. Representatives of the genera *Hippolais*, *Acrocephalus* and *Sylvia* winter in tropical Africa. Only the Streaked Scrub Warbler (*Scotocerca inquieta*) makes just short-distance movements within its breeding range.

Goldcrests (Regulidae)

These birds stay within the breeding range during the winter and do not make any long-distance migrations. Severtzov's Tit Warbler (*Leptopoecile sophiae*) makes vertical movements. Goldcrests (*Regulus regulus*) move about quickly in small flocks, the members of which give frequent contact-calls; they often form mixed flocks with other resident passerines.

Flycatchers (Muscicapidae)

The European species in this family (Spotted Flycatcher (*Muscicapa striata*), Pied Flycatcher (*Ficedula hypoleuca*) and White-collared Flycatcher (*F. albicollis*)) migrate to Africa, mainly to the tropics. The eastern species fly to South-East Asia. Most flycatchers are solitary outside the breeding season, though small parties are occasionally recorded. The Asiatic Paradise Flycatcher (*Terpsiphone paradisi*) is a partial migrant, moving to the more southerly parts of its breeding range for the winter.

Tits (Paridae, including Remizinae), Nuthatches (Sittidae), and Treecreepers (Certhiidae)

The Penduline-Tit (*Remiz pendulinus*) and most representatives of the tits, nuthatches and treecreepers make only local movements, generally staying within the breeding range. In winter, they typically roam about in small mixed flocks, quickly moving on in a characteristically rather hectic search for food.

Finches (Fringillidae)

The majority of Chaffinches (*Fringilla coelebs*) from breeding grounds in Russia migrate to Western Europe and North Africa, though some spend the winter in southern Russia. Most Bramblings (*F. montifringilla*) migrate to South Asia, but some winter in Russia – in the Transcarpathian region, the Crimea, Central Asia, and Transbaikal. Birds ringed in the St. Petersburg region take on average 50 days to reach Italy, Latvian-ringed birds 29 days, and those from Kaliningrad 31 days. The approximate travelling speed is thus 45-50 km per day. Chaffinches and Bramblings migrate in flocks of varying size. In Central Asia, in the south-west Kyzylkum, the two species migrate singly or in small flocks of up to five birds, often both species together.

Many finch species do not make long-distance southward migrations and some even stay in or near their nesting territories all year round, making only local movements.

European Goldfinches (*Carduelis carduelis*) ringed on the Kursiu Peninsula (Kaliningrad region), a climatically favourable area for overwintering, have been recorded in the autumn-winter period in Belgium, 1,150-1,260 km west and south-west of the ringing site. In Russian Asia, the Siberian Goldfinch (*C. c. major*) regularly appears in the Semirechye ("Seven Rivers") area of south-east Kazakhstan in early November.

High-altitude species (Hodgson's Rosy Finch (*Leucosticte nemoricola*), Brandt's Rosy Finch (*L. brandti*), Twite (*Acanthis flavirostris*), Crimson-winged Finch (*Rhodopechys sanguinea*), Red-mantled Rosefinch (*Carpodacus rhodochlamys*), Himalayan Red-mantled Rosefinch (*C. grandis*), and Red-breasted Rosefinch (*Pyrrhospiza punicea*)) all descend to the lower parts of mountains for the winter. Among the longer-distance migrants in this group are the Scarlet Rosefinch (*Carpodacus erythrinus*) and another species whose movements are irregular but which sometimes reaches Indochina – Pallas's Rosefinch (*C. roseus*).

The three crossbill species (*Loxia*), the Northern Bullfinch (*Pyrrhula pyrrhula*) and the Hawfinch (*Coccothraustes coccothraustes*) all remain within the breeding range for the winter, moving only short distances to the south. From its breeding grounds in the south of Siberia, the Grey Bullfinch (*Pyrrhula cineracea*) migrates to more southerly parts of the country, or still further south, into China.

In Russian Central Asia, in the Kyzylkum, the Scarlet Rosefinch usually migrates in flocks of 40-60 birds, the flocks sometimes joining together and swelling to 100 or more birds. Flight altitude in this region is 10-50 m. Finches commonly migrate during the day, especially just after sunrise and before sunset.

Buntings (Emberizidae)

Most bunting species are migratory, and spend the winter in the south of Asia and in Africa, the eastern species in South-East Asia. The Corn Bunting (*Emberiza calandra*), Yellowhammer (*E. citrinella*), Godlewski's Bunting (*E. godlewskii*), and Long-tailed Bunting (*E. cioides*), are basically resident and any movements take place within the limits of the breeding range. The Rock Bunting (*E. cia*) makes altitudinal movements, descending to the foothills for the winter.

As already mentioned, the Rybachiy Observatory (former Vogelwarte Rossiten) plays an enormously important role in Russian bird migration studies. The station director is Professor V.R. Dol'nik, whose work has gained international recognition. A mass of very detailed data has been gathered at Rybachiy since the 1960s, through the trapping (huge Heligoland-style funnel traps are employed) and ringing (aluminium and colour rings are used) of birds, as well as the "processing" – i.e. weighing and measuring, etc. – of live birds. Fundamental research at Rybachiy has clarified the understanding of such concepts as the migratory condition of birds, general fluctuations in numbers and their cyclical nature, as well as energy budgets during migration.

Thanks to intensive ringing programmes, ornithologists now know far more about where different geographical populations spend the winter. A species that has been particularly well studied in this respect is the Starling. Starlings from the European part of Russia migrate quite long distances, some to the Mediterranean, some to the Middle East. Populations from Finland and the Baltic states mostly winter in the British Isles. There is evidence that different geographical populations do not necessarily use separate migration routes and wintering areas. For example, in the Song

Thrush, Finnish, Estonian, Latvian and Lithuanian birds congregate and mix freely in optimal habitat on the wintering grounds.

The existing classic division of species into the categories resident, dispersive, and migratory is now considered extremely relative. In the Russian bird fauna, 47% of non-passerines and 39% of passerines belong to the category "partial-migrant". In almost all gull species, many ducks, waders, auks, corvids, tits and other groups there are populations of all three categories – migratory, dispersive, and resident. The migratory status of a given population is far from constant and may change quite rapidly with a change in the combination of factors which are called "migratory condition". At the same time, the transition to more or less migratory again takes place fairly quickly, as has been witnessed in the Baltic republics with such birds as Rook, Mallard, Common Starling, and others.

Further interesting results have emerged which show a relationship between the angle (degree) of dispersal of ringed birds and the number of races of a given species: the wider the angle, the fewer the races. Thus, for example, the Siskin (*Spinus spinus*), which disperse through 298°, is monotypic, while the Robin, with a dispersal of 98°, is represented by five subspecies in Russia. Several other passerines show a similar pattern. The inevitable result of a wide angle of dispersal is that individuals from different populations will spend the winter together in one place.

Studies undertaken on the Kursiu Peninsula cast doubt on the widely held belief that the first individuals of a particular species to arrive in a given area are the local breeders (as for young birds – i.e. those ringed as nestlings – 75-90% of these return to breed within the confines of their own natal population). For example, Chaffinches from Finland are among the first of their kind to arrive on the Kursiu Peninsula, while the arrival of the breeding population does not take place until later. Reverse migration is a well-known phenomenon: strange as it may seem, experience at Rybachiy has shown that southward movements in spring are in most cases not the result of any obvious external factors. It has been established that up to 30-65% of all migrants at Rybachiy move south rather than north as expected throughout the month of April.

Finally, studies over many years reveal how numbers of certain migrants fluctuate between years. Data on the numbers of birds trapped can be used as an objective measure of the total number passing through a given area, as has been proved statistically. Figures 9 to 11 show population trends of certain species based on trapping data from Rybachiy Observatory.

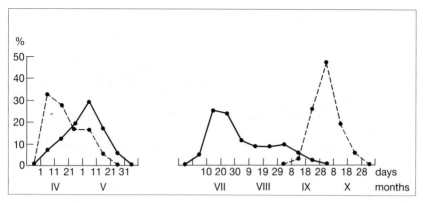

Fig. 9 *Timing of passage through the Kursiai Peninsula of the Finnish popu-lation (broken line) of the Chaffinch* (Fringilla coelebs) *compared with arri-val and departure times of local birds.*
Vertical axis shows the proportion of the total number of trapped birds with rings over the years 1957-89

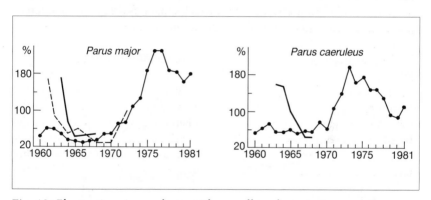

Fig. 10 *Fluctuations in numbers, with overall tendency to increase, in two species of birds (Great Tit* (Parus major) *and Blue Tit* (Parus caeruleus)) *trapped on the Kursiai Peninsula (line with dots) compared with trends shown by these species in Poland (solid line) and Helgoland, West Germany (broken line).*
Vertical axis shows the proportion of the mean annual number of birds trapped in these years

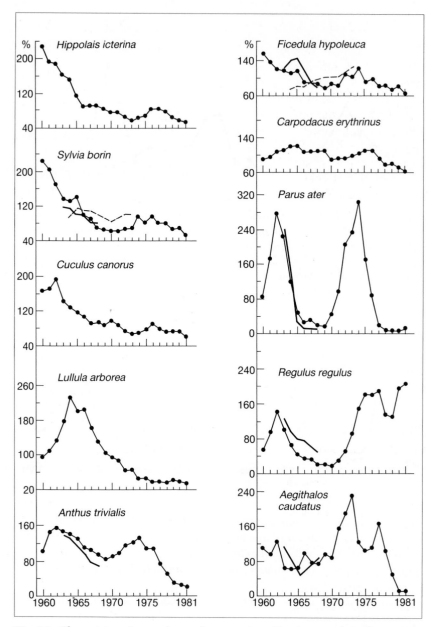

Fig. 11 *Fluctuations in numbers of ten species of bird trapped on the Kursiai Peninsula (line with dots) compared with trends shown by these species in Poland (solid line) and Sweden (broken line). Axes as in Fig. 10*

BIRD CONSERVATION IN RUSSIA

Like all the links in the intricate web of natural communities, birds everywhere are suffering increasingly from the impact of human activities, and Russia is of no exception. The threats for birds here are generally the same as in the rest of the world – pollution, destruction of habitats, legal and illegal hunting. Birds and other animals also suffer a great deal from different military establishments throughout the country, be it at ordinary military bases where the officers will shoot everything that moves many miles around it or sophisticated airforce unit using an island densely populated by bird colonies as a target for their exercise. Among the common threats are also disappearing wetlands, which is occuring mostly in the European part of Russia.

Conservation-minded people amongst the general public are still a rarity in more developed parts of the country, let alone places like Central Asia, the Far East and most of Siberia, even though the conservation programmes carried out by our scientific community have won significant approval from the world's conservation community and many prominent conservation bodies.

In very general outline, the development of nature conservation, which naturally includes birds, proceeded in the former Soviet Union as follows. A commission for nature conservation was set up in 1909 under the auspices of the Russian Geographical Society. The first nature reserves were established in Estonia in 1910, and in 1916, a law on reserves initiated by the Geographical Society was passed in Russia.

During the first years following the 1917 Revolution over 200 decrees and resolutions concerned with conservation were issued – most of them, surprisingly, on the authority of Lenin who was indeed responsible for the establishment, in 1919, of Astrakhan wildlife refuge in the Volga delta. A state Committee for Nature Conservation was set up in 1921, and the All-Russian Society for the Protection of Nature came into being in 1924.

During the darkest times of Stalin regime there was no place for conservation and the idea of conquering nature was widely publicised. Stalin, with the help of anti-scientific "scientists", like the famous academician Lysenko who refused boldly to recognise the fact of genetic inheritance and sent those who did not share his views on the problem to the concentration camps, created "The Great Stalin plan for the Improvement of Nature", the results of which are very obvious today.

During the Khrushchev and Brezhnev eras little interest was paid to conservation either. The results of this gross negligence and complete lack of understanding of the natural processes in the world are the drying seas and lakes, massive erosion, continuing sand storms and incredible pollution.

Entire regions, particularly in Central Asia, have been rendered inhospitable for humans.

In the past couple of decades the increased conservation efforts by a number of enthusiasts have been moving things on slowly, but steadily. Article 18 of the new Constitution, passed by Brezhnev in 1977 and still effective today, reads: "In the interests of the present and future generations in Russia, measures are being taken to ensure the conservation and scientifically based, rational use of the land and its mineral, water, plant and animal resources, and further to secure and maintain clean air and water, to safeguard the renewal of natural riches and to improve the quality of the environment". Although this sounds quite encouraging, it is, however, impossible to understand how such law was enforced, since until recently the category of "ecological crime" was unheard of.

There is a law "On protection and rational exploitation of the animal world" which also looks very encouraging indeed. It declares the preservation of animals living naturally on land, water, in the atmosphere and in the soil, animals residing permanently and temporarily in the territory of Russia.

Animals enjoying special protection are those in the rare and endangered categories, also those considered as game and others of economic importance to man. None the less, animal protection in Russia does not preclude the idea of combating the harmful species. These include rodents and certain predators. Among birds, a few members of the crow family may be legally shot by hunters during the year, especially where they pose a threat to large concentrations of breeding waterfowl. All birds of prey are fully protected by law, but this does not prevent illegal hunting, particularly in the remote areas. The Marsh Harrier, being a numerous species, can do a lot of damage in wildfowl reserves, as can the Goshawk when it occurs in pheasant-rearing areas. These raptors are not shot but trapped and then released far away from such places. This is particularly true in Latvia, where this initiative originated.

Conservation of Rare and Endangered Species – Red Data Books

Rare species of birds and other animals are normally included in the IUCN/ICPB Red Data Book and the country in whose territory they are found has a moral responsibility to protect and conserve them. A number of endangered species of birds are found in Russia, and various measures are being taken to safeguard their survival. Some of their habitats are protected areas, and a number of species are being bred in captivity with the aim to create an "emergency reserve". Direct measures in this area are carried out by eminent Russian scientist Professor Dr Vladimir Flint (Fig.

Fig. 12 *Dr Vladimir Flint in Saratov captive breeding unit for Great Bustards.*
Photo V. Mosseikin

12). It was indeed Dr Flint's initiative that led to the setting up of special captive breeding programmes for rare animals.

The Russian Red Data Book was launched with the idea of attracting the attention of the general public and of state organisations to the problem of endangered species. It contained, arranged in special categories, those species of plants and animals that are rare and endangered in Russia. Red Data Books were later compiled and published in each of the fifteen former Soviet Union republics. In 1984, a new, thoroughly revised and enlarged two-volume edition of the Russian Red Data Book appeared, one volume being devoted to animals, the other to plants. At present, there are 80 bird species listed in the Russian Red Data Book. Species included in the IUCN/ICPB Red Data Book automatically figure in the Russian National one.

Determining an order of priorities for the implementation of conservation measures depends on the animal's status and this has meant the introduction of a more clearly defined set of five categories.

Category I: Endangered species – i.e. threatened with extinction and doomed unless special measures are taken to save them.

Category II: Vulnerable species whose numbers are still relatively high, yet declining catastrophically so that they may soon be faced with the threat of extinction.

Category III: Rare species not at present endangered, but occurring in such low numbers or within such restricted range that they may be wiped out if there is an unfavourable, natural or man-introduced change in their habitat.

Category IV: Indeterminate species whose biology is not well known; the size and condition of their populations cause concern, but the lack of appropriate information means that they can not be assigned to any of the first three categories.

Category V: Species that have recovered and now out of danger, but still not to be exploited commercially and continued regular monitoring of their populations is essential.

Red Data Books have also been published commercially for the various former Union republics. An initial printing of 60,000 copies of the Lithuanian Red Data Book sold out immediately in this small republic with its population of 3.6 million.

Bird Species Included in the Russian Red Data Book

Category I
1. *Diomedea albatrus* – Short-tailed Albatross
2. *Nipponia nippon* – Japanese Crested Ibis
3. *Ciconia boyciana* – Oriental White Stork
4. *Anser cygnoides* – Swan Goose
5. *Tadorna cristata* – Crested Shelduck
6. *Anas angustirosrtis* – Marbled Teal
7. *Haliaeetus leucoryphus* – Pallas's Sea Eagle
8. *Gypaetus barbatus* – Lammergeier
9. *Falco biarmicus* – Lanner Falcon
10. *Falco pelegrinoides* – Barbary Falcon
11. *Grus japonensis* – Red-crowned Crane
12. *G. leucogeranus* – Siberian White Crane
13. *Chlamydotis undulata* – Houbara Bustard
14. *Ibidorhyncha struthersii* – Ibisbill
15. *Tringa guttifer* – Spotted Greenshank
16. *Numenius tenuirostris* – Slender-billed Curlew
17. *Larus relictus* – Relict Gull
18. *Ketupa blakistoni* – Blakiston's Fish Owl
19. *Picus squamatus* – Scaly-bellied Woodpecker
20. *Paradoxornis polivanovi* – Polivanov's Parrotbill
21. *Emberiza jankowskii* – Jankowski's Bunting

Category II
1. *Pelecanus onocrotalus* – White Pelican
2. *P. crispus* – Dalmatian Pelican
3. *Phalacrocorax aristotelis* – Shag
4. *Platalea leucorodia* – White Spoonbill

5. *Ciconia nigra* – Black Stork
6. *Phoenicopterus ruber roseus* – Greater Flamingo
7. *Rufibrenta ruficollis* – Red-breasted Goose
8. *Aix galericulata* – Mandarin Duck
9. *Mergus squamatus* – Chinese Merganser
10. *Aquila rapax* – Steppe Eagle
11. *A. heliaca* – Imperial Eagle
12. *A. chrysaetos* – Golden Eagle
13. *Haliaeetus albicilla* – White-tailed Sea Eagle
14. *Falco peregrinus* – Peregrine Falcon
15. *Falcipennis falcipennis* – Siberian Spruce Grouse
16. *Tetraogallus caspius* – Caspian Snowcock
17. *Francolinus francolinus* – Black Partridge
18. *Grus vipio* – Japanese White-naped Crane
19. *Anthropoides virgo* – Demoiselle Crane
20. *Porphyrio porphyrio* – Purple Gallinule
21. *Otis tarda* – Great Bustard
22. *Tetrax tetrax* – Little Bustard
23. *Chettusia gregaria* – Sociable Plover
24. *Larus ichthyaetus* – Great Black-headed Gull

Category III
1. *Calonectris leucomelas* – White-faced Shearwater
2. *Oceanodroma monorhis* – Swinhoe's Storm Petrel
3. *Philacte canagica* – Emperor Goose
4. *Anser indicus* – Bar-headed Goose
5. *Pandion haliaetus* – Osprey
6. *Circaetus gallicus* – Short-toed Eagle
7. *Haliaeetus pelagicus* – Steller's Sea Eagle
8. *Falco rusticolus* – Gyrfalcon
9. *F. cherrug* – Saker Falcon
10. *Grus monacha* – Hooded Crane
11. *Eurynorhynchus pygmeus* – Spoon-billed Sandpiper
12. *Numenius minutus* – Little Curlew
13. *Pagophila eburnea* – Ivory Gull
14. *Larus brunnicephalus* – Brown-headed Gull
15. *Sterna aleutica* – Aleutian Tern
16. *Hypocolius ampelinus* – Grey Hypocolius
17. *Passer simplex* – Desert Sparrow

Category IV
1. *Egretta eulophotes* – Swinhoe's Egret
2. *Oxyura leucocephala* – White-headed Duck
3. *Milvus milvus* – Red Kite
4. *Accipiter brevipes* – Levant Sparrowhawk

5. *Butastur indicus* – Grey-faced Buzzard-Eagle
6. *Gyps himalayensis* – Himalayan Griffon Vulture
7. *Tetraogallus tibetanus* – Tibetan Snowcock
8. *T. altaicus* – Altai Snowcock
9. *Porzana exquisita* – Swinhoe's Yellow Rail
10. *Gallinago hardwickii* – Japanese Snipe
11. *Limnodromus semipalmatus* – Asiatic Dowitcher
12. *Syrrhaptes tibetanus* – Tibetan Sandgrouse
13. *Columba leuconota* – Snow Pigeon
14. *Saxicola insignis* – Hodgson's Bushchat

Category V
1. *Branta leucopsis* – Barnacle Goose
2. *Cygnus bewickii* – Bewick's Swan
3. *Lyryrus mlokosiewiczi* – Caucasian Black Grouse
4. *Rhodostethia rosea* – Ross's Gull

Any classification naturally entails an element of formality and the present status of certain species in the above list is very much open to debate. It is, for example, difficult to agree with the claim that both the Lammergeier and Ibisbill will disappear from most of the great mountain ranges in Russia if measures to prevent this are not taken as a matter of urgency. Similarly contentious is the assertion that Red-breasted Goose numbers are "declining catastrophically".

Specially Protected Areas

Within the general system of nature and bird conservation in Russia, these areas play an outstandingly important role. The main type of specially protected area in Russia is the zapovednik, or nature reserve. This is the highest level of nature conservation. The network of reserves is set up on scientific principles and, until recently, within the framework of national and republican state plans. All forms of economic activity are prohibited within their boundaries, and the reserves are also not open to unorganised visits by large numbers of non-specialists, including tourists.

Reserves of the type existing in Russia served as the basis for the organisation – an initiative launched by UNESCO – of an international system of biosphere reserves. Biosphere reserves, now created in many countries of the world, have the same aims as those worked out for the system of Russian zapovedniks. The prime objectives are the preservation of the plant and animal communities and of ecosystems in all their variety, together with the organisation of scientific research on the dynamics of natural processes.

CONSERVATION

There is an undeniable increase in the amount of land and water brought under special protection and growing interest in such areas throughout the world. We are witnessing the conclusion of a whole host of international agreements, conventions and treaties on nature conservation.

As already noted, reserves in Russia occupy a special place in the general system of nature conservation. When a reserve is set up, a significant area of land or part of a water body, with all the attendant natural resources, is taken out of any commercial production. In such cases, conservation organisations quite often find themselves in conflict with the bureaucratic view that taking land out of production hinders economic development and hence is at odds with the interests of society and the material prosperity of the people. Yet this is a far cry from the truth: taking land out of economic production certainly does not mean that no use is being made of the natural resources at all – it is one way of using them! When an area is designated a reserve its natural resources are indeed no longer exploited in pursuit of short-term economic benefit, but at the same time the protected objects can be used for scientific investigation of their ecological and genetic variety. What is most important here in the final analysis are the aesthetic and ethical aspects, the moral question of responsibility to future generations for the protection and conservation of nature and natural resources.

There are now about 170 nature reserves in the former USSR, occupying an area of nearly 200,000 km^2. For a country whose territory takes up about one sixth of the Earth's land surface, this is admittedly not a lot. However, we are talking only about the area that comes under reserves. By the beginning of 1993, the country also had 14 national parks.

National parks are fairly recent phenomenon in the former Soviet Union. The first such park was set up in Estonia in 1972, this being followed by further parks in Latvia and Lithuania, and now other republics have them as well. The role of Russian national parks is somewhat different from that of reserves. National parks have a number of different zones. Agricultural and other human activities are not completely prohibited in them. There is usually a specially protected zone – the most valuable one – where economic activity is permitted and which is out of bounds to tourists.

There is one more type of protected area in the Russian system of nature conservation. This is the so-called zakaznik, for which there is not really an equivalent term in another language. Zakazniks are areas partially taken out of economic production because they contain valuable plants, rare animals, colonies of nesting birds, and so on. They are of various types – landscape, botanical, zoological, ornithological and others. A significant number of zakazniks are seasonal, e.g. for breeding colonies of birds. The area concerned is taken out of production and no visits are allowed during the breeding season, but, for example, cattle can be grazed when the birds have finished nesting.

International Cooperation in Bird Conservation

Birds, of course, do not recognise state boundaries and the idea of their breeding and wintering grounds lying within different political systems is meaningless to them.

It is obvious therefore that the complex task of bird protection can be resolved only through internationally co-ordinated efforts. The first steps along the road to such cooperation were taken at the beginning of this century, but the main development came only in the post-war years when over 250 international treaties, agreements and conventions concerned with nature conservation were concluded, and more than 300 different international conservation bodies created.

The world's oldest conservation organisation is the International Council for Bird Preservation, founded in 1922. A UNESCO initiative in 1948 led to the foundation of the International Union for the Conservation of Nature and Natural Resources (IUCN) which had about 50 member-countries. The World Wildlife Fund and IUCN have since combined to form a new and larger body called the World Wide Fund for Nature.

A Convention on the protection of migratory and endangered birds and their habitats signed by Russia and Japan has been in operation since 1974. About 12,000 swans, 6,000 geese and more than one million ducks breeding in Russia winter in Japan. Several rare species are found as breeding birds in both countries.

Russian-American cooperative projects aimed at conservation of the Snow Goose (*Chen hyperboreus*) and the Siberian White Crane (*Grus leucogeranus*) are developing successfully. The status of the Wrangel Island Snow Goose population is causing concern among scientists as there has been a steady decline in the number of breeding pairs. One of the factors in the conservation battle is the hunting of these geese in the United States, where the Wrangel Island population winters together with the local birds. Sightings of Wrangel Island birds fitted with plastic neck-collars have revealed the population's winter quarters, and ornithologists have proposed to Government bodies in the USA that wildfowling should be strictly controlled at waters where the geese winter.

Dr V. E. Flint and the Director of International Crane Foundation (ICF) Dr George Archibald have been responsible for the launch of "Operation Siberian White Crane", described already in many sources. For the work in nature conservation and especially for the part he played in "Operation Siberian White Crane" Dr Flint was awarded the 1987 Audubon Gold Medal.

Wetlands of International Importance

One of the main aims of the International Wetlands Programme is to protect migratory birds which may breed in one country and winter in another. Under this programme, Russia has designated as of international importance those wetlands which have the greatest significance for the conservation of both breeding birds and passage-migrants. Most such wetlands were established on the sites of already existing reserves and their territory now greatly exceeds that occupied by the former sanctuary. Examples are Matsalu Bay (Estonia) based on the Matsalu reserve, Kandalaksha Bay (White Sea) based on Kandalaksha reserve, the Volga delta based on the Astrakhan reserve and so on. These wetlands are of considerable importance for bird conservation during spring and autumn migration, when huge numbers of birds congregate there to rest and feed.

Matsalu reserve was set up in 1957 with an area of 39,700 hectares as the largest and richest place for the breeding and migration of birds in the Baltic region. This reserve now constitutes a large part of the internationally important wetland "Matsalu Bay, Baltic Sea" and now covers an area of 48,600 hectares.

The wetland sanctuary was established in Kandalaksha nature reserve in 1975 with an area of 208,000 hectares called "Kandalaksha Bay, White Sea". This reserve also includes islands in the Barents Sea – the "Seven Islands" and the Ainov Islands, these making a total of 58,100 hectares.

The Black Sea reserve was established in 1927 in the Kherson region in Ukraine on the northern Black Sea coast and covers 71,899 hectares of which 19,699 hectares are dry land. The main territory consists of five sections in Kherson region and islands in Yagorlitsk and Tendra Bays. Since 1975, the various sections of the reserve have constituted the wetland of international importance "Danube delta, Yagotlitsk and Tendra Bays, Black Sea" with a total area of 103,799 hectares.

One of the country's oldest wildlife sanctuaries, having been set up, with the direct support of V. Lenin, in 1919 is the Volga delta. Since 1975 all the reserve area has been included in this internationally important wetland, which has an area of 650,000 hectares. The Volga delta supports huge waterbird colonies, moulting and passage sites for migrant wildfowl in spring and autumn.

SYSTEMATIC REVIEW OF THE BIRDS OF RUSSIA

DIVERS – ORDER GAVIIFORMES

The divers or loons (Gaviiformes) are a small order of highly specialised birds found on lakes and coasts in the tundra and taiga zones. All five species of diver have been recorded in Russia and four out of five are breeders.

The commonest are the **Red-throated Diver** (*Gavia stellata*) and **Black-throated Diver** (*G. arctica*) (Plate 12). These birds reach the tundra lakes in May and their far-carrying wailing calls reverberate in echoes all around. They inhabit various types of lakes and nest on the lake shore or on a small island close to the water's edge. The nest is no more than a depression in the ground where the female lays two dark brownish-olive eggs in the first half of June. As their name suggests, divers are really at home in the water, being superb swimmers on and below the surface. They are rather clumsy on dry land and in flight and require a run across the water into the wind to take off. Divers are normally shy birds. Fish makes up the main part of their diet.

On the edge of their distribution, divers increasingly find themselves under pressure from humans during the nesting period. For example, in Lithuania, the Black-throated Diver is recorded breeding only in several places in the north-east. Nests, which are usually situated on the small islands and peninsulas in the forest lakes, are often simply deserted because

Fig. 13 *Distribution range of the Pacific Diver* Gavia pacifica. *1. breeding range; 2. wintering range*

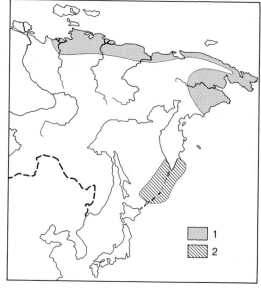

of frequent disturbance by tourists. This species is included in the Lithuanian Red Data Book.

Formerly considered a subspecies of the Black-throated Diver, the **Pacific Diver** (*Gavia pacifica*) (Plate 12) has now, after detailed investigation, been given the status of a separate species. It was by no means easy to single out *pacifica* from *arctica*, because the morphological differences are minimal. The most significant difference was the fact that the eastern subspecies of Black-throated Diver, *G. a. viridigularis*, lives together with the Pacific Divers in the tundras of Eastern Siberia but they do not form mixed pairs. This reproductive isolation within the same breeding grounds was sufficient to regard Pacific Diver as a separate species. The biology of the Pacific Diver is akin to that of the Black-throated. It is a tundra nester of Eastern Siberia and Chukotka (Fig. 13).

The largest of the country's divers is the **White-billed Diver** (*Gavia adamsii*) (Plate 12). This is a purely tundra species, found in the tundras of Russia and Alaska. The species is monotypic and weighs up to 6.5 kg. The White-billed Diver is a rare species, and numbers within the breeding range are extremely uneven. It arrives at its breeding grounds in mid-June. Divers usually settle in large lakes, but are sometimes found in small ones as well. The nest is situated on the shore just by the water's edge, and in late June or beginning of July one or two eggs are laid. As with the other divers, breeding takes place only once a year. Incubation takes about 25 days, and the hatched young spend their first day in the nest before leaving for water. The diet consists mainly of fish.

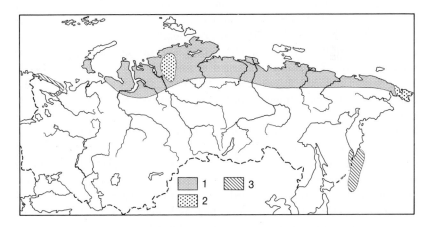

Fig. 14 *Distribution range of the White-billed Diver* Gavia adamsii.
1. breeding range; 2. areas with comparatively high breeeding density;
3. wintering areas

White-billed Divers winter off the coasts of Kamchatka, the Kuril Islands, Japan, Canada, and in the Barents Sea (Fig. 14).

The **Great Northern Diver** (*Gavia immer*) is regarded in Russia as an irregular vagrant. The only confirmed records come from the Commander Islands in the North Pacific. The records of Great Northern Divers in the Baltic and Barents seas are not confirmed by collection material or suitable pictures.

GREBES – ORDER PODICIPEDIFORMES

The grebes is also a compact and highly specialised group of water birds occurring, unlike divers, throughout the world. Different authors put the total number of species between 17 and 21. There are five species recorded in Russia, all of which breed there.

The smallest of all Russian grebes is the **Little Grebe** (*Podiceps ruficollis*). In Russia, it is distributed in three main areas – European Russia and Caucasus, Central Asia and the very south of the Russian Far East. It breeds in small lakes and river deltas, densely covered by aquatic vegetation. Little Grebes are secretive and shy and therefore quite difficult to see. They are monogamous and pairs are formed for the whole breeding season or even longer. As with all grebes, its nests are built right on the water. Incubation takes 20-21 days and is performed by both parents. Its food consists of a number of aquatic animals.

The **Black-necked Grebe** (*Podiceps nigricollis*) inhabits lakes and other water bodies in Europe, Asia and North America. In Russia, it is a reasonably common species in suitable places, but its distribution is patchy. In some places, like Central Asian mountains, the Black-necked Grebe can be found breeding as high as 3000 m. Considerable fluctuations in numbers are reported in different years. The nest is built on the water surface and the clutch consists of three to six eggs incubated by both parents for about 20-22 days. The food consists mostly of different aquatic invertebrates. The Black-necked Grebe commonly breeds in colonies, frequently mixed with other birds like Terns.

The **Slavonian Grebe** (*Podiceps auritus*) (Plate 13) is the northernmost species of Grebe in Eurasia. The southern boundary of its distribution lies between Scandinavia, Lithuania to Lake Baikal and the Amur river delta. In the north, the species is reported breeding in northern Norway, in Eurasia to the 65 parallel, while in Canada it breeds even further north. It also breeds in oligotrophic lakes in the mountains as high as 3000 m. In lowlands, it usually favours smallish water bodies with dense vegetation. The clutch, starting from the beginning of May, consists of one to seven eggs (usually 4-5) and the breeding takes both parents 22-25 days. The young are also fed by both adults.

The **Red-necked Grebe** (*Podiceps grisegena*) has a patchy distribution in

Russia from the western borders to the Far East. It is nearly as large as the familiar **Great Crested Grebe** (*P. cristatus*) which is the most common species of grebe in Russia, distributed from the western borders to the river Yenisey in the east.

TUBENOSES – ORDER PROCELLARIIFORMES

The tubenoses is the only order in the Russian bird fauna where the breeders are outnumbered by vagrant species. There are 18 species recorded in the country, and only five of them breed. Worldwide, there are about 100 species of tubenoses, which are solely marine birds.

Three species of albatrosses were recorded as vagrants in Russia. These include the **Short-tailed Albatross** (*Diomedea albatrus*) which was recorded in the Seas of Okhotsk and Japan as well as in several parts of the Pacific Ocean in the territorial waters of Russia; the **Laysan Albatross** (*D. immutabilis*), and the **Black-footed Albatross** (*D. nigripes*), both of which were recorded near the Kamchatka peninsula and Kuril islands in the Far East.

The well-known **Northern Fulmar** (*Fulmarus glacialis*) is widely distributed in Russia. It nests in the west of the Arctic region, including Franz Josef Land and Novaya Zemlya (New Land) as well as in the east, in the Bering Sea and northern Pacific, including the Kamchatka peninsula and Commander Islands. In the Kuril islands there are about 1.5 million breeding pairs, and on the Commander Islands about 0.5 million pairs.

Three species of the genus *Pterodroma* were recorded in Russia. **Solander's Petrel** (*P. solandri*) is supposed to visit the coasts near the southern Kuril Islands irregularly, while **Peale's Petrel** (*P. inexpectata*) visits the Sea of Okhotsk, Bering and other parts of the northern Pacific. The **Bonin Petrel** (*P. hypoleuca*), breeding in the Pacific Islands, was recorded in Russia near Sakhalin Island and in the southern part of the sea of Okhotsk.

There is only one species of Shearwater which breeds in Russia, namely the **White-faced Shearwater** (*Calonectris leucomelas*). It has been recorded breeding in small numbers on the islands in the Bay of Peter the Great not far from Vladivostok. Its main breeding population is concentrated on the islands around Japan. The nests are made in burrows excavated in the loose soil on marine islands. On Karamzin Island the eggs are laid in the second half of June. After the single white egg is laid, the male replaces the female on the nest for about eight days. After that the partners alternate more frequently, but sometimes the nest is empty for one to three days. Incubation takes 51-60 days and young are hatched in August. The parents start to feed them from the first day after they hatch, usually once a day, but sometimes less frequently, like twice in three days. The young spend at least two and a half months in the burrows before they appear for the first time outside.

They take off and leave the islands at the end of October. The main food for the White-faced Shearwater is small pelagic fish.

The **Manx Shearwater** (*Puffinus puffinus*) has been recorded as a vagrant species in the Black Sea and in the Sea of Azov, while all our records on Shearwaters come from the Far East. The **Pale-footed Shearwater** (*P. carneipes*) irregularly visits southern coasts of Ussuriland and southern Kuril Islands. The **Sooty Shearwater** (*P. griseus*) appears in the very north-east of the country, e.g. in Anadyr Bay of the Bering Sea. Up to the Bering Straits in the north it is possible to spot the **Short-tailed Shearwater** (*P. tenuirostris*), while the **Grey-backed Shearwater** (*P. bulleri*) has been recorded by the coasts of southern Kuril Islands.

The **British Storm Petrel** (*Hydrobates pelagicus*) has been recorded twice in the Black Sea and in the Sea of Azov. Bearing in mind that this species breeds on Lafontain Islands, it is possible that it also visits the Barents Sea.

Leach's Storm Petrel (*Oceanodroma leucorhoa*) (Plate 13) is widespread along the coasts and islands in the temperate expanses of the north Pacific and Atlantic Oceans. In Russia, this species breeds in the Kuril Islands, where about 350,000 breeding pairs were recorded. It also breeds on the Commander Islands in the North Pacific.

The Verkhovsky Islands in the Bay of Peter the Great are home for a colony of **Swinhoe's Storm Petrel** (*Oceanodroma monorhis*) (Plate 13). This area is the edge of distribution for this species, and the islands on which it breeds, including Karamzin Island, are not far from Vladivostok. We had the opportunity to visit the Verkhovsky islands which are simply several cliffs appearing out of the Sea of Japan. Apart from the large colony of Swinhoe's Storm Petrel we were astonished by the numbers of breeding Pacific Swifts (*Apus pacificus*), with nests in every possible niche or crevice in the rocks. Also common were Spectacled Guillemots (*Cepphus carbo*). As we predicted, we did not see any petrels during the day time and only the nesting burrows situated in every possible place where the loose black soil was present gave us an idea of the size of the colony. Altogether, on Verkhovsky and Karamzin Islands, there are about 12,000 breeding pairs. Its worth mentioning that Karamzin Island was selected by the local military as a target for air force exercises. A great number of different sea birds nest there, and it was constantly bombarded by military planes during our visit to the neighbouring Verkhovsky Islands. As it was pointed out by our colleagues working in this region, the coasts of Karamzin Island are literally covered by dead birds of different species, including Swinhoe's Storm Petrels.

The breeding biology of Swinhoe's Storm Petrel is much the same as that of many tubenoses. It breeds in burrows in the loose soil which it excavates. It also occupies the burrows of some Alcids, like the Ancient Murrelet

(*Synthliboramphus antiquus*). Starting from mid-June, a single white egg is laid and incubation takes about 40 days. Incubation is conducted by both parents. The young leave the islands by the end of October – beginning of November.

The **Fork-tailed Storm Petrel** (*Oceanodroma furcata*) is the common breeding species in the islands of the North Pacific. In Russia, it breeds mainly on the Commander and Kuril Islands. On the five islands of the Kuril chain, at least 200,000 breeding pairs were recorded. Its food consists mainly of pelagic invertebrates.

Harcourt's Petrel (*Oceanodroma castro*) is probably a visitor to the coasts of the southern Kuril Islands.

PELICANS AND ALLIES – ORDER PELECANIFORMES

This group of medium-size to huge marine birds has twelve species recorded in Russia, eight of which breed, three of which are vagrants and one of which became extinct in the recent past.

One species of the Family Fregatidae (Frigatebirds) was recorded in Russia as a vagrant species. It is the **Lesser Frigatebird** (*Fregata ariel*) which was seen at the coasts of Ussuriland and in the lower reaches of the Amur River in the Russian Far East.

The true Pelican family (Pelecanidae) is represented in Russia by two breeding species – the **White** (*Pelecanus onocrotalus*) (Plate 14 and Fig. 15) and the **Dalmatian** (*P. crispus*) (Plate 14). The first is a large bird weighing up to 11 kg. Its preferred habitat in Russia is the shores of large lakes and the deltas of rivers which empty into the Black and Caspian Seas. White Pelicans also live on the salt lakes of Kazakhstan. They nest in colonies of up to 700 pairs, though recent declines mean that colonies of that size do not exist any longer. Birds start building nests from mid-April. When there are many nests together, a peculiar kind of raft-like structure develops, and artificial rafts (nesting platforms) are now being provided for the pelicans nesting in the nature reserves. The nest itself is usually a massive structure, but building is completed by the female very rapidly – within two or three days. White Pelicans will steal nest material if they get the chance, especially from their close relative, the Dalmatian Pelican. The female sits on the nest until she has laid her two eggs which are then incubated for 33 days. Newly hatched chicks are fed by regurgitation of semi-digested food, but the parents start to bring them small fish later. Departure for the wintering grounds starts only with the first frosts. Pelicans feed mainly on fish, which they catch by immersing the head and top half of the body. They quite often hunt co-operatively, driving the fish towards the shore and catching them there.

The Dalmatian Pelican is frequently found in mixed colonies with the

Fig. 15 *White Pelicans (*Pelecanus onocrotalus*) in the River Ili delta.*
Photo O. Belialov

White. Their life-history is basically similar, though the Dalmatian lays more eggs – the normal clutch is four. It also has a slightly wider distribution.

The present status of both Pelican species in Russia is giving serious cause for concern. Their breeding ranges have contracted sharply in recent years. Larger, more significant concentrations of nesting birds have survived in the Ili river delta and on some islands of Lake Balkhash, at Lake Sasyk-Kol (all in the southern Kazakhstan), and on the lower reaches of the Turgay River. There are also several less important sites – where numbers are low or breeding is irregular – along the southern borders of Russia.

The Russian population of White Pelicans numbers 2,000–2,500 breeding pairs or, counting offspring and immature non-breeders, 7,000-9,000 birds. The status of the Dalmatian Pelican is similar – an estimated 1,500-2,000 breeding pairs and the total population after breeding is 7,000-9,000 birds.

The Family Sulidae (Boobies) is represented in Russia by two vagrant species. The **Northern Gannet** (*Sula bassana*) was recorded several times in the Barents Sea near Murman. The **Red-footed Booby** (*S. sula*), which breeds on the islands in the Indian Ocean and in the western part of the Pacific Ocean, was recorded in Tartar Straits in the Far East.

There are six breeding species of cormorant (*Phalacrocorax*) in Russia. One species – *P. perspicillatus* – became extinct before 1852. The **Great Cormorant**

(*P. carbo*) is the most common and most widespread cormorant in Russia. It has characteristically patchy distribution, which is closely connected with suitable habitats, namely reasonably large water bodies rich in fish. It favours big, shallow lakes and river deltas. The Great Cormorant usually nests in colonies, frequently together with other water birds. The colonies are very varied as are the coasts and banks of water bodies on which they occur. If there are suitable trees around, as is usually the case in the temperate zone rivers and lakes, the cormorants willingly settle on them. In the south, where the reedbeds are abundant and the coasts are usually treeless, the colonies are situated in the reedbeds or on bald tiny islands built on the sand. Cormorants also favour huge sea and lake rocks and cliffs to build their nests on. In April, the clutch consisting usually of three to four eggs is laid and incubated for about 28-31 days. The young leave the nest when they are about 50 days old. Cormorants, needless to say, feed on fish; their extraordinary fishing skills sometimes cause concern to fish farmers.

A close relative of the Great Cormorant is **Temminck's Cormorant** (*Phalacrocorax filamentosus*) (Plate 14) which inhabits the southern part of the Russian Far East as well as the sea islands around Japan, Korea and north-east China. Unlike the Great Cormorant, this species does not favour the inland waters and is exclusively marine. Their breeding colonies are situated on huge, inaccessible cliffs along the coasts and islands. The clutch consists of three to four eggs. In the Kuril Islands e.g. on the Island of Shikotan, these cormorants form mixed colonies on the cliffs together with Red-faced Cormorants (*P. urile*) and Slaty-backed Gulls (*Larus schistisagus*).

The **Pelagic Cormorant** (*Phalacrocorax pelagicus*) (Plate 15) is another typical species of marine cormorant which inhabits the islands and shores of Chukotka and Kamchatka peninsula in the Far East as well as the Commander Islands. This species is common in suitable habitats and nests together with species of Alcids and other marine birds. More rare and scarcely distributed is the **Red-faced Cormorant** (*P. urile*). Apart from the islands in the Russian Far East it nests on the small islands around Hokkaido in Japan as well as on Aleutians.

Well known and common in Britain, the **Shag** (*Phalacrocorax aristotelis*) is not that common in Russia. It appears on two far separated places both on the edge of its distribution – the Barents Sea and the Black Sea.

The smallest cormorant in Russia is the **Pygmy Cormorant** (*Phalacrocorax pygmaeus*) (Plate 15). This species is very different from its marine relatives and does not favour sea coasts, appearing in different water bodies in the south of the country. The colonies, which are situated in the reed beds and bushes are usually shared with herons, egrets and other water birds. The clutch consists of three to five eggs.

HERONS, BITTERNS AND STORKS – ORDER CICONIIFORMES

This order has 25 representatives in Russia. Seventeen of them are breeders, one species is recently extinct and four are vagrants. Breeding is likely for the other three species but it is not yet proved.

Bitterns (*Botaurus*) and little bitterns (*Ixobrychus*) form a very specific and secretive group of birds closely associated with the dense vegetation of different water bodies from huge river deltas to small lakelets. There are five species in Russia and the best known is, of course, the **Eurasian Bittern** (*Botaurus stellaris*) (Fig. 16).

The size, body shape and plumage colour of this bird allow easy distinction from other herons in the field. In the spring and summer, Eurasian Bitterns are not often seen, but their presence is betrayed by the remarkable booming sound they make.

The Eurasian Bittern is mainly nocturnal and, unlike other herons in Russia, a solitary nester. Breeding starts immediately after arrival. The nest is built in a dense reedbed and will eventually contain three to seven eggs. Incubation takes 25-26 days and starts with the first egg, so that there is a considerable size difference between the chicks of a brood. The young fledge at about two months and the family soon splits up once juveniles are well grown, each bird then leading an independent existence. Bitterns mainly eat fish, but also take frogs, newts, and worms.

Widespread though rarely seen is the **Little Bittern** (*Ixobrychus minutus*). This species favours large and small lakes and slow-running rivers which

Fig. 16 *Eurasian Bittern (*Botaurus stellaris*) in Lithuania. Photo H. Sakalauskas*

abound in dense vegetation along the shores and islands. In Russia, it is found from the Baltic Sea to Central Siberia. There are five races of Little Bittern in the world, but the whole of Russia is only inhabited by one. It has a wide distribution in Africa, Asia, and Australia. The nest is built in dense vegetation like reedbeds or bushes up to two metres above land. It is a compact pile 20-25 cm high and is usually completed within two to four days. The clutch consists of five to six (rarely 4-9) eggs and the incubation by both sexes takes 17-19 days. The young leave the nest at 17-18 days of age and are concealed in surrounding vegetation. The food primarily consists of fish, amphibians and insects.

The Russian Far East has three species of little bittern recorded there. There have been several records of the **Chinese Little Bittern** (*Ixobrychus sinensis*) on Sakhalin and Kuril Islands. Although breeding has yet to be proved, it is certainly quite possible, especially bearing in mind the secretive and elusive habits of the whole bittern tribe. The Chinese Little Bittern's range covers East and South Asia.

Schrenk's Bittern (*Ixobrychus eurythmus*) (Fig. 17) is a fairly common breeder in Ussuriland, the Khabarovsk region and Sakhalin Island. It is, however, a secretive, skulking bird and is difficult to see in the great reed-grass swamps and wet meadows with sparse shrubs which are its haunt from the end of May. Schrenk's Little Bittern makes a nest of plant stems on the ground and lays four to six eggs. Hatching takes at least two days

Fig. 17 *Schrenk's Bittern (*Ixobrychus eurythmus*) in Central Ussuriland. Photo Y. Shibnev*

and both parents take care of the young. Departure from Ussuriland takes place in late August or early September. The breeding range of Schrenk's Little Bittern is fairly restricted and includes, apart from the south of the Russian Far East, north-east and south China, Korea and Japan. It winters in southern China, the Philippines and Indonesia.

The **Cinnamon Bittern** (*Ixobrychus cinnamomeus*) is a vagrant species which was recorded in southern Ussuriland. The breeding range of this species includes South and East Asia.

The heron tribe starts with the **Black-crowned Night Heron** (*Nycticorax nycticorax*) (Plate 15) which is almost cosmopolitan and is a typical nocturnal species whose period of activity begins at dusk and ends shortly before sunrise. Unlike other herons, the Night Heron is rather stockily built with a short neck. It favours marshy areas with trees and bushes, and nests sometimes in large colonies up to several thousand birds. The colonies are usually mixed with other herons and egrets. The nest is built at varying heights in a tree. In large colonies, Night Herons frequently take over the old nests of other small herons, reconstructing them to suit their own taste, so that night heron nests are quite variable in size and shape. The clutch ranges from three to five eggs, but four is the usual number laid. Laying takes place from mid-April and the eggs are incubated for 21-22 days. As soon as their feathers are developed, the young start to clamber about in the colony trees and large numbers gather on the outermost branches waiting for their parents to arrive with food. Like other herons, Black-crowned Night Herons eat animal food, mainly small aquatic animals, insects, frogs, lizards and rodents.

Walking along a small stream in Ussuriland, which winds between hills, its banks fringed with dense forest and willow thickets, you may see a small, greenish-grey heron-like bird fly across the stream. This is the **Striated**, or **Green-backed**, **Heron** (*Butorides striatus*) (Plate 15), a characteristic bird of riverine forest. The range of this species embraces China, Indonesia, Ceylon and South America. On misty mornings in June, the Green-backed Heron quietly stalks the shallows and sandbanks of the rivers, hunting the small fish which are its chief prey. Plumage smooth and sleek, the heron moves as if in a slow-motion film. Green-backed Herons are shy birds and if they spot a human some way off, they will hastily leave their feeding place, but they often return, apparently to see whether it is now safe to carry on fishing. These herons favour the dense willow thickets in river valleys for nesting and form colonies of four to five pairs or are solitary. The nest is a loose structure of willow twigs usually at a height of two to four metres. Timing of nesting and laying varies considerably in different parts of Ussuriland, and this leads to a very extended season. We have found fresh clutches of two to five eggs in "Cedar Valley" nature reserve in the extreme south in June when hatching was already taking place further north on the Bikin river.

The **Japanese Night Heron** (*Gorsachius goisagi*) was recorded as a vagrant many times in southern Ussuriland. It breeds only in Japan. The **Squacco Heron** (*Ardeola ralloides*) (Plate 16) is distributed in Africa and the western part of Asia, while in Russia it inhabits the southern part of European Russia and Central Asia. The Squacco Heron usually inhabits small forests and reedbeds on the shores of water bodies, preferably large ones. The breeding biology of this species is typical of egrets. In April, the birds start building their nest in the trees or in the reedbeds, and the clutch of four to seven eggs is laid in mid-May. Incubation takes 22-24 days and the young stay in the nests for about one month. They are fed by both parents. The Squacco Heron feeds mainly on fish and different aquatic invertebrates.

The **Chinese Pond Heron** (*Ardeola bacchus*) is believed to breed in the reedbeds of Lake Khanka in the south of Ussuriland, even though this has not yet been proved. The birds have been seen here many times. The breeding range of this species includes China and Indochina.

In the south of the country a small, mainly white heron with distinctive heavy jowl and short neck can sometimes be seen by the shores of rivers and lakes, in the agricultural fields. It is the **Cattle Egret** (*Bubulcus ibis*) which is widespread around the world in suitable habitats and is known for its recent expansion of range. This egret breeds in large colonies, nearly always mixed with other herons and egrets. Nests are usually in the trees, and the clutch of five to seven (rarely 4-9) eggs are laid in mid-May. It is incubated by both parents for 22-24 days.

The true egrets are united in the subgenus *Casmerodius* and there are four species in Russia. The largest is the **Great Egret** (*Egretta alba*) (Plate 16), a bird well known to ornithologists and birdwatchers. In Russia there are two subspecies of it. The nominal *E. a. alba* is widespread from the western borders to the Far East and there it inhabits Khanka lowland, whereas *E. a. modesta* lives in the very south of Ussuriland, in Lake Khasan.

The huge reedbeds of Lake Khanka in the south of Ussuriland are home for the rare **Intermediate Egret** (*Egreta intermedia*). Breeding here has been proved quite recently. The main distribution range includes South and South-East Asia.

Enjoying a wide distribution range in Africa, Asia and Australia, the **Little Egret** (*Egretta garzetta*) (Plate 16) lives in the very south of the European part of Russia, Caucasus and Central Asia. The habitats are like those of other egrets but this species is usually more numerous and noisy. It frequents agricultural fields, lagoons, gently flowing rivers and streams as well as saline coastal waters. It tolerates human presence well. The Little Egret is a typical colonial breeder and nests in the trees as well as reedbeds. The breeding season starts by the end of April.

Swinhoe's Egret (*Egretta eulophotes*) has been reported many times from the south of Ussuriland. There is a strong probability that it breeds in the huge reedbeds of Lake Khanka. The breeding range includes south-east China and Korea.

Distributed in the vast expanses of Africa, Europe and Asia, the **Grey Heron** (*Ardea cinerea*) is a very well known and studied bird. It inhabits all kinds of water bodies in Russia from the western borders to the Far East and breeds in colonies on inaccessible trees as well as the reedbeds (in the south). Here the Grey Heron is a very shy bird and does not share the habits this species is developing in Western Europe.

The **Purple Heron** (*Ardea purpurea*) is restricted to the water bodies in the south of Russia, including the usual places for many of the above mentioned species of egrets and herons. It includes the shores of the Black and Caspian Seas and the deltas of large rivers in Central Asia. It breeds both in the trees and in the reedbeds. Purple Herons form monogamous pairs for one breeding season and breed in colonies as well as in isolated pairs. The clutch consists of four to five eggs and is incubated by both sexes for about 26 days. The young, which are fed by both parents with fish, amphibians and various insects stay in their nest approximately 45 days. A different subspecies *A. p. manilensis* inhabits the southern part of Ussuriland.

The Family Threskiornithidae (Ibises and Spoonbills) begins with the **White Spoonbill** (*Platalea leucorodia*) (Plate 16). This unusual bird inhabits different types of water bodies in the south choosing dense reedbeds, shrubs and trees for breeding. It is a colonial species and preference is given to islands to breed on. The approximate number of breeding pairs in Russia is 2600-3600 and the White Spoonbill is included in the Russian Red Data Book as rare and declining.

The **Glossy Ibis** (*Plegadis falcinellus*) (Plate 17) has a more restricted distribution range than the White Spoonbill. In Russia, it breeds locally on the shores of shallow lakes, rivers and floods, forming mixed colonies with the many species already mentioned. It is more common than the Spoonbill and is not causing conservationists serious concern. Nests are built both in reedbeds and in the trees, and three to six eggs are laid in May. Incubation is performed by both sexes and takes approximately 21 days. The young fledge to maturity in about one month and are fed by both parents. The food of the Glossy Ibis consists mainly of small fish and a number of aquatic invertebrates.

The **Japanese Crested Ibis** (*Nipponia nippon*) is one of the word's rarest birds and is now extinct in Russia. It formerly bred in Ussuriland. It does, however, survive in very small numbers in Japan (no longer in the wild) and China.

Two species of the genus *Threskiornis* are registered in Russia as vagrants. The **Sacred Ibis** (*T. aethiopica*) was registered many times in the Black and Caspian Sea regions while the **Oriental Ibis** (*T. melanocephala*) was registered once in the south of Ussuriland.

The familiar **White Stork** (*Ciconia ciconia*) is represented in Russia by two subspecies (out of the world's two). The nominal inhabits the European part of the country while *C. c. asiatica* which is larger lives in Central Asia. Apart from traditional nesting places on the roofs of houses and in trees, the storks also settle on power lines. In 1988, we were shown a colony of twelve nests, each on a power line.

In the vast expanses of the Khanka lowland, along the Bikin River in Ussuriland and in the Amur region, you may see a bird that, from afar, you would quite likely mistake for the familiar White Stork in Europe. This is the **Oriental White Stork** (*Ciconia boyciana*) (Plate 17), a rare and declining species, which is registered in the IUCN/ICPB Red Data Book. As a breeding bird, it is found mainly in Russia. This species is distinguished from its European cousin by its larger size and, especially, by its thick black bill. It always nests far from man and is an exceptionally shy and wary bird. Its nests are built at varying heights in the trees – it depends on what is available, though tall, thick-trunked trees are preferred and the birds often use one with a broken, flat top. Arrival at the breeding grounds takes place from mid to late March. Three to four eggs (the clutch ranges from two to five) are laid in the first half of April and incubated by both adults. The young spend more than two months in the nest, fledging at 65-68 days. Departure from breeding grounds takes place in September and October.

In the Bureya-Arkhara lowland (Amur region) Dr S. Vinter has found 45 nests of the Oriental White Stork. A further eight to ten pairs nest at Lake Khanka. It is also a scarce breeder in the Bikin Valley and along the Ussuri River. Outside Russia, there are small populations in north-east China and Korea.

The **Black Stork** (*Ciconia nigra*), which is mostly a forest species, has wide but patchy distribution in Russia. Everywhere it is quite rare and secretive. Separate populations inhabit the European forests of Russia, the Central Asian mountains, and the immense forests of the Far East.

FLAMINGOES – ORDER PHOENICOPTERIFORMES

There is only one species of this order in Russia which is the **Greater Flamingo** (*Phoenicopterus ruber roseus*) (Fig. 18). It has a single breeding colony in the country located in Kurgaldzin Nature Reserve in Central

Fig. 18 *Flock of Greater Flaminoges (*Phoenicopterus ruber roseus*) wintering to the south of the Caspian Sea. Photo L. Veisman*

Kazakhstan. The number of breeding birds here differs from year to year but recently did not exceed 11,000 pairs. This population winters on the shores of the Caspian Sea on both eastern and western sides.

DUCKS, GEESE AND SWANS – ORDER ANSERIFORMES

This order is very well represented in Russia mainly because of the huge tundra belt and the abundance of marshes and swamps still unaffected by human activities. There are 62 species recorded in Russia altogether, 52 of which breed, nine are vagrants and one species (the Crested Shelduck) is believed to be extinct.

Genus *Branta* has four species in Russia. The **Canada Goose** (*B. canadensis*) is recorded as vagrant, with three subspecies found in the north of the Russian Far East including Chukotka and the Commander Islands.

The **Barnacle Goose** (*Branta leucopsis*) breeds in the high Arctic latitudes including the Novaya Zemlia and Vaigach islands. It also was registered as a breeder at Matsalu nature reserve in Estonia.

Being strictly coastal and more aquatic than other geese, the **Brent Goose** (*Branta bernicla*) inhabits the coastal areas of the high Arctic from the Yamal peninsula to the Khatanga river delta in Taimyr. The **Pacific Brent Goose** (*B. nigricans*), which is now regarded as a separate species by Russian ornithologists, inhabits the area from the Lena river delta to the Chukotka peninsula.

A Russian endemic restricted to the tundra of the Taimyr, Yamal and Gydan peninsulas is the **Red-breasted Goose** (*Rufibrenta ruficollis*) (Plate 18). Numbers of this species are uneven within the restricted area of distribution. This bird migrates to the south-east, southern and south-west shores of the Caspian for the winter, but individual geese have been recorded in winter in almost all the countries of Europe. Large numbers are now wintering in Bulgaria and Romania.

Typical Red-breasted Goose nesting habitat is the driest and highest parts of the tundra, most frequently terraces and steep slopes by river banks. Nest-building starts soon after the return to the breeding grounds, and the geese tend to form small colonies of four to six pairs. The base and walls of the nest are made of dry grass and other plant stems and the cup is lined with down. As is well known, Red-breasted Geese tend to nest near birds of prey – Peregrines or Rough-legged Buzzards. Even stranger apparently is the habit of nesting in the colonies of large gulls. It is remarkable that the gulls do not harm the goslings, but the geese nesting in the gull colonies are known to sit much more tightly and can be practically touched on the nest. The whole question of the complex inter-relationships between the potential enemies deserves more detailed investigation. Red-breasted Geese lay three to ten eggs which are incubated by the female alone for a period of about 26 days. It is rare for the loss of eggs to exceed 15-20 per cent. In the years when lemming numbers are low, more goose eggs are lost to foxes. The average brood size is 5.5. While the female is incubating, her mate stays on the bank or water nearby. When leaving the nest for a break from incubation, the goose covers her eggs with down and other nest material. After hatching, and when the goslings are dry, the male joins the family which now stays in place where there is fresh growth of grass.

Red-breasted Geese undergo a complete moult in summer, while fledged juveniles have a partial autumn-winter moult. Before the summer moult which renders the birds flightless, the geese join in flocks and then all renew their flight feathers more or less simultaneously over a period of 15-20 days. Most adults and juveniles start to fly again about August 20th. The main food of this species is various parts of grasses and other herbaceous plants.

Three of the four representatives of the genus *Anser* have their breeding grounds in the tundra. The **Greylag Goose** (*A. anser*) has really varied and patchy distribution in different geographical zones of Russia from the western borders to the Far East.

The **Bean Goose** (*Anser fabalis*) and the **Greater White-fronted Goose** (*A. albifrons*) are common tundra nesters. The **Lesser White-fronted Goose** (*A. erythropus*) has recently suffered a sharp decline in numbers, which is a matter of growing concern to ornithologists and conservationists. The Greater White-fronted Goose is the most numerous goose in Russia and is found in damp, low-lying tundra and wooded tundra. It nests in dry sites amidst areas of bushy tundra with an abundance of rivers and lakes. Four to six eggs are laid from mid-June. After rearing a brood, the adults start their moult and become temporarily flightless. White-fronts eat mainly young plant shoots.

The Bean Goose also occurs in the taiga zone. It nests in marshy tundra where there are many lakes or on remote streams and lakes in the taiga. The nest is sited on a dry hummock or slope, often on a river island. A clutch of three to six eggs is laid from the first half of June and incubated by the female, her mate remaining close by. Both adults care for the young. From mid-July the Bean Geese start their moult and in suitable places flocks up to 3000 birds can still be seen. For example, in the Kamchatka peninsula in the valley of the Moroshechnaya River several subspecies gather for the moult and are easily distinguishable from each other.

Of the rarer tundra geese, the **Snow Goose** (*Chen hyperboreus*) (Plate 18) has a colony in the Wrangel Island nature reserve in the Chuktchi Sea. **Ross's Goose** (*Chen rossi*) is registered as vagrant on Wrangel Island, and the **Emperor Goose** (*Philacte canagica*) (Plate 19) breeds on the Chukotka peninsula.

The high mountains of Pamir are home for the **Bar-headed Goose** (*Anser indicus*). The colony breeds on the shore of Lake Kara-Kulat at around 4000 m. It has also been found breeding in the nests of birds of prey in the trees along the rivers in Tuva in southern Siberia.

The **Swan Goose** (*Anser cygnoides*) is very rare in Russia and is included in the Russian Red Data Book. The number of breeding pairs in the whole country is estimated at 300 to 400. The several remaining spots of its once considerable range of distribution are in the Transbaikal and the Far East.

There are four swan species in the country, the most familiar of which is the **Mute Swan** (*Cygnus olor*) (Plate 19). It is interesting to note that there are many places in Russia where this species is extremely shy and wary and has no similarities to the behaviour of the Mute Swan in Europe. For example, in Lake Alakol in Eastern Kazakhstan the Mute Swans we encountered were probably the most shy of all birds. The area of distribution of Mute Swans in Russia is very patchy but huge, expanding from the western borders to the Far East. There are many places in this area where swans are irregular breeders.

The **Whooper Swan** (*Cygnus cygnus*) is rather common nester in the taiga zone and has very wide distribution throughout the country. Especially popular in Britain, thanks to the efforts of the late Sir Peter Scott, is **Bewick's Swan** (*C. bewickii*) (Fig. 19). Bewick's Swan inhabits low-lying and very marshy tundra within a range extending east to the Kolyma River in Siberia. Part of the population winters in Britain, stopping off on migration at Matsalu nature reserve in Estonia and in the Netherlands. Rather scarce and unevenly distributed, Bewick's Swan breeds amidst the tundra with countless lakes and

Fig. 19 *Bewick's Swans* (Cygnus bewickii) *wintering at Slimbridge.*
Photo A. Knystautas

winding rivers. The nest, sited on a dry mound by a lake or on an island, is a fairly massive structure of moss and sedge. A clutch of three to four eggs is laid from early June and incubated by the female alone, the male staying nearby. The **Tundra Swan** (*C. columbianus*) which also breeds in the Chukotsk tundra is treated as a separate species by Russian ornithologists.

Colourful Shelducks have two breeding species in Russia and one regarded as extinct. The **Ruddy Shelduck**'s (*Tadorna ferruginea*) breeding range covers huge expanses of Asia, mostly its mountainous part. This beautiful bird breeds in very diverse landscapes from deserts to the high mountains. Their characteristic calls resound in the mountain lakes as high as 4000 m or even higher. The nests are situated in holes in the ground or among the rocks and cliffs. The usual clutch consists of eight to nine eggs and is incubated by the female alone for about 28-29 days. The brood is reared by both parents. When disturbed, adults show great agitation and come quite close to humans particularly when one of the young is caught.

The **Common Shelduck** (*Tadorna tadorna*) is distributed in Europe and Asia up the Trans-Baikal region. In Russia, it lives mostly in southern part of the country, choosing different water bodies mainly in steppe and desert zones.

The last record of the **Crested Shelduck** (*Tadorna cristata*) was in 1964 in the Bay of Peter the Great near Vladivostok. This bird is believed to be extinct even though there have been attempts by ornithologists of different

Fig. 20 *European Widgeon* (Anas penelope) *which come from Russia to winter in Britain. Photo A. Knystautas*

countries to discover its possible breeding places. There have been no encouraging results reported up to now.

There is quite a number of common ducks which breed widely in Russia, mostly in tundra and taiga belts. Many of them breed in Europe or are very familiar to European birdwatchers during the winter. Among them are the **Mallard** (*Anas platyrhynchos*), **Green-winged Teal** (*A. crecca*), the **Gadwall** (*A. strepera*), the **European Widgeon** (*A. penelope*) (Fig. 20), the **Northern Pintail** (*A. acuta*), the **Garganey** (*A. querquedula*) and the **Northern Shoveller** (*A. clypeata*) (Plate 19).

The **Spotbill Duck** (*Anas poecilorhyncha*) nests quite commonly in the Transbaikal region, Amur region and Ussuriland. Numbers of breeding ducks on the huge Lake Khanka in Ussuriland are directly dependent on the water level in the particular year, and increase when the water level rises. Like most of other ducks, the Spotbill nests in a well-concealed site on the ground. It usually lays seven to nine eggs. Its breeding range covers South and East Asia, Australia and Tasmania.

The Russian endemic is the **Baikal Teal** (*Anas formosa*) (Fig. 21), a delicate and beautiful duck whose breeding range covers Eastern Siberia. In the north it breeds also in a wooded tundra. The breeding biology resembles that of other ducks of this genus. The Baikal Teal is an uncommon species and has an uneven distribution. It winters in South-East Asia.

Fig. 21 *Male Baikal Teal (*Anas formosa*) on Lake Khanka. Photo Y. Shibnev*

The **Falcated Teal** (*Anas falcata*) (Plate 19) is one of the most beautiful of all ducks. A typical East Asian species, it is a characteristic but rather scarce breeder of various waters in the southern part of the Russian Far East. Only a few pairs nest in Lake Khanka, but in August, when Falcated Ducks assemble there to moult, they comprise about 22 per cent of all the moulting waterfowl in the lake. The species is a ground nester and lays eight to ten eggs. It is distributed in East Siberia, the Far East, north-east China and Japan.

The **Marbled Teal** (*Anas angustirostris*) (Plate 20) is now very rare in Russia and is included in the Russian Red Data Book in Category I – species facing danger of extinction. Its breeding area in the Caspian region has been drastically reduced and the numbers of recorded individuals are extremely low. In the 1930s this species used to winter in the deltas of large rivers in huge flocks. Now it is very rare and breeds in lowland parts of Azerbaidjan. It is no longer recorded in summer or in winter in the places where it used to be common.

Among the ducks of the genus *Anas* there are two which are registered as vagrants in Russia; the **Common Teal** (*A. carolinensis*), and the **American Widgeon** (*A. americana*) which were recorded in the areas close to Alaska.

The **Mandarin Duck** (*Aix galericulata*) leaves a wonderful impression in the wild in its native habitats. If you are lucky, you may see a pair of small ducks moving rapidly downstream in the clear water of the rock-strewn river which flows through the majestic forest. Such is the splendour of the drake's plumage, it is difficult to believe the vision is real. It is not easy to come to your senses after such an encounter: you are held spellbound by the gentle gurgling of the river, the sparkling crystals of spray, moss encrusted stones on the bank, the delicate green of the forest, the swirling shreds of mist, and the ducks swimming past – birds which Nature seems to have adorned with all the colours of the rainbow. Of course, many people are familiar with this astonishing duck. Many will have seen it in pictures or in zoos or in wildfowl collections, but how many ornithologists and birdwatchers will have dreamt of seeing in the primeval, untouched Ussuri forest, its natural habitat. The Mandarin Duck, which feeds mainly on acorns, is a declining species, included in the Russian Red Data Book. There has been a 1.5 to 2-fold decline in its numbers over the last 20 years.

Mandarins inhabit the remote river valleys in the taiga and are found in both lowland and mountain regions. This pearl of Manchuria returns from its winter quarters in late March or early April and seeks out first ice-free patches and rills or the springs which do not freeze in winter. Some Mandarins arrive in pairs; the others, probably younger birds, in small flocks. By mid-April, when all the ice has melted, the unpaired birds may be seen indulging in their fantastic courtship displays. The drakes are truly splendid sight this time: with crests slightly raised and upstanding orange "sails" on their wings, they parade all their rainbow finery before the ducks. Following pair formation, Mandarins start nesting. They use a tree-cavity, sometimes as much as 15-20 m up, or more rarely nest on the ground under a fallen tree or dead broken-off branch. The female lays seven to twelve uniformly pale, slightly tinted eggs directly on the wood dust and debris in the cavity, adding only a little down plucked from her breast. The drake remains near the nest for a long time and flies off with his mate to feed at nearby watercourses, usually in the early morning and in the evening. The eggs hatch after 28-31 days. Once they are more or less dry, the ducklings leap down to the ground from the tree hole and follow the female to the water. Broods keep to the most remote river arms and creeks. The ducklings fledge in July and August, but some birds breed late so that young still unable to fly are sometimes seen in September. In October, the Mandarins fly south. They winter in Japan and south-east China.

We will not discuss in detail a group of diving ducks which are common in Russia and are well known to Western European birdwatchers. Among them are the **Red-crested Pochard** (*Netta rufina*) (Plate 20), the **Common Pochard** (*Aythya ferina*), the **Ferruginous Duck** (*A. nyroca*), the **Tufted Duck** (*A. fuligula*) (Fig. 22) and the **Greater Scaup** (*A. marila*). Except for the Scaup which is primarily a maritime species of duck, the other species prefer different kinds of water bodies and are widely distributed in the country.

Fig. 22 *Tufted Ducks (*Aythya fuligula*) near St. Petersburg. Photo A. Sokolov*

The Red-crested Pochard and the Ferruginous Duck are more common in the southern parts of the country, in steppe and desert zones.

The **Redhead** (*Aythya americana*) is registered as vagrant in the New Siberia archipelago in the Arctic Ocean.

In Ussuriland, you may be lucky enough to catch a glimpse of **Baer's Pochard** (*Aythya baeri*), a rare duck with a restricted range. These ducks arrive in Ussuriland in late March or early April and at first they are found, together with great numbers of other duck species, on the unfrozen water patches. Later, some move north, while the rest disperse to breed at various rivers and lakes. They start nesting in the second half of May and by early June most birds will be incubating full clutches of nine to thirteen eggs. The nest is made of plant stems, grass blades and a little down, and is usually sited on flooded lowlands among tussocks, but near Khasan, nests were found about 150 m from lagoons, on a dry bank. At Lake Khanka, nests are often in colonies of gulls and terns. The first broods are usually noted from about mid-July. The birds are very sensitive at this time, tending to lurk in the half-flooded patches of swamp vegetation.

When the water level falls at Khanka, Baer's Pochard numbers are also low and the density is about 1-2 pairs per square kilometre. This figure increases to nearly twice as many if the water level rises. Their diet consists mainly of seeds and the green parts of aquatic plants, but insects and small fish are also eaten. This species breeds in north-east China as well as in Ussuriland and the Amur region. The **Lesser Scaup** (*Aythya affinis*) was recorded in the Kamchatka peninsula as a vagrant species; it breeds in North America. The **Harlequin Duck** (*Histrionicus histrionicus*) breeds on the

Fig. 23 *Long-tailed Duck* (Clangula hyemalis) *in Taimyr. Photo A. Sokolov*

shores of mountain rivers and streams, and on marine islands in Eastern Siberia and the Far East.

Among the ducks typical to the tundra ecosystem, mention should be made of the **Long-tailed Duck** (*Clangula hyemalis*) (Plate 20 and Fig. 23). This common, locally numerous species inhabits wet grassy tundra from the Kola peninsula east to Chukotka. The nest is in a dry site – among grass or under a willow bush, close to the water's edge. Six to eight eggs are laid from mid-June and the incubating female will allow humans to approach the nest closely. The drakes take no part in the care of eggs or young, but together with non-breeding females they form huge flocks in coastal bays or on lakes. Long-tailed Ducks eat insect larvae, aquatic invertebrates and fish.

The **Common Goldeneye** (*Bucephala clangula*) is a fairly common species in Russia with a huge breeding range from the western borders to the Far East. It nests in tree holes on the shores of forest lakes. Two other species of the same genus are registered as vagrants. **Barrow's Goldeneye** (*B. islandica*) was recorded on the lakes Ilmen and Onega in north-west Russia while the **Bufflehead** (*B. albeola*) was found in different parts of the Russian Far East.

There are four species of eider which nest in Russia. The **Common Eider** (*Somateria mollissima*) (Fig. 24) is a fairly common bird and nests mostly on marine islands. Eiders only come to dry land during the breeding season. Otherwise they spend their time on the open sea or closer inshore. Following their spring arrival, eiders congregate in rafts of tens or hundreds in quiet bays and inlets. The drakes stand out in such rafts, their strikingly attractive, mainly black-and-white plumage contrasting with sombre mottled brown

Fig. 24 *Common Eider* (Somateria mollissima*) at Matsalu, Estonia.*
Photo A. Knystautas

females. Eiders feed by frequently diving. Underwater, they use their wings to swim about and they stay down for 25-30 seconds. Pair-formation takes place where the ducks spend the winter. The nests are built on different islands and sometimes form quite large colonies. A shallow scrape, usually protected by a stone, cliff or log, serves as a nest and the four to seven eggs are laid in May or June, depending on location. All the incubation is by the female, and it is interesting that she eats almost nothing during that period, managing to live off her large fat supply. By the end of incubation, the female eider will have lost nearly a whole kilogram in weight. After hatching, the ducklings will spend another couple of days in the nest before leaving for the water. They become independent when they reach full adult size, i.e. at about two to three months old. Eiders eat mainly animal food, including aquatic worms, molluscs, and small crabs. The species is, of course, famed throughout the world for its exceptionally warm down which the female plucks from her breast to line the nest.

The drake **King Eider** (*Somateria spectabilis*) (Plate 20) is splendidly adorned. This species has an uneven distribution in the Russian tundras. It often breeds far from the coast, and nests in a dry, well-concealed, or sometimes completely open, site. Four to six eggs are laid from the end of June and incubated by the female alone. The drakes gather for the moult in July. Their diet is various aquatic invertebrates.

Fig. 25
White-headed Duck
(Oxyura leucocephala).
Photo A. Knystautas

Of striking and bizarre appearance is the drake **Spectacled Eider** (*Somateria fischeri*) (Plate 21). This is a rather rare species found in coastal tundra of the mainland and islands in East Siberia and Chukotka. It is a solitary nester in tundra rich in lakes and marshland. The nest is usually near a small lake, often on a tussock. The clutch of five to seven eggs is laid in July. While the female incubates, the drakes are already assembling to moult.

Steller's Eider (*Polysticta stelleri*) is found in similar habitats in Eastern Siberia with the breeding range extending west to the Taimyr peninsula. It also inhabits the American Arctics.

Out of five species of scoters (*Melanitta*) four are recorded as breeders and one as vagrant. All scoters are tundra and taiga species breeding on the shores of rivers and lakes, on the marine islands. Better known and more common are the **Velvet Scoter** (*M. fusca*) and the **Black Scoter** (*M. nigra*) (Plate 21). In the Eastern Siberia and the Far East two more species nest – the **American Scoter** (*M. americana*) and **Pied-billed Scoter** (*M. deglandi*). The **Surf Scoter** (*M. perspicillata*) was recorded as vagrant in the Commander Islands and in Estonia.

The lakes in steppe and desert zones in Kazakhstan and Central Asia are inhabited by the rare and poorly studied **White-headed Duck** (*Oxyura leucocephala*) (Fig. 25). Since the 1960s a considerable reduction of numbers was reported and at present there are about 700-900 breeding pairs in the whole breeding region within Russia. The world total in the wild is about 15,000 birds. This species appears in the Russian Red Data Book.

Quite unusual for their group are the mergansers (*Mergus*), four species of which breed in Russia. While the **Smew** (*M. albellus*) (Fig. 26), the **Goosander** (*M. merganser*) and the **Red-breasted Merganser** (*M. serrator*)

Fig. 26 *Spring displays of Smew* (Mergus albellus). *Photo A. Knystautas*

(Plate 21) have a rather wide distribution in Russia and are well known in the West, the **Chinese Merganser** (*M. squamatus*) is very exotic. It lives along the rivers which flow through mixed forests in the Sikhote-Alin mountains, Amur region and in the small territory of north-east China. This is an extremely interesting bird and is not often seen by ornithologists. Imagine pushing your way through a dense forest. Now and again you have to wade through shallow water channels, springs, creeks and backwaters, and there are more of these the closer you get to the clear waters of the main river. There is still ice by the water edge. Quietly and carefully raising a branch that hinders your view, you see a pair of Chinese Mergansers by the opposite bank. They seem to have an almost unreal beauty of the spring. The scaly pattern on the flanks of the drake is clearly visible through binoculars. This is the scene you may be fortunate enough to witness on a river in Sikhote-Alin in mid-March, when the first mergansers arrive in the region. At that time, the lower reaches of the rivers are still ice-covered, while on the middle reaches you see here and there the sparkle of the first ice-free rills. The first flocks of mergansers are small – three to five, rarely seven, birds. Spring passage is light: small flocks are seen flying upstream, keeping low and following exactly each bend in the river, only occasionally taking a short cut. Some of the birds land where there are open patches and here they will fish, even diving under ice. In mid-April, groups of five to nine birds will indulge in communal display, chasing one another, splashing, and diving. Having moved a little away from the main group, a pair will perform their courtship ritual – head-bobbing in a special way which usually culminates in copulation. After a bout of display, the whole flock will rest for a time on the river bank.

Chinese Mergansers nest in holes in trees, sometimes very high up. The female lays up to twelve white eggs on wood dust and debris in the cavity. Incubation starts in late April and the first broods are seen in the last days of May. The ducklings leap down to the ground from the nest-hole and quickly make their way to the water. They dive expertly and will disappear under the water if threatened, coming up again 5-7 m away under the protection of a steep bank or floating debris. The drakes probably moult very rapidly at this time, as you will no longer see them in the splendour of their breeding plumage by the end of May. In October, the merganser flocks move downstream and single birds only occasionally remain to winter on unfrozen stretches of river. Taking into consideration the rivers on which Chinese Mergansers can breed, the total population in Sikhote-Alin mountains is unlikely to exceed 1,000-1,500 breeding pairs.

BIRDS OF PREY – ORDER FALCONIFORMES

Altogether there are 54 species of birds of prey in Russia. Forty-eight species breed, another two are likely to breed but this is not yet proven and there are four vagrant species.

The sole representative of the Osprey family (Pandionidae), the **Osprey** (*Pandion haliaetus*) (Fig 27) has a very wide distribution in Russia as well as in the rest of the world. The total number of breeding pairs in Russia is estimated at 10,000. This bird is included in the Russian Red Data Book, Category III – rare bird.

The **Black-shouldered Kite** (*Elanus caeruleus*) is recorded as vagrant and was found in the southern part of Russian Central Asia, near Termez.

Apart from the familiar **Western Honey Buzzard** (*Pernis apivorus*) which breeds in Russia from the western frontiers to Western Siberia, the country has another species of *Pernis* – the **Crested Honey Buzzard** (*P. ptilorhynchus*) (Plate 22). It is fairly widespread in South-East and East Asia and inhabits various types of forests. The species is migratory in the north of its range, dispersive or migratory in the south. In Russia, all the populations are migratory. It is a scarce breeder in Eastern Siberia from Lake Baikal to Ussuriland, where it is commoner than elsewhere in the country, and Sahkalin Island. Arriving fairly late (during May) on their breeding grounds, birds settle to breed straight away. Having established a territory, the pair sets about repairing the old nest, and they also display at this time: both birds circle high in the sky and from time to time hover briefly on vertically raised and quivering wings. The nest is built high up in a tree fork. One or two eggs are laid from early June and the chicks hatch in the first week of

Fig 27 *Osprey (*Pandion haliaetus*) at Markakol Nature Reserve in the Altai Mountains. Photo A. Knystautas*

July. They are brooded by the female while the male brings food. Crested Honey Buzzards eat larvae of wasps and bumble-bees, less commonly frogs. As the male brings the whole honey-combs, a few larvae are not eaten and survive to turn into adult wasps, and the chicks amuse themselves by trying to catch them. When the chicks are older, the female also starts hunting, usually close to the nest where she catches mainly frogs. The male travels further afield to search out wasp nests. The young fledge from late August. Crested Honey Buzzards, like their European cousins, breed late in order to coincide with the appearance of their insect prey. In September and October they leave Russia, migrating to their winter quarters in South-East Asia and Indonesia.

There are two species of kite (*Milvus*) in Russia. The **Red Kite** (*M. milvus*) nests scarcely in the western part of the country and in Caucasus. The **Black Kite** (*M. migrans*) is rather common throughout its huge distribution range in Russia which includes European Russia, Caucasus, Central Asia, Siberia and the Far East.

As for the harriers, there are five breeding species in Russia. These are birds of open spaces, nesting in the fields and reedbeds, tall grass meadows and among bushes. The most exotic one, apart from the better known and common **Marsh Harrier** (*Circus aeruginosus*) (Fig. 28), **Hen Harrier** (*C. cyaneus*) and **Montagu's Harrier** (*C. pygargus*) is the **Pied Harrier** (*C. melanoleucus*) (Plate 22).

Fig. 28 *Marsh Harrier (*Circus aeruginosus) *in Lithuania. Photo H. Sakalauskas*

The Pied Harrier nests in the Far East and is locally common, but overall is not a numerous species and the population is declining owing to agricultural development of its breeding grounds. It inhabits wet meadows with various herbaceous plants and shrubs. In the north of Ussuriland it nests on the raised sphagnum-moss bogs ("mari") and in the Khanka lowland, in sedge and reed-grass marshes. Pied Harriers arrive to breed in early April. The nest, of thin twigs, reeds and grass, is built on the ground, on a tussock in thick grass or reeds, or in a low bush. Four to five eggs are laid in mid-May. Before nesting, the harriers often perform aerial courtship displays which are a delight to watch. Both birds will fly up high into the sky, and they seem to be almost wallowing in the air as they throw themselves from side to side, sharply loop-the-loop and fly upside-down. The black-and-white male especially is shown to best advantage in this wonderful display.

Incubation is mainly by the female, the male taking over very occasionally. His prime task is to hunt and bring prey to the nest. Pied Harriers eat various rodents and frogs, sometimes pounce on small birds, and also take insects. Food is passed in the air, the female flying from the nest to meet the male and snatching the prey as she approaches him from below. Sometimes the male drops what he is carrying and the female catches it in flight.

Young harriers fledge at the end of July, and departure from the breeding grounds is in late August or early September. However, an abundance of

Fig. 29
Northern Goshawk
(Accipiter gentilis)
in central Lithuania.
Photo U. Pilinkus

mice and voles will keep birds in the area until November and some Pied Harriers may even winter in the south of Ussuriland. The breeding range embraces the south of the Russian Far East as well as north-east China.

The **Pallid Harrier** (*Circus macrourus*) is a typical steppe and semi-desert species which has characteristically patchy distribution due to the agricultural changes in its habitat. More than other harriers, it prefers entirely open terrain. The main breeding range is within Russia.

Following the harriers is the genus of true hawks (*Accipiter*) which has six breeding species in Russia. The well known **Northern Goshawk** (*A. gentilis*) (Fig. 29) is widely distributed as far as the Far East, and in the north-east of the country a wonderful white subspecies can be found. Also very familiar is the **Northern Sparrowhawk** (*A. nisus*). The southern parts of the country are inhabited by the **Shikra Sparrowhawk** (*A. badius*) and **Levant Sparrowhawk** (*A. brevipes*). Both the latter are rather scarce and unevenly distributed.

The most exotic of the sparrowhawks which breed in Russia is probably **Horsfield's Sparrowhawk** (*Accipiter soloensis*) (Plate 22). Its range embraces Korea and Eastern China. Only four nests of this species have been found in Russia and the author and his colleagues were fortunate enough to make such a discovery. Horsfield's Sparrowhawk occurs only in the extreme south of Ussuriland, which is the northern edge of its range. Birds arrive on their breeding grounds in early May and are soon seen performing display-flights. Nesting then follows in late May or early June. The nest is built in a tree fork, near the trunk or on an outer branch, and at a height of 8-12 m. The lining of the nest is green foliage. A clutch of three to four eggs is laid from about mid-June. Both parents share the incubation and the feeding of their young. The male normally hunts far from the nest and, when approaching with prey, announces his arrival to the female with a loud call which is reminiscent of the Eurasian Sparrowhawk, and not at all like the Besra Sparrowhawk (*Accipiter gularis*) which also breeds in Ussuriland. The female leaves the nest to collect the prey from her mate. She also hunts, but tends to stay closer to the nest. Horsfield's Sparrowhawks actively defend their nest against crows and other predators. They will attack squirrels and even man, striking with their talons. The young hawks start to fly at 22 days and a week later they will be hunting for themselves. On July 8, 1981, we found a nest in "Cedar Valley" nature reserve. It was about 8 m up in the almost horizontal fork of a Mongolian Oak, one of a stand of this species on a south-facing slope. The nest contained three incubated eggs and these hatched on the 12-13th July. The parents fed their young mainly with frogs, also some small birds and insects. During three days' observation, the male came to the nest only four times, each time bringing fresh green foliage.

Unlike Horsfield's Sparrowhawk, the **Besra Sparrowhawk** (*Accipiter gularis*) (Plate 23) occasionally nests slightly higher up on the slopes of hills. The riverain forest is where the Besra's nest is most likely to be found. If you approach and see the hawk flying from tree to tree, calling loudly, that is a sure sign it is no use searching here for the nest. Besras are very secretive and wary near the nest, but their behaviour changes abruptly once the nest has been discovered. Then these diminutive hawks actively defend the nest with quite remarkable energy and vigour. The female especially launches repeated dive-attacks on anyone attempting to climb the Elm or Korean Willow near the top of which the small nest is visible. The attacks reach their highest intensity if the intruder should reach the nest itself. Besras are late breeders, not laying before early June, which means that the young fledge in mid-August. These hawks feed almost exclusively on small birds. They spend the winter in South and South-East Asia.

There are four breeding species of buzzards (*Buteo*) in Russia. The well-known **Eurasian Buzzard** (*B. buteo*) is one of the most common birds of prey in the European part of the country. Its breeding range extends all the way to the Pacific Ocean.

A typical raptor of the tundra is the **Rough-legged Buzzard** (*Buteo lagopus*) (Fig. 30). It has a circumpolar distribution in the tundras of Eurasia and America. Clutch size is closely linked with feeding conditions in a given year, more precisely with lemming numbers which, as is well known, are subject to marked fluctuations. The usual clutch size is three to four eggs

Fig. 30 *Rough-legged Buzzard* (Buteo lagopus) *in Taimyr Nature Reserve. Photo A. Ouwerkerk*

but up to seven may be laid in a favourable year. On the other hand, if the lemming population drops to an exceptionally low level, Rough-legged Buzzards make no attempt to breed at all.

The **Upland Buzzard** (*Buteo hemilasius*) (Plate 23) has a quite restricted distribution range in the Transbaikal region. It is a typical steppe species and is common locally. The numbers of Upland Buzzards fluctuate considerably from year to year. The clutch consists of two to four eggs and the laying takes place by the end of May. The young fledge by the end of July. The food consists of birds and their eggs, and various rodents.

The **Long-legged Buzzard** (*Buteo rufinus*) (Plate 23) is a bird of steppes and semi-deserts on the lower reaches of the Volga river, in Central Asia and Kazakhstan. It is migratory in the northern part of its range, resident in the south. Numbers of these buzzards are closely dependent on the sate of rodent populations, as these animals form their main prey. In the south of its range (Turkmenistan), breeding starts in late March, in other parts of the range in April. The nest is built on a cliff ledge or a steep clay bank or hill, sometimes in a tree. Four eggs is the usual clutch, though between two and five are sometimes recorded. The young fledge in late June.

Closely related to the true Buzzards is the **Grey-faced Buzzard-Eagle** (*Butastur indicus*) (Plate 23) which is a very characteristic bird of the south of the Russian Far East, particularly Ussuriland. It is also found in north-east China, Korea and Japan. The valleys of the larger rivers, such as the Iman or Bikin, usually hold about one pair per 4-5 km. On the eastern slopes of the Sikhote-Alin mountains it is already rare in the area of Terney Bay. In

Ussuriland, the species inhabits both broad-leaved and mixed forests near wide meadows, fields and hummocky bogs with scattered trees. It is also found on low hills near open expanses and sparse forest. Birds arrive in the region in the first half of April. Aerial display is not infrequent, and high-soaring by two pairs together a quite common sight. As for the nest, this is built at varying heights in the crown of a tree and is remarkably small considering the size of the bird. Thin twigs are used for the basic structure which is then lined with grass and fresh leaves. Three to four eggs are laid in early May. The loud, drawn-out food-calls of the fledged young are heard from mid-July, but it will be mid- to late August before the juveniles start to hunt independently. The birds leave Ussuriland for their wintering grounds in South-East Asia in September.

The **Short-toed Eagle** (*Circaetus gallicus*) is known for its unattractive diet consisting mainly of snakes. It is a rare bird in Russia and is included into the Russian Red Data Book. The breeding range includes forests of the European part of the country (very rare) and the steppes, deserts and mountains of Caucasus and Central Asia.

Hodgson's Hawk-Eagle (*Spizaetus nipalensis*) has been observed many times in Ussuriland and there is a possibility that it breeds in the Sikhote-Alin nature reserve. The **Booted Eagle** (*Hieraaetus pennatus*) is unevenly distributed from the western borders to Lake Baikal, but mostly in the south. The closely related **Bonelli's Eagle** (*H. fasciatus*) (Plate 24) is very rare in Russia and is found nesting only in the south of Russian Central Asia, on the borders with Iran, mostly in the Kopet Dag mountains.

The aptly named **Steppe Eagle** (*Aquila rapax*) (Plate 24) is widely distributed in open areas of both Asia and Africa. The Russian range stretches from the country's western borders to the Transbaikal. Steppe Eagle numbers are declining rapidly owing to man's impact on the environment and the species is one of several raptors included in the Russian Red Data Book. Birds from Russia winter in Africa, the Near East, India and China. The Russian population is put at some tens of thousands of pairs. At the present time, up to 10 per cent of the whole population are killed each year during migration through collision with electric power cables.

Steppe Eagles first breed at three to four years old. They pair for life and occupy the same nesting territory for many years. The nest is normally built on the ground, but birds have more recently taken to using stacks, electrical pylons and telegraph poles. The two (1-4) eggs are laid in the second half of April and incubated for about 45 days. Juvenile mortality reaches 50 per cent and higher, and up to 80 per cent of nests are lost to direct persecution by man, ploughing or grazing. Steppe Eagles prey chiefly on susliks (ground squirrels), young marmots, and gerbils.

The **Greater Spotted Eagle** (*Aquila clanga*) and the **Lesser Spotted Eagle** (*A. pomarina*) are two closely related species associated with the forest ecosystem. The first one is a rare and poorly studied bird distributed from Poland to the Far East, with very insignificant populations outside Russia. The Lesser Spotted is better known to European birdwatchers and its breeding range is restricted to Europe, Turkey and Caucasus.

One of the most impressive eagles is the **Imperial Eagle** (*Aquila heliaca*). In Russia the nominal subspecies inhabits steppes, forest edges, semi-deserts and mountains of the European south, Caucasus, Kazakhstan and Central Asia and southern Siberia up to Lake Baikal. It is rare and declining due to various factors. The total number of breeding pairs in the whole country can be put very approximately at 500-1,000. The bird is included in the Russian Red Data Book.

Birds of prey are in many cases commoner in mountains than in temperate lowlands. For example, the **Golden Eagle** (*Aquila chrysaetos*) is relatively common in Russia only in the mountains of Central Asia and in certain parts of the north. It is indeed as a mountain bird that we tend to picture the Golden Eagle – soaring majestically in the blue sky amidst magnificent mountain scenery, making the marmots down in the valley whistle in alarm.

The Golden Eagle is included as a Category II species in the Russian Red Data Book. The total population is put at several thousand pairs. Though they attain sexual maturity in their second year, Golden Eagles do not usually breed before they are four or five years old. The species is monogamous and birds pair for life. The nest is built on a cliff – on a ledge or in a small cave – or sometimes in a tree. In Central Asia, the clutch of one to two eggs is laid in early March. Incubation takes about 45 days and the number of young reared varies between 0.8 and 1.3 per pair. The fledging period is about 2 months. Chick mortality is about 30-40 per cent due to the elder chick's attacks on its younger sibling. Golden Eagles take various rodents, birds, tortoises, and some carrion. They basically winter within the limits of their breeding range which covers nearly all the territory of Russia.

The breeding range of **Pallas' Sea Eagle** (*Haliaeetus leucoryphus*) covers some parts of Russian Central Asia but the bird is believed to be extinct since no nests have been found for a long time. If the bird still breeds in Russia, there would be no more than about ten pairs nesting very far from each other.

The **White-tailed Sea Eagle** (*Haliaeetus albicilla*) enjoys wide distribution in Russia from its western borders to the Pacific Ocean. Like the other large eagles, the White-tailed is also declining in most parts of its breeding range. It is included in the Russian Red Data Book and the total number of breeding pairs in Russia is approximately 2,000.

Fig. 31 *Steller's Sea Eagle (*Haliaeetus pelagicus*) on Sakhalin Island. Photo Y. Shibnev*

The **Bald Eagle** (*Haliaeetus leucocephalus*), an American species, has been recorded in the Kamtchatka peninsula and Kolyma river in Siberia.

Endemic to Russia, the majestic **Steller's Sea Eagle** (*Haliaeetus pelagicus*) (Plate 24 and Fig. 31) is distributed on the coasts and islands of the Pacific. It breeds in the Kamchatka peninsula, Sakhalin and northern Kuril Islands, and on the coasts of the Sea of Okhotsk. The highest breeding density is recorded in Kamchatka, where there is one breeding pair every 8-10 km along the coast, 1.5-2 km along the rivers and two to three breeding pairs in the one square kilometre of delta forest. High breeding density is recorded in the Amur river delta. Around Lake Orel in this region 50 breeding pairs were counted. The total number of Steller's Sea Eagles in Russia is thought to be 2,000 breeding pairs and about 5,000 non-breeding birds. This species starts to breed from four years of age. The nests are built in huge trees and are used for many years. Sometimes nests are built on the rocks and cliffs. The clutch of one to three eggs is laid in April and is incubated by both parents for about 35-40 days. The young fledge at about 70-75 days old.

Fig. 32
Egyptian Vulture
(Neophron
percnopterus)
*in the Tien Shan
Mountains.*
*Photo A. Knys-
tautas*

Usually the brood consists of one bird, very rarely two. The main food of this species is fish, in winter they also take carrion.

During the winter in the Kamchatka peninsula, near Lake Kamchatka, about 700 Steller's Sea Eagles may be seen wintering at the same time. They feed here on certain species of fish which breed here during the whole winter.

The **Lammergeier** or **Bearded Vulture** (*Gypaetus barbatus*) (Plate 24) is a typical mountain raptor and a very big bird, with a wingspan of about 2.5 m. It lives in all the great mountain ranges of the Caucasus and Central Asia, but it is rare everywhere and is consequently included in the Russian Red Data Book. This species rarely takes live prey and feeds mainly on carrion. It sometimes attacks marmots or pushes mountain goat kids over steep precipices.

Well known in Europe, the **Egyptian Vulture** (*Neophron percnopterus*) (Fig. 32), the **Griffon Vulture** (*Gyps fulvus*) (Fig. 33) and the **Black Vulture** (*Aegypius monachus*) (Plate 25 and Fig. 34) are distributed in many mountain ranges and plateaux in the south of the country.

The **Himalayan Griffon Vulture** (*Gyps himalayensis*) lives in the mountain systems of Russian Central Asia as well as most of the Himalayan system. It is usually regarded as a high mountain species and is included in the Russian Red Data Book. It is rare and insufficiently studied, breeding in high mountains sometimes in mixed colonies with Griffon Vultures. Only seven nests have ever been found in Russia. The clutch of one to two eggs

Fig. 33 *Griffon Vulture (Gyps fulvus) in Badkhyz Nature Reserve, Turkmenistan. Photo H. Sakalauskas/A. Blazys*

is laid in February-March. Incubation takes about 50 days while the whole breeding season is 6.5-7 months.

The **Oriental White-backed Vulture** (*Pseudogyps bengalensis*) is a vagrant species in Russia with a record near Rostov-on-Don (there is a possibility that this was an escaped bird).

The next large family of the birds of prey is the true falcons (Falconidae), with twelve species in Russia. The **Gyrfalcon** (*Falco rusticolus*) is a rare species found in the tundra and wooded tundra. Numbers of this raptor are relatively stable. It has circumpolar distribution along the coasts and islands of Arctic Eurasia and America, and favours crags along river valleys, tending to avoid the flat tundra. In the European part of Russia and in Kamchatka, it occurs on sea cliffs where there are large seabird colonies. The Russian population of Gyrfalcon is estimated at several hundred pairs. Gyrfalcons first breed at two years old. They are monogamous and show strict site-tenacity. At the end of April or in early May, the female lays two to five eggs in a nest located on a sea cliff or the side of a gorge, and incubates it for 26-30 days. Gyrfalcons feed on a variety of birds and also some rodents.

The **Saker Falcon** (*Falco cherrug*) (Plate 25) is another large species of falcon weighing around 1 kg. It is distributed in Eurasia from Hungary and Bulgaria to Mongolia and China in the east. Its favourite habitats are steppes and forest steppes, foothills and canyons. In suitable habitats it is not rare at all, even though is included in the Russian Red Data Book, and the total population in Russia is estimated at more than 1,000 breeding pairs. This figure is probably much lower than the real numbers. In several places in southern Kazakhstan we encountered a number of occupied nests in

Fig. 34
*European
Black Vulture
(*Aegypius
monachus*) in
the Tien Shan
Mountains.
Photo
O. Belialov*

comparatively small areas. In Serek-Tas, for example, several nests were destroyed by an Eagle Owl which was breeding nearby. Several beautifully arranged nests are located in Charyn river canyons where we found five grown-up young in one nest. This species starts to breed at two to three years of age. The nests are built on the trees or on the rocks in the foothills of a mountain. The clutch consists of three to four eggs, more rarely up to six. Saker Falcons feed on medium-size rodents and birds.

The **Lagger Falcon** (*Falco jugger*) is believed to breed on the rocks in the foothills in several places in Central Asia (Karatau, southern Turkmenistan). The **Lanner Falcon** (*Falco biarmicus*) is recorded as a breeder in southern parts of Armenia. Its main breeding range covers Africa and the Near East.

The **Barbary Falcon** (*Falco pelegrinoides*) breeds in Russia in the mountains of Central Asia, including Kopet Dag, Western Pamir, Alai system, Tien-Shan and others. The biology is very much the same as that of other large falcons, including the Peregrine. It is rare and poorly studied. It is believed that there are about 50 breeding pairs in Russia. Recently, a breeding pair was found in the mountains not far from Alma-Ata, the capital of Kazakhstan.

The **Peregrine Falcon** (*Falco peregrinus*) (Plate 25) has a wide distribution in Russia, being more common only in tundra habitats. The Peregrine is a Red Data Book species, whose catastrophic decline in numbers followed excessive use of toxic chemicals in agriculture. On the tundra, Peregrines favour river valleys with crags and hills; in other zones, forests or coastal cliffs are the preferred habitat. Even the tundra population has declined to a fifth or even an seventh of its original size in recent years.

Peregrines are monogamous and highly site-tenacious. Their nest is built in a tree, on the ledge of a steep cliff or, in the tundra, in a depression

Fig. 35 *Amur Red-footed Falcon* (Falco amurensis) *reaching its nest hole in a dead tree in central Ussuriland. Photo Y. Shibnev*

typically on a hillock or steep riverside bank. Depending on latitude, laying takes place from March to July and the full clutch is of three to four eggs. Incubation lasts 28-35 days and the young falcons fledge at 30-37 days old. Peregrines feed almost entirely on birds. Rodents are eaten only rarely.

There are several species of smaller falcons which are better known and some are common in many other countries. These include the **Northern Hobby** (*Falco subbuteo*) (Plate 25), the **Merlin** (*F. columbarius*), the **Western Red-footed Falcon** (*F. vespertinus*) and the **Common Kestrel** (*F. tinnunculus*).

The forests in the Far East are inhabited by the **Amur Red-footed Falcon** (*Falco amurensis*) (Fig. 35). Outside Russia, this bird breeds in Mongolia, Korea and China. This species favours forest margins, small forests and groups of trees, and often breeds in raised bogs in the taiga. The Amur falcons breed in isolated pairs or in small colonies. They use the nests of other birds, and also breed in tree holes. Egg laying takes place in May, the clutch consists of two to six eggs, usually three or four. Incubation by both parents takes 22-23 days. The food – small birds and insects – is brought to the nest by both sexes. The young stay in the nest for about one month.

Fig. 36 *Lesser Kestrels (*Falco naumanni*) in Uzbekistan. Photo A. Sokolov*

The **Lesser Kestrel** (*Falco naumanni*) (Fig. 36) is a small and fragile-looking falcon in some ways resembling a large swallow. It breeds in colonies on the steep clay and sand banks along the rivers in Central Asia. Its nest is usually a hole in a slope. There are 15-25 nests in a colony. Egg-laying takes place in May and the clutch consists of three to six eggs. The food of this species consists mainly of large insects.

The **American Kestrel** (*Falco sparverius*) was recorded in Estonia but this was possibly an escaped bird.

PHEASANTS AND GROUSE – ORDER GALLIFORMES

This order has two families and 21 species in Russia. The Family Tetraonidae has eight species and the family Phasianidae thirteen species. All 21 species are breeders.

Among the common and well-known species of grouse are the **Willow** and **Rock Ptarmigans** (*Lagopus lagopus* (Fig. 37) and *L. mutus* (Fig. 38)) which enjoy wide distribution in the lowland and mountain tundra as well as in many raised bogs in the taiga zone. Well-known though declining is the **Black Grouse** (*Lyrurus tetrix*) whose distribution range covers the territory from the western borders to the Far East.

An interesting species of grouse found in mountains is the **Caucasian Black Grouse** (*Lyrurus mlokosiewiczi*) (Plate 26 and Fig. 39). In the early morning,

Fig. 37 *Willow Ptarmigan* (Lagopus lagopus). *Photo A. Sokolov*

Fig. 38 *Rock Ptarmigan* (Lagopus mutus). *Photo H. Sakalauskas/A. Blazys*

when the summits of the mountains are blanketed in mist while the ravines below are still in darkness and the delicate scent of spring alpine flowers is wafted on the gentlest of breezes, you may catch the far-carrying whistling sound made by the wings of displaying grouse. This species is resident and occurs mainly in the subalpine and alpine belts of the Great Caucasus, its breeding range extending by way of other mountains into Turkey and Iran. Scarce everywhere, the Caucasian Black Grouse leads a more or less sedentary life, making only short movements in response to the changing seasons. Spring display is a remarkable affair: the males gather in groups or display singly, fly up silently and beat their wings, producing the whistling sound alluded to above. The nest is on the ground under a bush in thickets of rhododendron, juniper and low birches. Laying takes place from the end of May and there are five to eight eggs. Incubation and the care of the young are carried out by the female alone. She sits very tightly, allowing humans to approach very closely. Caucasian Black Grouse eat leaves, buds and seeds of various plants.

Unlike its European relative the **Western Capercaillie** (*Tetrao urogallus*) (Plate 26), the **Black-billed Capercaillie** (*Tetrao parvirostris*) is much less well-known or seen. The latter breed mainly in the sparse larch forests in eastern Siberia and Sakhalin Island. The lifestyle and behaviour of both species is quite similar. The Black-billed Capercaillie is more active in winter

Fig. 39 *Adult female Caucasian Black Grouse* (Lyrurus mlo-kosiewiczi) *in Caucasus Nature Reserve. Photo H. Sakalauskas*

as its east Siberian homeland has relatively little snow to prevent it from moving on the ground.

Unlike the widespread **Hazel Grouse** (*Tetrastes bonasia*) (Plate 26), the **Siberian Spruce Grouse** (*Falcipennis falcipennis*) (Plate 26) has a restricted distribution. It lives in the south-east of Siberia and the Far East, inhabiting dense forests of larch, spruce, or mixed spruce and fir. It is resident all year round. As its name suggests, it lives chiefly on conifer buds, shoots and needles, supplementing its diet with berries, insects and spiders. The Siberian Spruce Grouse is monogamous. During the spring courtship ritual, the males may shake their wings, fan their tails and leap into the air with outstretched necks, giving a raucous call. The nest is well concealed and the six to ten eggs are laid by the end of May. The female is very reluctant to leave the nest during the 17 day incubation period. The males play no part in incubation or care of their chicks. This species has an unfortunate combination of tasty flesh and remarkable tameness. They are easily caught by hunters armed with nooses. The Siberian Spruce Grouse is included in the Russian Red Data Book.

The genus *Tetraogallus* (Snowcocks) has five species all of which breed in Russia. The **Caucasian Snowcock** (*T. caucasicus*) is found only in Great Caucasus and is thus a Russian endemic; the **Altai Snowcock** (*T. altaicus*) inhabits the Altai mountains, and the **Caspian Snowcock** (*T. caspius*) lives in various ranges of the Little Caucasus as well as in Iran and Turkey. Mountains of the Himalayan system are the home of the **Himalayan Snowcock** (*T. himalayensis*) (Plate 27) and the **Tibetan Snowcock** (*T. tibetanus*). The Himalayan has the more northerly distribution, in the Tien Shan and the Pamir Alay systems, while the range of the Tibetan Snowcock extends far from the Pamir massif south into the Himalayas.

Snowcocks are amazing birds in various ways. Any ornithologist finding a snowcock's nest, which is built on the ground amidst stones and surrounded by high cliffs, can count themselves fortunate indeed. Most often one sees a single brood or even several joined together, accompanied by one or several females. Once the birds have seen you, they will run rapidly up the steep slope, but if they sense there is a real threat, for example that they will be overtaken by someone on horseback, the hens, cackling loudly, will suddenly take off and, with bowed but completely motionless wings, fly downhill with a whistling call, the chicks following. Snowcocks have the habit of not landing in sight of humans, so they first top the ridge, then dive down and disappear from view behind it. It is no use trying to follow them as they are wily and cautious birds.

It is only during the peak courtship period that one has a chance to find out a little more about the life and behaviour of snowcocks, and this means observing them from a hide at the places they particularly favour, namely large thawed patches and on the snow-line. The mobile snow-line is indeed a real boundary for these birds: it dictates their movements up and down the mountains with the changing seasons. They are geneally sedentary and undertake only these insignificant vertical movements.

The northernmost species – the Altai Snowcock – has to contend with the especially hard winters characteristic of the Altai mountains. In the breeding season, they range no higher than 3,000 m, and in winter they come down even into the river valleys. In contrast, the Tibetan Snowcock, the true high-mountain specialist, ascends to 5,000 m in the Pamirs. The Himalayan Snowcock is found in a far wider range of habitats and sometimes nests at an altitude of only about 1,000 m. This is a clear demonstration of greater plasticity than in the other snowcocks. The Caspian Snowcock breeds at altitudes of between 1,800 and 3,500 m and favours dry slopes. Even in the hardest winters, these birds do not descend below the tree-line. Endemic of Russia, the Caucasian Snowcock is intimately linked with the alpine zone of the Great Caucasus. It inhabits remote

Fig. 40 *Chukar Partridge (*Alectoris chukar*) in the Syugaty Mountains, Eastern Kazakhstan. Photo A. Knystautas*

and inaccessible rocky habitat with scattered mixed-herb meadows at altitudes of between 2,600 and 3,700 m. In winter, the birds move down to the south-facing slopes which form their breeding grounds.

The **Chukar Partridge** (*Alectoris chukar*) (Fig. 40) is widely distributed in a number of mountain ranges in Russia. They live in different habitats starting from low mountain slopes to the truly sub-alpine areas. It is a very popular game species.

Two uncommon species on the edge of their distribution are the **See-See Partridge** (*Ammoperdix griseogularis*) (Plate 27) and the **Black Partridge** (*Francolinus francolinus*) (Plate 27). Two species of the genus *Perdix* live in Russia – the common and well-known **Grey Partridge** (*P. perdix*), and, inhabiting southern parts of Central Asia and Siberia, the **Daurian Partridge** (*P. dauuricae*).

The story of the **Common Quail** (*Coturnix coturnix*) in many parts of European Russia is a sad tale. For example, once common in Lithuania, it has become extremely rare. The excessive use of chemicals in agriculture and alteration of its habitat are to be blamed. Numerous in the lowlands in the Far East is the **Japanese Quail** (*C. japonica*) which once was considered a subspecies of the Common Quail. It has a very distinctive voice completely different from that of its European cousin and places like Khanka lowland resounds with the calls in May.

The **Common Pheasant** (*Phasianus colchicus*) is fairly widely distributed in Russia and is well known for the great number of its subspecies – there are 30 altogether. Many of them occur in Central Asia where they live quite close to each other. A distinctive subspecies inhabits Ussuriland. As in other countries this pheasant is a very popular game bird and is bred in captivity for this purpose.

CRANES, BUSTARDS AND ALLIES – ORDER GRUIFORMES

This order has four significant suborders in Russia, the representatives of which are very varied indeed. The first suborder is the buttonquails (Turnices) with only one species in Russia. The next is the cranes (Grues) with seven breeding species in the country, then water rails (Ralli) with thirteen species, twelve of which breed and one is vagrant, and finally bustards (Otides) with three breeding species.

The **Yellow-legged Buttonquail** (*Turnix tanki*) inhabits forest edges, and rich grass meadows with occasional bushes in the south of Ussuriland. This is an uncommon species mainly because it is on the northern edge of its distribution. Buttonquails arrive at their breeding ground in Ussuriland in May. The nests are small scrapes under hummocks, and egg-laying takes place in the first half of June. The clutch consists of four eggs and is incubated by the female for about twelve days. The young leave the nest soon after hatching and are able to fly when about ten days old. The Yellow-legged Buttonquail feeds on insects and plant seeds.

The true cranes (Grues), with seven breeding species in Russia, are at the centre of conservation efforts. Due to the reduction of habitats, pollution of wintering sites and disturbance during the breeding season their numbers have fallen dramatically.

The awe-inspiring beauty of the **Red-crowned** or **Manchurian Crane** (*Grus japonensis*) (Plate 28) is reflected in such names as "jewel of Asia" and "queen of the birds" while in Japan it is known as "the bird of happiness". Sadly, the world population is alarmingly small and the species figures in the IUCN/ICPB Red Data Book. It is feared that the Red-crowned Crane may be on the verge of extinction in Russia. There has been a sharp contraction in its range, which formerly covered a large part of Ussuriland and the Amur region. At the present time, Red-crowned Cranes breed at Lake Khanka, in the Amur region, and on the river Bikin. The small range is an indication of a relict species.

The cranes arrive at Khanka in late March and by early April they will be in pairs or small groups of up to six birds. Typical nesting habitat is extensive flooded marshlands. The nest is built on a small island surrounded by reed-grass and sparse, low-growing reeds. Two eggs are laid from late April or early May, about a month after the birds arrive. Pairs often fail to breed successfully at Khanka. The species is extremely sensitive to disturbance and all too readily deserts the nest. Another negative factor is the periodic rise in water levels, while the destructive practice of reed-burning by the local people to increase the area of land used for hay meadows means that all the eggs laid by this rarest of rare birds in a given year are immediately lost. Hatching at Lake Khanka takes place in late May. The Red-crowned Crane population in all the shore-belt around Khanka numbers 20-25 breeding pairs, and 20-30 non-breeding birds. When there is no reed-burning, the breeding success amounts to just under one chick per pair. The cranes leave Khanka at the end of November.

Dr S. Vinter has made a detailed study of the breeding biology of Red-crowned Cranes in the Bureya-Arkhara lowland (Amur region) where eight pairs live in an area of 162 square kilometres. The cranes arrive here at the same time as the Khanka birds, and the main laying period is 16th-22nd April. The first and second eggs are laid two to four days apart, and incubation takes 29-31 days.

In 1981, a new Red-crowned Crane breeding site was discovered by Yuri Shibnev on the lower reaches of the Bikin river. The sphagnum-moss bogs in that area are huge open expanses, stretching for 5-10 km or more. On the side near the river, they are bordered by forest, while on the other side hills clothed in mixed taiga forest rise up and form the boundary. There have been several records of Red-crowns in this locality. In 1981, two breeding pairs were noted and one nest was described. The latter was built on one of the many moss cushions and was constructed of reed-grass; it was 8 cm high and 70 cm across. The eggs hatched over the two last days of May. A second pair of cranes nested about 5-6 km away. Outside Russia, Red-crowned Cranes breed in north-east China and, in very small numbers, in Japan.

A magnificent member of the crane family, now well known for its rarity and attempts to save it, is the **Siberian White Crane** (*Grus leucogeranus*) (Plate 28). A Russian endemic, it is listed in the Russian Red Data Book. The Siberian Crane breeds in two widely separated ranges. One is in northern Yakutia and the other on the lower Ob' river. In Yakutia, the breeding range is located in the tundras lying between the Yana and Indigirka rivers. The Ob' population nests on the right (east) bank of the Kunovat river basin.

Cranes of the Yakut population migrate across Transbaikal to winter quarters on the right (east) bank of the Yangtzee river in China. At the same time, birds from the Ob' valley migrate across the Turgai to Central Asia and the Volga delta; there are two separate wintering groups, one in India and the other in northern Iran.

There are some differences between the nesting habitats of the two populations. In Yakutia, the birds inhabit extensive tracks of level and very marshy tundra dotted with lakes. On the lower Ob', they nest in great bogs with, on the higher ground, northern taiga in the form of patches of Siberian Stone Pine (*Pinus sibirica*) forest. The Yakut population is estimated to number 200-250 birds, including about 60 breeding pairs. The Ob' population barely exceeds 50 birds. The main threat to the Siberian White Crane is changes to the wintering grounds: these include gradual dessication of the lakes, reduction of the food-base, disturbance, and the possibility of birds being poisoned by pesticide residues. Many cranes fall victim to poachers during migration. The breeding grounds are relatively secure, though disturbance may occur even there. Siberian White Cranes do not mate until they are six years old. They pair for life. The species is a solitary nester, pairs being 10-20 km or sometimes only 2-3 km apart. Two eggs are normally laid, but only one chick survives. Incubation takes 28-30 days. Egg and chick mortality can be as high as 70 per cent: the Siberian Crane is an exceptionally shy bird and will leave the nest on sighting a man even at a considerable distance and this means that the eggs are exposed and can easily be lost to a predator.

Siberian Cranes eat both animal and plant food: chiefly plant tubers and other underground plant parts, but during the breeding season small animals and aquatic invertebrates are also taken.

The **Common Crane** (*Grus grus*) nests in raised bogs and swamplands from the western borders to eastern Siberia. It is the most common crane in Russia. The **Sandhill Crane** (*G. canadensis*) is primarily an American species which also breeds in the tundras of eastern Siberia, Chukotka and Kamchatka peninsulas.

The most important breeding populations of the **Japanese White-naped Crane** (*Grus vipio*) are in north-west China and Mongolia, and the range runs through Ussuriland and the Amur region. The total wild population is put at 2,000 to 3,000 birds. Very small numbers now breed at Lake Khanka and probably also in the Ussuri river valley which forms the state boundary between Russia and China.

Most mysterious and legendary of our cranes is the **Hooded Crane** (*Grus monacha*) (Plate 28 and Fig. 41). It was, after all, only as recently as 1974 that the first nest was discovered on the middle reaches of the Bikin river in Ussuriland, and the eggs and chicks first described. The Hooded Crane is listed in the IUCN/ICPB Red Data Book. Its main population breeds within Russia but it may well be that some nest in parts of China bordering Ussuriland, e.g. on taiga bogs in the Little Khingan. The foundation of their nest is constructed of moss and is built on an animal trail across the partially flooded ground; it is trampled to make a solid base. A second layer consists of twigs from bushes and the final lining is of sedge. Two eggs are laid. Some bogs have quite a high density of breeding cranes and the bugling calls of four or five pairs may be heard from one spot early in the morning.

Birds are not easy to see on the bog as they follow the paths made by animals between the high cushions of moss, dwarf birches and low larches. In these places, they will allow approach to within about 50-70 m, but out in the

Fig. 41
*Hooded
Cranes (*Grus
monacha*) in
the Bikin
River Valley,
central
Ussuriland.
Photo Y.
Shibnev*

middle of the bog, where they can be seen a kilometre or more away, they tend to be much less approachable. The onset of laying very much depends on the weather condition in a particular year, and nesting begins correspondingly early in an early and warm spring. There is, for example, a record of two families with chicks four to five days old on 23rd May at a site where no cranes had been seen on 14th April. It appears that Hooded Cranes are unlike White-naped Cranes and Red-crowned Cranes in that they start to nest more or less immediately after their arrival on the breeding grounds. The total winter population in Korea, Japan and China is in excess of 4,000 birds.

One of the loveliest and most impressive breeding birds of Russian steppes and deserts is the **Demoiselle Crane** (*Anthropoides virgo*) (Plate 28). As a declining species, it is listed in the Russian Red Data Book, but it is gratifying to report that this crane is showing signs of adapting to the man-made environment. In the southern Ukraine Demoiselles are starting to colonise arable fields, and successful breeding has been confirmed in this habitat. The total number of these cranes in Russia is estimated at 45-50,000. Demoiselles return to their breeding grounds in April and immediately begin their communal courtship displays in which all the breeding birds of a particular area participate. The nest is a shallow depression in the ground lined with a few carelessly arranged plant stems. Two eggs are laid, very rarely three. These cranes feed mainly on plant material, to a lesser extent on insects.

The rails, gallinules and coots (Ralli) are well known for their secretiveness and the difficulties involved in their study. Among the species which are well

Fig. 42 *Water Rail* (Rallus aquaticus) *on Sakhalin Island. Photo Y. Shibnev*

known in Europe and breed in Russia are the **Water Rail** (*Rallus aquaticus*) (Fig. 42), the **Spotted Crake** (*Porzana porzana*), the **Little Crake** (*P. parva*), **Baillon's Crake** (*P. pusilla*), the **Corncrake** (*Crex crex*), the **Moorhen** (*Gallinula chloropus*) and the **Black Coot** (*Fulica atra*). Most of the rest are Far Eastern species with the exception of the **Purple Gallinule** (*Porphyrio porphyrio*) which breeds in the huge reedbeds along the Caspian coast.

The **Water Cock** (*Gallicrex cinerea*) is registered as an uncommon breeder in the southern part of Ussuriland and the Khanka lowland. It also breeds on the southern Kuril islands.

The **Ruddy-breasted Crake** (*Porzana fusca*) is an East Asian species. It has been found to breed on Sahkalin Island. There have been a number of records in various parts of Ussuriland, including in Peter the Great Bay, in the extreme south, and on the middle reaches of River Bikin, where displaying birds have been seen in a marshy part of the river valley with hummocky sedge bogs. There is little doubt that the breeding range of this species also covers southern Ussuriland.

Another crake, the **Band-bellied** (*Porzana paykullii*), has a restricted range but is a characteristic bird of Ussuriland. It is fairly common there, but is sporadically distributed in wet tussocky meadows with rich herbaceous vegetation and sparse scrub. The Band-bellied Crake does not arrive in the region before mid-May, and the seven to nine eggs are laid from early June. Courtship calls are given from arrival up to mid-July. The range of this species covers only Ussuriland and north-east China.

Rare and poorly studied and thus included in the Russian Red Data Book is **Swinhoe's Yellow Rail** (*Porzana exquisita*) which was found breeding at Lake Khanka and in Transbaikal. The real boundaries of its breeding range

Fig. 43 *Femal Great Bustard (*Otis tarda*) in the Saratov region. Photo V. Mosseikin*

are yet to be established. The **White-breasted Water Hen** (*Amaurornis phoenicurus*), which has a wide distribution in South and East Asia has been recorded several times in southern Ussuriland.

There are three breeding species of bustard (Otides) in Russia. The **Great Bustard** (*Otis tarda*) (Plate 29 and Fig. 43) is one of the largest birds in the country and typically inhabits open areas in the forest and forest-steppe zones, semi-deserts and the fringe of the desert, also penetrating into montane steppes. It is migratory in the north and resident in the south. The range formerly embraced a large part of the steppe zone and adjoining areas from the country's western borders to Lake Khanka in the Far East. A sharp decline in the 1970s led to a fragmentation of the breeding range and its reduction to a number of isolated islands. The wintering grounds are located in the Transcaucasus, Turkmenistan and Kazakhstan.

Many different kinds of open areas are occupied and only true desert is avoided. Intensification of agricultural practices means that the natural nesting habitat of the Great Bustard is being steadily eroded. On the more positive side, the birds are showing a clear tendency to move onto farmland and now nest in various crops. There are estimated to be at least 3,000 Great Bustards in Russia, with the highest population in the Saratov region where 683 nests were counted in 1980. The eastern race *O. t. dybowskii* totals only 300 birds of which 150-200 live in the Buryat autonomous republic on the eastern side of Lake Baikal.

Both polygamous and monogamous mating systems have been reported for this species, with the maximum breeding productivity confirmed for the second of these. Males do not breed before they are five to six years old, females not before four to five years. In early spring, with the first warmer temperatures and the beginning of the thaw, the bustards settle to breed. Depending on latitude, this happens in March or April. For their impressive display, the males choose a flat, open area which offers an unimpeded view all around. Birds display in groups and singly, usually in the morning before sunrise. The nest is a shallow pit in the ground. All incubation (taking 23-30 days) and later care of the young is by the female. An incubating hen bustard blends perfectly with the surrounding vegetation. The chicks start to fly at about 35 days when they have attained half the weight of the female. Great Bustard weight varies between 4 and 11 kg according to season. An exceptionally large male may reach 16 kg.

The **Little Bustard** (*Tetrax tetrax*) (Plate 29) weighs only 600-950 g and is thus far smaller than the previous species. Like the Great Bustard, it has become rare owing to human impact on the steppe environment and is thus also listed in the Russian Red Data Book. The former range spanned the whole steppe zone and a considerable part of the semi-desert zone in a broad band from the country's western borders east to Altai. This range is now very much reduced and within it the species is distributed very unevenly. Census data indicated Russia population in 1980 to be at least 5,000 birds, or about 8,000 after the breeding season. However, winter counts in Transcaucasus suggest a much bigger population of between 13,000 and 16,800 birds. Little Bustards nest in solitary pairs, arriving on their breeding grounds in mid-April when the steppe is completely free of snow. Males display singly, adopting a number of peculiar and characteristic postures. The nest is a slight hollow in the ground lined with a thin layer of plant stems. Three to four eggs are laid and incubated by female alone for 20-21 days, her mate usually staying close by. The first chicks are normally seen around the end of May. For the first few days, the brood stays in the general area of the nest, but by early August, the juveniles will be flying well and they then assemble in flocks which depart in September or October. Little Bustards eat various plant parts, insects, and small vertebrates.

Of the three bustard species, one is a characteristic bird of the sand and clay deserts of Central Asia. This is the **Houbara Bustard** (*Chlamydotis undulata*) (Plate 29), now a rare bird included in the Russian Red Data Book. There is a group of these birds kept in Bukhara captive breeding unit for rare animals with the hope that they will start to breed in captivity. Available data says that the only place they have been bred was in Tel Aviv zoo in Israel. Their nest is a hollow in the ground completely open and unlined. Two to three eggs are laid around mid-April. The female does all the incubation and cares for the young alone. This shy and generally not very vocal bird eats insects as well as the shoots and seeds of various plants.

WADERS AND ALLIES – ORDER CHARADRIIFORMES

This group of birds is the second largest after the passerines for the number of species found in Russia. It has 147 species altogether, 93 species of waders and jacanas, 34 species of gulls and terns and 20 species of Alcids.

The suborder jacanas (Jacanae) has one species in Russia. The **Pheasant-tailed Jacana** (*Hydrophasianus chirurgus*) has been recorded in Ussuriland twice.

The suborder Charadrii, true waders, begins with the **Stone Curlew** (*Burhinus oedicnemus*) (Plate 29) which is distributed in Russia from the western borders to the south of western Siberia. It is not rare in suitable habitats and it now uses agricultural lands for breeding.

The **Greater Painted Snipe** (*Rostratula benghalensis*) has been recorded many times in southern Ussuriland and there is a strong possibility that it may breed there.

The genus *Pluvialis* has four species in Russia. The largest one is the **Grey Plover** (*P. squatarola*) which breeds in the Arctic belt of Eurasia and America and winters in Africa, South America and South Asia. Nesting birds tend to stick to the higher and drier parts of the tundra, rarely using lower-lying areas. On passage and in winter it haunts sandy beaches and sand-banks in the shallows of rivers and lakes. Grey Plovers are monogamous and nest as widely dispersed pairs. A simple scrape is made by the female and her four eggs are laid from mid-June. As soon as the young fledge and become independent, the adults begin their migration, usually from the end of August. As in most waders, non-breeders or failed breeders move away much earlier.

The controversy surrounding two species of Arctic plovers – the **Pacific Golden Plover** (*Pluvialis fulva*) (Plate 30) and the **American Golden Plover** (*P. dominica*) has been in favour of dividing these two forms into separate species. The first inhabits the tundras of Eurasia from the Yamal peninsula to the Chukchi peninsula in the East and also Alaska. The American Golden Plover is regarded in Russia as vagrant and was recorded in the Chukotka and Kamchatka peninsulas and on Wrangel Island.

The **European Golden Plover** (*Pluvialis apricaria*) inhabits both taiga and tundra zones choosing raised bogs in the latter. It is a typical and well-known swampland bird which gives a certain character to the bogs and marshes. Its breeding range extends from the western borders to the Taimyr peninsula in the east.

The sandplovers (*Charadrius*) are quite well represented in Russia with eight breeding and one vagrant species. Among these birds, which traditionally are regarded as coastal, are the true desert species, which live very far from the nearest water body and are nearly the only birds found in some habitats, particularly in the clay deserts.

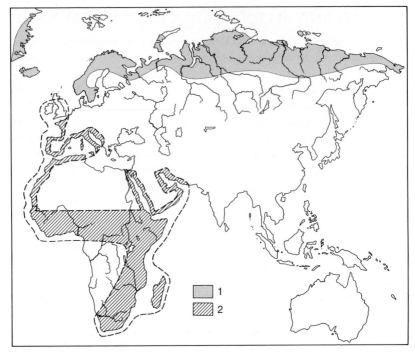

Fig. 44 *Palaearctic breeding range (1) and wintering grounds (2) of the Ringed Plover (*Charadrius hiaticula*)*

Among the common and well known species which are widespread in Russia are the **Ringed Plover** (*Charadrius hiaticula*) (for breeding range see Fig. 44), the **Little Ringed Plover** (*C. dubius*) and the **Kentish Plover** (*C. alexandrinus*), the latter being found on the shores of southern water bodies.

The **Long-billed Ringed Plover** (*Charadrius placidus*) is a Far Eastern species found in Russia in Ussuriland. It also inhabits Japan and east China. The life story of this uncommon species is similar to that of other shore species of ringed plovers. It inhabits sandy and gravel riversides and arrives at the breeding grounds from its wintering quarters in Indochina in May. A nest is a small scrape in sand or gravel. The usual clutch consists of four eggs which are incubated by both parents for 23-25 days. The young leave the nest soon after hatching and are incredibly well camouflaged in the surrounding landscape.

The most interesting and exotic group of plovers of this genus are those which form a rather compact group of four species and all have orange-like colouring. They are the **Lesser Sand Plover** (*Charadrius mongolus*) (Plate

126

30), the **Caspian Plover** (*C. asiaticus*) (Plate 30), the **Greater Sand Plover** (*C. leschenaultii*) (Plate 30) and the **Eastern Sand Plover** (*C. veredus*).

The Greater Sand Plover is a highly specialised wader of clay, salt and stone deserts, ranging from the southern Caucasus to China and Mongolia, and migrating to the coasts of Africa, Asia, Indonesia and Australia for the winter. It is not rare in suitable habitats, though rather few nests have been found so far. Greater Sand Plovers are solitary breeders, sometimes living in such harsh conditions in stone and clay deserts that they are virtually the only bird species found there. The nest is a shallow scrape, in which usually three, less commonly four eggs are laid in early May. Both parents care for the young, feeding them with various insects. This species is also wonderfully camouflaged in the remote landscape in which it lives and it is always difficult to locate the bird in the deserts following its mournful whistle. Needless to say, the breeding female is virtually impossible to see, as well as the eggs themselves. For birdwatchers this bird is very exciting to see on its breeding grounds somewhere around geographical centre of Eurasia.

There is no apparent pattern to the Lesser Sand Plover's distribution. With the populations in the Chukotka and Kamchatka peninsulas, near Lake Baikal, in Tien-Shan and the Pamir mountains it represents a true puzzle for specialists.

The Caspian Plover inhabits the same habitats as the Greater Sand Plover and their life stories are very much the same. The Eastern Sand Plover is a rare species in Russia on the edge of its distribution. It occurs in Tuva and the Transbaikal region.

Regarded as a vagrant, the **Semipalmated Plover** (*Charadrius semipalmatus*), an American species, was found breeding on Wrangel island in 1988.

The **Eurasian Dotterel** (*Eudromias morinellus*) in Russia inhabits dryer parts of lowland tundra as well as montane tundra from the Kola peninsula to the Far East.

The **Sociable Plover** (*Chettusia gregaria*) (Plate 30) is a Russian endemic, inhabiting dry steppes and semi-deserts. It has a sporadic breeding distribution from the east bank of the Volga river in the west to the Zaisan depression in the east. The wintering grounds lie in north-east Africa, Iran, Iraq, north-west India and Pakistan. Sociable Plover's numbers are declining rapidly as ever more land comes under the plough, and the species is thus included in the Russian Red Data Book. In the southern Urals, Sociable Plovers nest on arable fields. During the breeding season, birds are otherwise found in clay and stony steppe with sparse vegetation, sometimes on bare clay patches of solonets (leached saline soil – where there is surface salt on the soil). They are able to nest far from water. The world population is estimated at several tens of thousands of birds. Numbers are highest in the

Tengiz-Kurgaldzin depression in Central Kazakhstan where the density can reach about one pair per square kilometre.

Depending on the latitude and weather conditions, Sociable Plovers return to their breeding grounds between early March and mid-May. They form colonies of a few or sometimes up to 20-30 pairs. The nest is on the ground, often sheltered by grass. Three to four eggs are laid and incubation lasts 21-25 days. Both sexes incubate and care for the young. Various insects are the main food eaten.

The **Northern Lapwing** (*Vanellus vanellus*) enjoys wide distribution in Russia. It breeds in swamplands and agricultural fields throughout the temperate zone of nearly the whole country.

The **White-tailed Plover**'s (*Chettusia leucura*) (Plate 31) range extends from Syria to Pakistan and incorporates southern parts of Russian Central Asia. Common in suitable habitats, this species settles on the shores of different water bodies including canals in semi-desert and desert zones. This attractive wader usually forms loose colonies in suitable places. These birds are noisy like other species of lapwings, and meet furiously any intruders which appear in the vicinity of the breeding colony. White-tailed Plovers arrive at their breeding sites in Central Asia in the first half of April and soon start reproduction. The nest is a simple scrape in the ground where three to four eggs are laid in the second half of April. Incubation takes 22-24 days, and the fledging period is about 30 days. Both parents take care of the young. The food consists of various insects. In August, White-tailed Plovers start their migration to the winter quarters situated in north-west India and Egypt.

The **Grey-headed Lapwing** (*Vanellus cinereus*) has been recorded many times in southern Ussuriland and on Sakhalin Island. There is a strong possibility that it may breed there.

In the very south of Russia near the borders with Iran and Afghanistan, the rare **Red-wattled Lapwing** (*Lobivanellus indicus*) is found. This species is on the edge of its distribution in Russia, and its main breeding range covers the Middle East, India and Sri Lanka.

The **Spur-winged Plover** (*Vanellus spinosus*) was recorded as vagrant near Odessa in the Ukraine. It breeds in some places in southern Europe, Africa and the Middle East.

The **Ruddy Turnstone** (*Arenaria interpres*) (Fig. 45) has circumpolar distribution. Common though unevenly distributed, it favours the coasts in the tundra zone and in some places of temperate forest zone like Estonia. Its American relative, the **Black Turnstone** (*Arenaria melanocephala*), has been recorded twice on Wrangel Island and the Chukotka peninsula and is thus listed as vagrant.

Its extraordinary appearance instantly singles out the **Black-winged Stilt**

Plate 1

Spring in Wrangel Island.
Photo L. Veisman

Arctic desert, New Siberian
Islands. Photo L. Veisman

Spotted tundra, Yakutia.
Photo L. Veisman

Forest-tundra in Taimyr.
Photo L. Veisman

Plate 2

Above: Middle reaches of
River Bikin, Ussuriland.
Photo Y. Shibnev

Above right: Upper reaches
of Podkamennaya Tunguska
River, Central Siberia.
Photo L. Veisman

Right: Autumn in the mountains east of Lake Baikal.
Photo L. Veisman

Sunset in Northern
Sakhalin. Photo Y. Shibnev

Sikhote Alin Mountains,
Ussuriland. Photo Y. Shibnev

Plate 3

Pine wood in Lithuania.
Photo A. Knystautas

Forest in european Russia,
north-east of Moscow.
Photo L. Veisman

Feathergrass steppe, north Kazakhstan. Photo A. Knystautas/O. Belialov

Plate 4

Stony semi-desert south of
Lake Balkhash. Photo
O. Belialov/A. Knystautas

Spring in the Sary
Ishikotrau desert,
Kazakhstan. Photo
A. Knystautas/
O. Belialov

Singing Mountain National
Park, east Kazakhstan.
Photo A. Knystautas/
O. Belialov

Repetek Nature Reserve,
Turkmenistan.
Photo H. Sakalauskas

Plate 5

Singing Mountain National
Park, east Kazakhastan.
Photo A. Knystautas/
O. Belialov

Kara Kala Nature Reserve,
Turkmenistan. Photo
H. Sakalauskas/A. Blazys

Delta of the Ak Kem River, Altai.
Photo A. Knystautas

Western Pamir Mountains.
Photo H. Sakalauskas

Plate 6

Right and below: Trans Ili Mountain Range, Kazakhstan. Photo A. Knystautas/O. Belialov

Below: Mountain spring in Western Pamir Mountains. Photo H. Sakalauskas

Above: Trans Ili Mountain Range, Kazakhstan. Photo A. Knystautas/O. Belialov

Plate 7

Lake Karakul in the
Pamirs. Photo A. Liutkus

Caucasus Nature Reserve.
Photo H. Sakalauskas

Karkarala National
Park, east Kazakhstan.
Photo O. Belialov/
V. Morozov

Ak Tau Mountains,
east Kazakhstan.
Photo A. Knystautas/
O.Belialov

Plate 8

Hot springs in Kamchatka.
Photo A. Sokolov

Red Canyon of
Charyn, Kazakhstan.
Photo O. Belialov

Ustyurt Nature Reserve, west
Kazakhstan. Photo O. Belialov

Plate 9

Zuvintas Nature Reserve,
Lithuania. Photo H. Sakalauskas

Lake Teletskoje, Altai.
Photo A. Knystautas

Lake Baikal. Photo H. Sakalauskas/
A. Blazys

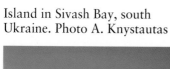

Island in Sivash Bay, south
Ukraine. Photo A. Knystautas

Plate 10

Lake Issyk Kul,
Kirghistan. Photo
A. Knystautas

Swamp in central
Ussuriland. Photo
Y. Shibnev

Delta of the River
Atrek, Turkmenistan.
Photo H. Sakalauskas

Plate 11

Northern Kuril Islands. Photo A. Sokolov

Baltic Sea, Lithuania. Photo A. Knystautas

Coast of the Sea of Japan, Ussuriland. Photo Y. Vaskovsky

Bay of Peter the Great, south Ussuriland. Photo A. Knystautas

Plate 12

Red-throated Diver *(Gavia stellata)*
in Taimyr Nature Reserve.
Photo H. Sakalauskas/A. Blazys

Black-throated Diver *(Gavia arctica)*
in Taimyr Nature Reserve.
Photo H. Sakalauskas/A. Blazys

Pacific Diver
(Gavia pacifica)
in the Chukchi
Peninsula. Photo
P. Tomkovich

White-billed
Diver
(Gavia adamsii)
in the Chukchi
Peninsula. Photo
P. Tomkovich

Plate 13

Slavonian Grebe *(Podiceps auritus)* in the St. Petersburg region. Photo A. Sokolov

Leach's Storm Petrel *(Oceanodroma leucorhoa)* in the Kuril Islands. Photo A. Sokolov

Swinhoe's Storm Petrel *(Oceanodroma monorhis)* in the Verkhovsky Islands, the Sea of Japan. Photo A. Knystautas

Plate 14

White Pelican *(Pelecanus onocrotalus)* in the Ili River Delta. Photo O. Belialov

Dalmatian Pelican *(Pelecanus crispus)* in the Ili River Delta. Photo O. Belialov

Temminck's Cormorant *(Phalacrocorax filamentosus)* on the Kuril Islands. Photo A. Sokolov

Plate 15

Pelagic Cormorants
(Phalacrocorax pelagicus) in
Kamchatka. Photo L. Veisman

Pygmy Cormorants
(Phalacrocorax pygmaeus)
in south Azerbaidjan.
Photo L. Veisman

Black-crowned Night Heron
(Nycticorax nycticorax) in south
Ukraine. Photo V. Siokhin

Striated or Green-Backed Herons *(Butorides striatus)* in south
Ussuriland. Photo Y. Shibnev

Plate 16

Squacco Heron *(Ardeola ralloides)* in south Ukraine. Photo V. Siokhin

Great Egret *(Egretta alba)* in south Ukraine. Photo V. Siokhin

White Spoonbill *(Platalea leucorodia)* in Azerbaidjan. Photo L. Veisman

Little Egret *(Egretta garzetta)* in south Ukraine. Photo V. Siokhin

Plate 17

Glossy Ibis
(Plegadis falcinellus)
in south Ukraine.
Photo V. Siokhin

Oriental White Stork
(Ciconia boyciana) on
Lake Khanka, Ussuriland.
Photo Y. Shibnev

Plate 18

Red-breasted Geese
(Rufibrenta ruficollis)
in Taimyr Nature
Reserve. Photo A.
Liutkus

Red-breasted Goose
(Rufibrenta ruficollis) in
Taimyr Nature Reserve.
Photo A. Liutkus

Snow Goose
(Chen hyperboreus)
in Wrangel Island.
Photo L. Veisman

Plate 19

Emperor Goose *(Philacte canagica)* in Chukchi Peninsula. Photo P. Tomkovich

Mute Swans *(Cygnus olor)* in the Baltic Sea, Lithuania. Photo A. Blazys

Falcated Teal *(Anas falcata)* at Slimbridge. Photo. A. Knystautas

Northern Shovellers *(Anas clypeata)* at Slimbridge. Photo A. Knystautas

Plate 20

Marbled Teal
(Anas angustirostris)
at Slimbridge.
Photo A. Knystautas

Red-crested Pochard
(Netta rufina) at
Slimbridge. Photo
A. Knystautas

Long-tailed Duck
(Clangula hyemalis)
in Lithuania.
Photo H. Sakalauskas

King Eider
(Somateria spectabilis) in
Taimyr Nature Reserve.
Photo A. Sokolov

Plate 21

Spectacled Eider *(Somateria fischeri)* at Slimbridge. Photo A. Knystautas

Black Scoter
(Melanitta nigra)
in Kamchatka.
Photo A. Sokolov

Red-breasted Merganser
(Mergus serrator) at
Slimbridge.
Photo A. Knystautas

Crested Honey Buzzard
(Pernis ptilorhyncus)
in Ussuriland.
Photo Y. Shibnev

Pied Harrier
(Circus
melanoleucus)
in Ussuriland.
Photo Y. Shibnev

Horsfield's Sparrowhawk
(Accipiter soloensis) in
Ussuriland. Photo A.
Knystautas/A. Baltenas

Plate 23

Besra Sparrowhawk
(Accipiter gularis)
in Ussuriland.
Photo Y. Shibnev

Long-legged
Buzzard
(Buteo rufinus)
in southern
Kazakhstan.
Photo O. Belialov

Upland
Buzzard
*(Buteo
hemilasius)*
in Mongolia.
Photo
N. Formozov

Grey-faced Buzzard-Eagles *(Butastur indicus)* in Ussuriland. Photo Y. Shibnev

Plate 24

Bonelli's Eagle *(Hieraaetus fasciatus)* in south Turkmenistan. Photo H. Sakalauskas/A. Blazys

Steppe Eagle *(Aquila rapax)* in the Saratov region. Photo V. Mosseikin

Steller's Sea Eagle chick *(Haliaeetus pelagicus)* in the Sakhalin Islands. Photo Y. Shibnev

Bearded Vulture *(Gypaetus barbatus)* in the Tien Shan Mountains. Photo O. Belialov

Plate 25

Saker Falcon *(Falco cherrug)*
in the Saratov region.
Photo V. Mosseikin

Black Vulture *(Aegypius monachus)*
in the Tien Shan Mountains.
Photo A. Knystautas/A. Baltenas

Peregrine Falcon
(Falco peregrinus) in
Taimyr Nature
Reserve. Photo A.
Liutkus/V. Siokhin

Altai ssp. (?) of Saker Falcon
(Falco cherrug) in the Altai
Mountains. Photo A. Blazys

Hobby *(Falco subbuteo)* in the
Voronezh region. Photo V. Nechaev

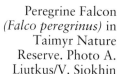

Plate 26

Right: Male Caucasian Black Grouse *(Lyrurus mlokosiewiczi)* in Great Caucasus. Photo A. Sokolov

Left: Male Western Capercaillie *(Tetrao urogallus)* in Finland. Photo H. Hautala

Siberian Spruce Grouse *(Falcipennis falcipennis)* in central Ussuriland. Photo Y. Pukinsky

Hazel Grouse *(Tetrastes bonasia)* in Lithuania. Photo A. Knystautas

Plate 27

Himalayan Snowcock *(Tetraogallus himalayensis)*. Photo O. Belialov

See-See Partridge
(Ammoperdix griseogularis)
in south Turkmenistan. Photo
H. Sakalauskas/A. Blazys

Black Partridge *(Francolinus
francolinus)* in south
Turkmenistan. Photo V. Morozov

Plate 28

Red-crowned or Manchurian Cranes *(Grus japonensis)* in central Ussuriland. Photo Y. Shibnev

Siberian White Crane *(Grus leucogeranus)* in the Kolyma Delta. Photo E. Nazarov

Hooded Crane *(Grus monacha)* in central Ussuriland. Photo Y. Shibnev

Demoiselle Crane *(Anthropoides virgo)* in the Saratov region. Photo V. Mosseikin

Plate 29

Below: Little Bustards *(Tetrax tetrax)* in Azerbaidjan. Photo L. Viesman

Above: Male Great Bustard *(Otis tarda)* in the Saratov region. Photo H. Sakalauskas/A. Blazys

Houbara Bustard *(Chlamydotis undulata)* in the Bukhara region, Uzbekistan. Photo O. Belialov

Stone Curlew *(Burhinus oedicnemus)* in the Saratov region. Photo V. Mosseikin

Plate 30

Pacific Golden Plover
(Pluvialis fulva) in the Chukchi
Peninsula. Photo V. Flint

Greater Sand Plover *(Charadrius leschenaultii)* in east
Kazakhstan. Photo O. Belialov

Caspian Plover
(Charadrius asiaticus)
in central Kazakhstan.
Photo O. Belialov

Lesser Sand Plover *(Charadrius
mongolis)* in the Chukchi
Peninsula. Photo V. Flint

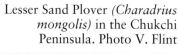

Sociable Plover *(Chettusia
gregaria)* in the Saratov
region. Photo V. Mosseikin

Plate 31

White-tailed Plover
(Chettusia leucura) in
south Uzbekistan.
Photo A. Knystautas/
H. Sakalauskas

Black-winged Stilt
(Himantopus himanto-
pus) in south Ukraine.
Photo V. Siokhin

Ibisbill *(Ibidorhyncha*
struthersii) in the Tien
Shan Mountains. Photo
A. Knystautas/O. Belialov

Ibisbill *(Ibidorhyncha*
struthersii) in the Tien Shan
Mountains. Photo V. Morozov

Plate 32

Spotted Greenshank chick *(Tringa guttifer)* on Sakhalin Island. Photo Y. Shibnev

Marsh Sandpiper *(Tringa stagnatilis)* in the St. Petersburg region. Photo A. Sokolov

Spotted Greenhank *(Tringa guttifer)* on Sakhalin Island. Photo W. Müller

Spotted Redshank *(Tringa erythropus)* in Taimyr Nature Reserve. Photo H. Sakalauskas/ A. Blazys

Grey Phalarope *(Phalaropus fulicarius)* in Taimyr Nature Reserve. Photo A. Ouwerkerk

Plate 33

Above: Red-necked Phalarope *(Phalaropus lobatus)* in Taimyr Nature Reserve. Photo A. Ouwerkerk

Below: Spoon-billed Sandpiper *(Eurynorhynchus pygmeus)* in Chukchi Peninsula. Photo P. Tomkovich

Red-necked Stint *(Calidris ruficollis)* in the Chukchi Peninsula. Photo P. Tomkovich

Little Stint *(Calidris minuta)* in Taimyr Nature Reserve. Photo H. Sakalauskas/A. Blazys

Long-toed Stint *(Calidris subminuta)* in the Sakhalin Islands. Photo Y. Shibnev

Plate 34

Right: Baird's Sandpiper *(Calidris bairdii)* in the Chukchi Peninsula. Photo V. Flint

Left: Temminck's Stint *(Calidris temminckii)* in the Kolyma Delta. Photo H. Sakalauskas/A. Blazys

Above: Rock Sandpiper *(Calidris ptilocnemis)* in the Chukchi Peninsula. Photo P. Tomkovich

Above: Curlew Sandpiper *(Calidris ferruginea)* in the Taimyr Nature Reserve. Photo A. Sokolov

Right: Sharp-tailed Sandpiper *(Calidris acuminata)* in the Kolyma Delta. Photo P. Tomkovich

Plate 35

Pectoral Sandpiper
(Calidris melanotos) in
Taimyr Nature Reserve.
Photo A. Sokolov

Great Knot
(Calidris tenuirostris)
in the Koryak
Mountains.
Photo V. Flint

Western Sandpiper
(Calidris mauri) in the
Chukchi Peninsula.
Photo P. Tomkovich

Pintail Snipe *(Gallinago stenura)*
in Taimyr Nature Reserve.
Photo H. Sakalauskas/A. Blazys

Plate 36

Far Eastern Curlew
(Numenius madagascariensis) in
Ussuriland. Photo Y. Shibnev

Common Pratincole
(Glareola pratinola)
in east Kazakhstan.
Photo O. Belialov

Black-winged Pratincole
(Glareola nordmanni) in
south Turkmenistan.
Photo H. Sakalauskas/
A. Blazys

Plate 37

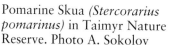

Pomarine Skua *(Stercorarius pomarinus)* in Taimyr Nature Reserve. Photo A. Sokolov

Arctic Skua *(Stercorarius parasiticus)* in the Barents Sea Islands. Photo A. Liutkus

Relict Gull *(Larus relictus)* in Alma Ata Zoo. Photo A. Knystautas

Long-tailed Skua *(Stercorarius long-icaudus)* in Taimyr Nature Reserve. Photo A. Sokolov

Great Black-headed Gulls *(Larus ichthyaetus)* in south Ukraine. Photo V. Siokhin

Plate 38

Relict Gulls
(Larus relictus) at
Lake Alakol, east
Kazakhstan. Photo
A. Knystautas/
H. Sakalauskas

Mediterranean
Gulls *(Larus
melanocephalus)* in
south Ukraine.
Photo V. Siokhin

Little Gull
(Larus minutus) in
the St. Petersburg
region. Photo A.
Sokolov

Slender-billed Gulls
(Larus genei) in
south Ukraine.
Photo A. Knystautas

Brown-headed
Gulls *(Larus
brunnicephalus)*
in the Pamir
Mountains.
Photo A. Liutkus

Plate 39

Left: Eastern Herring Gull *(Larus cachinnans)* in south Ukraine. Photo V. Siokhin

Below: Slaty-backed Gulls *(Larus schistisagus)* in the Kuril Islands. Photo A. Sokolov

Above: Slaty-backed Gull *(Larus schistisagus)* in the Kuril Islands. Photo A. Sokolov

Glaucous Gull *(Larus hyperboreus)* in Taimyr Nature Reserve. Photo A. Sokolov

Black-tailed Gull *(Larus crassirostris)* in the Sea of Japan, south Ussuriland. Photo A. Knystautas

Plate 40

Ross's Gull *(Rhodostethia rosea)* in the Indigirka Delta. Photo V. Flint

White-winged Black Tern *(Chlidonias leucopterus)* in the St. Petersburg region. Photo A. Sokolov

Gull-billed Tern *(Gelochelidon nilotica)* in south Ukraine. Photo V. Siokhin

Caspian Terns *(Hydroprogne caspia)* in south Ukraine. Photo V. Siokhin

Sandwich Terns *(Sterna sandvicensis)* in south Ukraine. Photo V. Siokhin

Plate 41

Spectacled Guillemot *(Cepphus carbo)* in the Verkhovsky Islands, Sea of Japan. Photo A. Knystautas

Ancient Murrelet *(Synthli-boramphus antiquus)* in the Kuril Islands. Photo A. Sokolov

Horned Puffin *(Fratercula corniculata)* in Kamchatka. Photo L. Veisman

Plate 42

Pin-tailed Sandgrouse
(Pterocles alchata) in
central Kazakhstan.
Photo A. Levin

Black-bellied Sandgrouse
(Pterocles orientalis) in east
Kazakhstan. Photo O. Belialov

Pallas's Sandgrouse
(Syrrhaptes paradoxus) in east
Kazakhstan. Photo O. Belialov

Plate 43

Eversmann's Dove *(Columba eversmanni)* in the Ili River Valley, east Kazakhstan. Photo V. Morozov

Rufous Turtle Dove *(Streptopelia orientalis)* in Ussuriland. Photo Y. Shibnev

Laughing Doves *(Streptopelia senegalensis)* in Alma Ata, Kazakhstan. Photo O. Belialov

Oriental Cuckoo *(Cuculus saturatus)* in Ussuriland. Photo A. Knystautas

Plate 44

Snowy Owl *(Nyctea scandia-ca)* in the Chukchi Peninsula. Photo L. Veisman

Eurasian Scops Owl *(Otus scops)* in Turkmenistan. Photo H. Sakalauskas

Northern Eagle Owls *(Bubo bubo)* in Ussuriland. Photo Y. Shibnev

Blakiston's Fish Owl *(Ketupa blakistoni)* in Ussuriland. Photo Y. Shibnev

Plate 45

Indian Scops Owl *(Otus sunia)* in Ussuriland. Photo Y. Shibnev

Hawk Owl *(Surnia ulula)* in Finland. Photo H. Hautala

Great Grey Owls *(Strix nebulosa)* in Ussuriland. Photo Y. Shibnev

Collared Scops Owl *(Otus bakkamoena)* in Ussuriland. Photo Y. Shibnev

Brown Hawk Owl *(Ninox scutulata)* in Ussuriland. Photo Y. Shibnev

Plate 46

Above: Jungle Nightjar *(Caprimulgus indicus)* in Ussuriland. Photo Y. Shibnev

Left: Greater Pied Kingfisher *(Ceryle lugubris)* in the Kuril Islands. Photo Y. Shibnev

Above: European Roller *(Coracias garrulus)* in Turkmenistan. Photo H. Sakalauskas

Eastern Broad-billed Roller *(Eurystomus orientalis)* in Ussuriland. Photo Y. Shibnev

Plate 47

Above: European Kingfisher *(Alcedo atthis)* in Kazakhastan. Photo O. Belialov

Above: Blue-cheeked Bee-eaters *(Merops superciliosus)* in central Kazakhstan. Photo O. Belialov

Left: Great Spotted Woodpecker *(Dendrocopos major)* in Ussuriland. Photo A. Knystautas

Below: White-winged Woodpecker *(Dendrocopos leucopterus)* in east Kazakhstan. Photo A. Knystautas/O. Belialov

Above: Black Woodpecker *(Dryocopus martius)* in the Kaluga region. Photo A. Sokolov

Plate 48

Japanese Pygmy
Woodpecker
(Dendrocopos kizuki)
in Ussuriland.
Photo Y. Shibnev

Below: Northern Three-
toed Woodpecker *(Picoides
tridactylus)* in the St.
Petersburg Region.
Photo A. Sokolov

Sand Martin *(Riparia
riparia)* in the Kaluga
region Photo A. Sokolov

Grey-headed Pygmy Woodpecker
(Dendrocopos canicapillus) in
Ussuriland. Photo Y. Shibnev

Red-rumped Swallow *(Hirundo daurica)*
in east Kazakhstan. Photo O. Belialov

Plate 49

Crested Lark *(Galerida cristata)* in east Kazakhstan. Photo O. Belialov

Lesser Short-toed Lark *(Calandrella rufescens)* in east Kazakhstan. Photo A. Knystautas/O. Belialov

Short-toed Lark *(Calandrella cinerea)* in central Kazakhstan. Photo O. Belialov

Calanadra Lark *(Melancorypha calandra)* in Turkmenistan. Photo H. Sakalauskas/A. Blazys

Plate 50

Bimaculated Lark *(Melanocorypha bimaculata)* in central Kazakhstan. Photo O. Belialov

Male Black Lark *(Melanocorypha yeltonensis)* in east Kazakhstan. Photo O. Belialov/V. Morozov

Female Black Lark *(Melanocorypha yeltonensis)* in east Kazakhstan. Photo O. Belialov

Shore Lark *(Eremophila alpestris)* in Taimyr. Photo A. Sokolov

Plate 51

Richard's Pipit *(Anthus richardii)* in Ussuriland. Photo A. Knystautas/ Y. Shibnev

Buff-bellied Pipit *(Anthus rubescens)* in Ussuriland. Photo Y. Shibnev

Olive-backed Pipit *(Anthus hodgsoni)* in Kamchatka. Photo A. Sokolov

Yellow Wagtail *(Motacilla taivana)* in the Sakhalin Islands. Photo V. Shibnev

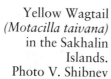

Plate 52

Forest Wagtail
(Dendronanths indicus) in Ussuriland. Photo Y. Shibnev

Kamchatka Wagtail *(Motacilla lugens)* in Kamchatka. Photo A. Sokolov

Masked Wagtail *(Motacilla personata)* in the western Tien Shan Mountains. Photo A. Knystautas

CitrineWagtail *(Motacilla citreola)* in the Taimyr Nature Reserve. Photo H. Sakalauskas/A. Blazys

Plate 53

Brown Shrike
*(Lanius crista-
tus)* in
Ussuriland.
Photo
Y. Shibnev

Isabelline Shrike
*(Lanius isabelli-
nus)* in south
Kazakhstan.
Photo
V. Morozov

Bull-headed Shrike *(Lanius
bucephalus)* in Kunashir Island,
Kurils. Photo Y. Shibnev

Lesser Grey Shrike *(Lanius
minor)* in south Kazakhstan.
Photo V. Morozov

Plate 54

Black-naped Oriole *(Oriolus chinensis)* in Ussuriland. Photo Y. Shibnev

Daurian Starling *(Sturnia sturnina)* in Ussuriland. Photo A. Knystautas

Rose-coloured Starling *(Sturnus. roseus)* in east Kazakhstan. Photo V. Morozov

Plate 55

Siberian Jay
(Perisoreus infaustas) in
Finland. Photo H. Hautala

Pander's Ground Jay
(Podoces panderi) in
Turkmenistan.
Photo H. Sakalauskas

Azure-winged Magpie
(Cyanopica cyanus) in Ussuriland.
Photo A. Knystautas/Y. Shibnev

Plate 56

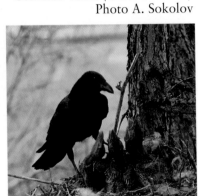

Common Crow *(Corvus corone)*
Photo A. Sokolov

Red-billed Chough *(Pyrrhocorax pyrrhocorax)* in the Tien Shan Mountains. Photo O. Belialov

Desert Ravens *(Corvus ruficollis)* in central Kazakhstan. Photo O. Belialov

Jungle Crows *(Corvus macrorhynchos)* in Ussuriland. Photo Y. Shibnev

Plate 57

White-throated Dipper *(Cinclus cinclus)* in the Tien Shan Mountains. Photo H. Sakalauskas/ A. Blazys

Brown Dipper *(Cinclus pallasi)* in Ussuriland. Photo Y. Shibnev

Bohemian Waxwing *(Bombycilla garrulus)* in Finland. Photo H. Hautala

Ashy Minivets *(Pericrocotus divaricatus)* in Ussuriland. Photo Y. Shibnev

Plate 58

Alpine Accentor *(Prunella collaris)* in the Swiss Alps. Photo W. Müller

Himalayan Accentor *(Prunella himalayana)* in the Pamir Mountains. Photo H. Sakalauskas

Brown Accentor *(Prunella fulvescens)* in the Altai Mountains. Photo A. Blazys

Siberian Accentor *(Prunella montanella)* in the Taimyr Peninsula. Photo H. Sakalauskas/ A. Blazys

Plate 59

Short-tailed Bush Warbler
(Urosphena squameiceps) in
Ussuriland. Photo Y. Shibnev

Japanese Bush Warbler
(Horeites diphone) in
Ussuriland. Photo Y. Shibnev

Cetti's Warbler *(Cettia cetti)* in
Uzbekistan. Photo A.
Knystautas/A. Blazys

Chinese Bush Warbler
(Bradypterus tacsanowskius) in
the Trans Baikal region.
Photo A. Sokolov

Gray's Grasshopper Warbler
(Locustella fasciolata) in Ussuriland.
Photo Y. Shibnev

Plate 60

Pallas's Grasshopper Warbler
(Locustella certhiola) in the
Trans Baikal Region.
Photo A. Sokolov

Middendorff's Grasshopper
Warbler *(Locustella ochotensis)*
in Sakhalin. Photo Y. Shibnev

Lanceolated Warbler
(*Locustella lanceolata*) in
Kamchatka. Photo A. Sokolov

Thick-billed Warbler
(Phragmaticola aedon)
in Ussuriland.
Photo Y. Shibnev

Black-browed Reed Warbler
(Acrocephalus bistrigiceps) in
Ussuriland. Photo Y. Shibnev

Plate 61

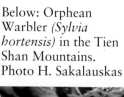

Below: Orphean Warbler *(Sylvia hortensis)* in the Tien Shan Mountains. Photo H. Sakalauskas

Above: Upcher's Warbler *(Hippolais languida)* in Kazakhstan. Photo O. Belialov

Lesser Whitethroat *(Sylvia curruca)* in Kazakhstan. Photo V. Morozov

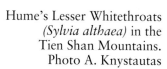

Hume's Lesser Whitethroats *(Sylvia althaea)* in the Tien Shan Mountains. Photo A. Knystautas

Plate 62

Ménétries' Warbler *(Sylvia mystacea)* in south Turkmenistan.
Photo H. Sakalauskas

Desert Warbler *(Sylvia nana)* in
Kazakhstan. Photo O. Belialov/
A. Knystautas

Arctic Warbler *(Phylloscopus borealis)* at
the Kolyma River. Photo H. Sakalauskas

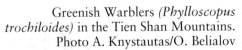

Greenish Warblers *(Phylloscopus
trochiloides)* in the Tien Shan Mountains.
Photo A. Knystautas/O. Belialov

Plate 63

Pale-legged
Leaf Warbler
*(Phylloscopus
tenellipes)* in
Ussuriland. Photo
A. Knystautas/
A. Baltenas

Sulphur-bellied Warbler
(Phylloscopus griseolus) in the
Tien Shan Mountains.
Photo V. Morozov

Dusky Warbler *(Phylloscopus
fuscatus)* in Kamchatka.
Photo A. Sokolov

Radde's Warbler *(Phylloscopus
scharwarzii)* in Ussuriland.
Photo A. Knystautas/Y. Shibnev

Plate 64

Severtzov's Tit Warbler
(Leptopoecile sophiae) in the Tien
Shan Mountains. Photo V. Morozov

Above and right: Male
Asian Paradise Flycatcher
(Terpsiphone paradisi)
in Ussuriland.
Photo Y. Shibnev

Plate 65

Yellow-rumped Flycatcher
(Ficedula zanthopygia) in
Ussuriland.
Photo Y. Shibnev

Spotted Flycatcher
(Muscicapa striata) in
Lithuania.
Photo A. Knystautas

Brown Flycatcher
(Muscicapa latirostris) in
Ussuriland. Photo A.
Knystautas/Y. Shibnev

Blue-and-White Flycatcher
(Cyanoptila cyanomelana)
in Ussuriland. Photo
A.Knystautas/Y. Shibnev

Plate 66

Desert Wheatear *(Oenanthe
deserti)* in Kazakhstan.
Photo V. Morozov

Isabelline Wheatear
(Oenanthe isabellina) in
Kazakhstan. Photo O. Belialov

Red-tailed Wheatear *(Oenanthe
xanthoprymna)* in the Pamir
Mountains. Photo H. Sakalauskas

Rufous Bush Chat
(Cercotrichas galactotes) in
Kazakhstan. Photo
A. Knystautas

Blue-headed Redstart
(Phoenicurus caeruleocephalus)
in the Tien Shan Mountains.
Photo O. Belialov

Plate 67

Black Redstart *(Phoenicurus ochruros)* in the Pamir Mountains. Photo H. Sakalauskas

Güldenstädt's Redstart *(Phoenicurus erythrogaster)* in the Pamir Mountains. Photo O. Belialov

Eversmann's Redstart *(Phoenicurus erythronotus)* in the Altai Mountains. Photo A. Knystautas

Daurian Redstart *(Phoenicurus auroreus)* in Ussuriland. Photo Y. Shibnev

River Chat *(Chaimarrornis leucocephalus)* in the Pamir Mountains. Photo H. Sakalauskas

Plate 68

Japanese Robin *(Luscinia akahige)*
in the Kuril Mountains.
Photo Y. Shibnev

Himalayan Rubythroat *(Luscinia pectoralis)* in the Tien Shan Mountains.
Photo O. Belialov/V. Morozov

Siberian Blue Robin *(Luscinia cyane)* in Ussuriland.
Photo Y. Shibnev

Red-flanked Bluetail
(Tarsiger cyanurus) in the
Kunashir Islands, Kurils.
Photo Y. Shibnev

White-throated Robin
(Irania gutturalis) in the Karatau
Mountains, Kazakhstan.
Photo O. Belialov

Plate 69

Grey-backed Thrush *(Turdus hortulorum)* in Ussuriland. Photo Y. Shibnev

Black-throated Thrush *(Turdus atrogullaris)* in Kazakhstan. Photo O. Belialov

Dusky Thrush *(Turdus eunomus)* in the Taimyr Peninsula. Photo H. Sakalauskas/A. Blazys

Blue Whistling Thrush *(Myiophonus caeruleus)* in the Tien Shan Mountains. Photo A. Knystautas/H. Sakalauskas

White's Thrush *(Zoothera dauma)* in Ussuriland. Photo Y. Shibnev

Plate 70

Little Forktail *(Microcichla scouleri)* in the Pamir Mountains. Photo H. Sakalauskas

Vinious-throated Parrotbill *(Suthora webbiana)* in Ussuriland. Photo Y. Shibnev

Male Bearded Tit *(Panurus biarmicus)* in Kazakhstan. Photo V. Morozov

Polivanov's Parrotbills *(Paradoxornis polivanovi)* in Lake Khanka, Ussuriland. Photo Y. Shibnev

Plate 71

Songar Tit
(Parus songarus) in the
Tien Shan Mountains.
Photo A. Knystautas

Siberian Tit *(Parus
cinctus)* in Finland.
Photo H. Hautala

Rufous-naped Tit *(Parus rufonuchalis)* in the
Tien Shan Mountains. Photo A. Knystautas/A. Baltenas

Plate 72

Boukhara Tit *(Parus bokharensis)* in east Kazakhstan.
Photo A. Knystautas

Azure Tit *(Parus cyanus)* in the northern Tien Shan Mountains. Photo A. Knystautas/O. Belialov

Yellow-breasted Azure Tit *(Parus flavipectus)* in the western Tien Shan Mountains. Photo A. Knystautas/H. Sakalauskas

Plate 73

Eastern Rock Nuthatch
(Sitta tephronota) in the
Tien Shan Mountains.
Photo O. Belialov

Chestnut-flanked White-eye *(Zosterops erythropleura)* in
Ussuriland. Photo Y. Shibnev

Plate 74

Spanish Sparrow
(Passer hispaniolensis) in east
Kazakhstan. Photo V. Morozov

Saxual Sparrow *(Passer
ammodendri)* in east
Kazakhstan. Photo A.
Knystautas/V. Morozov

Desert Sparrow *(Passer
simplex)* in Turkmenistan.
Photo H. Sakalauskas

Plate 75

Brambling *(Fringilla montifringilla)* in Finland. Photo H. Hautala

Chinese Greenfinch *(Chloris sinica)* in Ussuriland. Photo Y. Shibnev

Red-fronted Serin *(Serinus pusillus)* in Great Caucasus. Photo A. Sokolov

Redpoll *(Acanthis flammea)* in Taimyr Nature Reserve. Photo A. Sokolov

Grey-headed Goldfinch *(Carduelis caniceps)* in the Tien Shan Mountains. Photo A. Knystautas/A. Blazys

Plate 76

Hodgson's Rosy Finch *(Leucosticte nemoricola)* in the Tien Shan Mountains. Photo A. Knystautas/ O. Belialov

Crimson-winged Finch *(Rhodopechys sanguinea)* in the Tien Shan Mountains. Photo A. Knystautas

Mongolian Trumpeter Finch *(Bucanetes mongolicus)* in east Kazakhstan. Photo O. Belialov/ V. Morozov

Red-mantled Rosefinch *(Carpodacus rhodochlamys)* in the Tien Shan Mountains. Photo O. Belialov

Pallas's Rosefinch *(Carpodacus roseus)* in south Siberia. Photo V. Morozov

Plate 77

Great Rosefinch *(Carpodacus rubicilla)* in Great Caucasus. Photo A. Sokolov

Parrot Crossbill *(Loxia pytyopsittacus)* in Finland. Photo H. Hautala

Long-tailed Rosefinch *(Uragus sibiricus)* in Ussuriland. Photo Y. Shibnev

Pine Grosbeak *(Pinicola enucleator)* in Finland. Photo H. Hautala

Chinese Grosbeak *(Eophona migratoria)* in Ussuriland. Photo Y. Shibnev

Plate 78

White-capped Bunting
(Emberiza stewarti) in the Tien
Shan Mountains. Photo H.
Sakalauskas/A. Knystautas

Long-tailed Bunting *(Emberiza cioides)*
in Ussuriland. Photo Y. Shibnev

Pallas's Bunting
(Emberiza pallasi)
in the Taimyr
Peninsula.
Photo A. Sokolov

Plate 79

Tristram's Bunting *(Emberiza tristrami)* in Ussuriland. Photo Y. Shibnev

Rustic Bunting *(Emberiza rustica)* in Kamchatka. Photo A. Sokolov

Black-faced Bunting *(Emberiza spodocephala)* in Ussuriland. Photo Y. Shibnev

Yellow-breasted Bunting *(Emberiza aureola)* in Ussuriland. Photo A. Knystautas

Plate 80

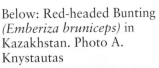

Below: Red-headed Bunting
(Emberiza bruniceps) in
Kazakhstan. Photo A.
Knystautas

Above: Grey-necked Bunting
(Emberiza buchanani) in
Kazakhstan. Photo
A. Knystautas/V. Morozov

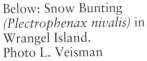

Below: Snow Bunting
(Plectrophenax nivalis) in
Wrangel Island.
Photo L. Veisman

Above: Lapland Bunting
(Calcarius lapponicus)
in the Taimyr Peninsula.
Photo A. Sokolov

Fig. 45 *Ruddy Turnstone (*Arenaria interpres*) in the Barents Sea Islands. Photo A. Liutkus*

(*Himantopus himantopus*) (Plate 31) from other birds. Unusually long legs and a stork-like appearance are characteristic of this species which has cosmopolitan distribution. In Russia, it breeds along the shores of mostly saline water bodies in the south of the country.

The symbol of the Royal Society for the Protection of Birds is the **Pied Avocet** (*Recurvirostra avosetta*) (Fig. 46). This beautiful and delicate wader has extremely uneven distribution in Russia and is found along the shores of different water bodies from the western borders to the Transbaikal region, favouring mostly saline bays and lakes in the south.

The **Palearctic Oystercatcher** (*Haematopus ostralegus*) has a highly fragmented breeding distribution in Russia, being found along sea coasts as well as in river valleys in many different parts of the country from the Baltic sea east to Kamchatka. Oystercatchers first breed at three years old. They nest on shingle, sand, shell, and rocky sea coasts in bays and inlets, where there are shallows and a wide littoral zone which is uncovered at low tide. Inland habitat is river and lake margins. A clutch of three to four eggs is laid in a simple, shallow scrape. Incubation takes 26-28 days and the chicks leave the nest on the day they hatch. It is a curious fact (and unusual for a wader) that the parent oystercatchers not only guard their offspring, but actually feed them bill to bill. Even a fully feathered chick is incapable of feeding itself. Fidelity of the territory once chosen has been confirmed several times by ringing – birds return to the same place year after year and often

Fig. 46 *Pied Avocet* (Recurvirostra avosetta) *in Eastern Kazakhstan. Photo O. Belialov*

even use the same nest-site. Oystercatchers have a varied diet, comprising mainly aquatic invertebrates.

Perhaps one of the most exciting of all the waders found in Russia is the **Ibisbill** (*Ibidorhyncha struthersii*) (Plate 31). This species is restricted to small areas of the Central Asian mountains. It is not, however, a truly alpine bird since it is associated not with the alpine habitats but with the valleys of high mountain rivers and can thus be found in lower altitudes as well.

In spring 1986, in the high mountains of Zailiisli Alatau, together with Oleg Belialov, I was lucky enough to study and photograph a pair of Ibisbills at their nest at about 2,500 m. This species occurs in the Russian Red Data Book and the estimated number in Russia is about 150 breeding pairs, though this may be higher. The inaccessibility of most breeding sites makes it very difficult to obtain more accurate data. Helicopters would be of immense help but scientific research bodies are quite limited in their finance so it is not always possible to use this expensive technique. The last data when the helicopter was used in 1989 revealed the following numbers in the northern Tien Shan mountains. The upper reaches of Chilik river had four breeding pairs, the valley of Chon Kimin river which has massive gravel-covered valleys and runs between the Zailiiski and Kungei Alatau ranges had ten breeding pairs and along the Kara Kara River in the Kungei Alatau range there were another ten pairs.

Fig. 47 *Common Greenshank* (Tringa nebularia) *on migration in the Ili River Valley, Kazakhstan.* Photo O. Belialov

The Ibisbill occurs in a very restricted mountain habitat, being confined to valleys, usually devoid of any vegetation, along which the rivers flow relatively slowly. It finds its prey which consists of insects, crustaceans, molluscs and small fish by probing with its bill beneath the pebbles or by raking its bill from side to side through the pebbles to dislodge its prey.

Ibisbills begin nesting in May, when their loud piping courtship calls can be heard across the mountain river valleys. The nest is a simple pit in the ground lined with flat pebbles containing from two to four eggs, and is extremely difficult to find against the pebble-strewn background. Indeed, the only way we spotted one was to climb high above the valley and scan the whole area with powerful binoculars. The incubation period is about 30 days, but many other details of the life story of this extraordinary bird still remain to be learned. In winter, the Ibisbill moves down to lower altitudes although it never leaves its mountain habitat.

The genus *Tringa* has eight species recorded in Russia, seven of which breed. Many species well known to western birdwatchers are common and widespread in Russia. They inhabit marshes, raised bogs in the taiga, lowland tundra and some even mountain river valleys. These are the **Green Sandpiper** (*Tringa ochropus*), the **Wood Sandpiper** (*T. glareola*), the **Common Greenshank** (*T. nebularia*) (Fig. 47), and the **Common Redshank** (*T. totanus*).

Surely the most exotic species of this genus in Russia is the **Spotted Greenshank** (*Tringa guttifer*) (Plate 32), an exceptionally rare shank which is endemic to Russia. It nests only on Sakhalin Island and is included as endangered in both IUCN/ICPB and the Russian Red Data Books. Its wintering grounds lie in south-east China, the Philippines, Indochina, and India.

This wader is unique in many respects. Its habitat in the Far East breeding range is marshy coastal lowlands adjoining sparse larch forest. Places like this have an abundance of shallow lakes and lagoons, mudbanks and dense thickets of typical marshland vegetation along the margins. This habitat has thus far suffered no significant changes, but the Spotted Greenshank's numbers are alarmingly low (a few hundred individuals at the most) and the status of this species gives grave cause for concern. The limits of the present breeding range have still not been clarified and no areas have been designated for special protection – rectifying this should be treated as a matter of the utmost urgency. It is worrying to report that several localities where Spotted Greenshanks formerly bred now have none.

These waders typically nest in loose colonies, with pairs 50 m or up to 7 km apart. One of the most remarkable facts in the life of this wader is that it builds its own nest in a tree. Tree-nesting in waders is not so unusual but, and this is the important difference, other species use the old nests of other birds, chiefly thrushes. The Spotted Greenshank builds a nest of dead twigs and lichen on a larch branch at 2-4.5 m up. The clutch of four eggs is laid in early June and incubated by both sexes; the exact period is not known. Hatching takes place in late June or early July. The main food is small fish and various aquatic invertebrates. Departure from the breeding grounds starts around mid- to late August.

The **Spotted Redshank** (*Tringa erythropus*) (Plate 32) is an elegant bird of strikingly beautiful plumage. It is a typical tundra species and apart from the most Arctic tundras of Russia inhabits parts of Finland, Sweden, and Norway. It penetrates also into wooded tundra and even into parts of the northern taiga belt. Its life story is much the same as those of other closely related species. The wintering grounds cover parts of Africa south of the Sahara, and southern Asia.

From the western borders east to Ussuriland the **Marsh Sandpiper** (*Tringa stagnatilis*) (Plate 32) is found. This species is associated with steppe and boreal zones. It favours marshes along fresh water bodies where the grass is not too dense. The wintering grounds cover Africa and south Asia. The melodious voice of this wader starts to resound in its breeding places from April. The nest is a well-hidden pit covered with dense vegetation. The clutch consists of four eggs which are laid in May. Even though this bird is common in several areas within its breeding range, a lot more still remains unknown about its life history.

The **Lesser Yellowlegs** (*Tringa flavipes*) is a vagrant species in Russia, recorded several times on Wrangel Island and Chukotka peninsula.

Endemic to Russia, the **Grey-tailed Tattler** (*Heteroscelus brevipes*) inhabits mountainous regions of wooded tundra and taiga of north-east Asia, south to Lake Baikal and the Sayan mountains, north to the Taimyr peninsula, the northernmost forests in the world. These birds appear at their breeding grounds in May since most of the grounds are cold areas of Siberia where the spring even in the south comes by the end of May. In June shanks are actively involved in their courtship displays, producing a sound resembling that of the Wood Sandpiper but much louder. They often interrupt their flight to sit on the tree-tops and are active all day and night. In June, four eggs are laid either in an old nest of a thrush or in a scrape on the ground camouflaged by dense vegetation or dead tree trunks.

A clutch is incubated by both sexes and parents are very active in defending their nest against any intruder. The alarm calls sometimes end with the courtship song. Both adults take care of the young. In mid-August, these birds start to make their way towards the wintering grounds in Indonesia, the Philippines, Australia and Tasmania.

The **Wandering Tattler** (*Heteroscelus incanus*), an American species, breeds in the Chukotka peninsula on the Anadyr and Koryak ranges. The main breeding area covers the north-west part of North America.

Very common and characteristic throughout the country is the **Common Sandpiper** (*Actitis hypoleucos*) which inhabits shores of rivers, lakes and streams in diverse habitats from the north to the high mountains of Central Asia. Its American counterpart, the **Spotted Sandpiper** (*A. macularia*), was recorded as a vagrant species in the Chukotka peninsula.

Another species of wader with its main breeding grounds in Russia is the **Terek Sandpiper** (*Xenus cinereus*). It has a very restricted breeding area in Finland, the rest being in Russia. It is mainly restricted to the boreal taiga zone but extends north into subarctic tundra as in the Taimyr peninsula. The Terek Sandpiper likes overgrown moist grasslands with plenty of shrubs, riverain forests and sandy river banks. It is noisy and its voice is most commonly compared to that of the Redshank. The Terek Sandpiper is a solitary nester. Nests are situated either in open areas or in short vegetation. Breeding starts in May or, in more northerly areas, by the end of June. The usual clutch consists of four eggs which are incubated for 23-24 days. It seems that both parents take care of the young. Autumn migration to the wintering grounds in Africa, South Asia and Australia starts in mid-August.

Three species of phalarope have been recorded in Russia, two of which breed. The American species, **Wilson's Phalarope** (*Phalaropus tricolor*) is regarded as vagrant. Both the **Red-necked Phalarope** (*P. lobatus*) (Plate 33) and the **Grey Phalarope** (*P. fulicarius*) (Plate 32) inhabit tundras of Russia.

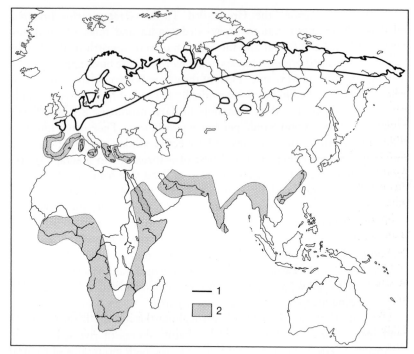

Fig. 48 *Breeding range and wintering grounds of the Ruff (*Philomachus pugnax). 1. Boundary of breeding range; 2. wintering grounds*

The latter species is solely a tundra breeder while the Red-necked is also found along the shores of inland waters in the forest-tundras. Both species are common in suitable habitats.

The **Ruff** (*Philomachus pugnax*) is well known for its spectacular spring displays when differently coloured males gather in a flat, drier place in the marsh or wet meadow to fight, apparently doing no harm to each other. This bird has wide distribution from the western borders to the Far East (Fig. 48).

Most western birdwatchers are familiar with the controversy surrounding Cox's Sandpiper, and a very interesting view on this problem has been expressed by Dr L. Stepanyan. He thinks that this bird is a hybrid between the Ruff and the Pectoral Sandpiper (*Calidris melanotos*). The theory is supported by several facts including the following. Cox's Sandpipers were found in winter and on migration only recently when the Ruff started expansion of its breeding range to the tundras of the Russian Far East. These regions in Eastern Siberia include the breeding range of the Pectoral Sandpiper in Russia. The male Pectoral Sandpiper has a little mantle distantly resembling that of the Ruff. The theory suggests that Cox's Sandpiper is a hybrid between a male Pectoral Sandpiper and a female Ruff. This theory is, of course, subjective and only time and additional research will give us proof.

The **Spoon-billed Sandpiper** (*Eurynorhynchus pygmeus*) (Plate 33) is an astonishing little wading bird, a relict species with a restricted range entirely within Russia. It breeds in a narrow, discontinuous belt along the coast of Chukotka and the Kamchatka isthmus. Spoon-billed Sandpipers migrate along the Pacific coast of Asia to wintering grounds in South-East Asia from eastern India to south-eastern China. The incredible shape of this bird's bill would appear to be a distinctive feature for its identification in the wild but this is not the case. In fact, it is very difficult to single out this bird among other sandpipers by its bill.

Spoon-billed Sandpipers inhabit the shores of coastal lagoons where there is an abundance of shallow saline lakes, and the innermost parts of marine bays where river estuaries provide a network of temporary water channels and moss-covered shingle banks. The present condition of this habitat gives no cause for concern for the species' survival and no significant changes are likely to take place.

The world population of Spoon-billed Sandpipers is estimated at 2,000-2,800 breeding pairs, with numbers varying locally from two to three and ten to fifteen pairs. In some places there are noticeable annual fluctuations, but no general decline in numbers has been detected.

This small wading bird is monogamous. Its nest is usually on a dry, relatively flat place with low tundra vegetation. Three to four eggs are laid at the end of June and incubated for 19-23 days. The chicks fledge at 15-18 days. Spoon-billed Sandpipers feed predominately on adult and larval insects. When foraging, they resemble a flamingo, moving about in the shallows and rapidly turning the head from side to side and thus sweeping the water surface with the bill in semi-circles.

The true sandpipers and stints of the genus *Calidris* are a large group of northern waders of which sixteen species breed on the Russian tundra and marshlands. The breeding range of the **Little Stint** (*Calidris minuta*) (Plate 33) stretches across the tundra of Eurasia from Norway to the lower reaches of River Lena. It is one of the smallest representatives of this genus, weighing 22-27 g. Wintering grounds lie on the southern Caspian, in south Asia and in Africa. Having arrived on their breeding grounds in early July, very rarely at the end of May, Little Stints immediately take up nesting territories and start to perform song-flights: flying at a fair height with wings raised, the bird hovers and gives a trill reminiscent of a stridulating bush-cricket. Displaying Little Stints not infrequently settle on small willow bushes. The

Fig. 49 *Temminck's Stint* (Calidris temminckii) *in the Kolyma Delta.*
Photo H. Sakalauskas/A. Blazys

nest is a simple scrape lined with flattened growth of last year's grass, often under a small bush. Four eggs are laid at the end of June. The Little Stint is one of the commonest of tundra waders.

Like many of its kind, the Little Stint is a bird of calm and placid habits, foraging in silence or giving only a quiet contact-calls. It is almost indifferent to the presence of man. An incubating bird will allow very close approach and, if forced off the nest, tends not to move away, attempting rather to drive off the intruder, by approaching and sometimes even by gently pushing at their hand. Little Stints are mainly insectivorous, but they also eat molluscs and small crustaceans.

The tundras of north-east Siberia and north-west America are home to the **Red-necked Stint** (*Calidris ruficollis*) (Plate 33) which closely resembles the Little Stint but is slightly larger. It winters in China, Japan, Australia, Tasmania and South Asia. Departure from the breeding grounds takes place from the end of August. Following arrival on the tundra in the beginning of June, Red-necked Stints start to display actively: the song-flight makes them easy to distinguish from the Little Stint as Red-necks move up and down like a yo-yo, holding the wings at body level and rarely raising them above that. The nest is a simple scrape and the normal clutch is four eggs.

The **Long-toed Stint** (*Calidris subminuta*) (Plate 33) is endemic to Russia. This is not a true tundra species and is widespread in the marshes of the taiga zone from the river Ob' basin to the Far East. It also breeds on the

Fig. 50 *Dunlin* (Calidris alpina) *in Kamchatka. Photo A. Sokolov*

Pacific islands including the Commander Islands, the Kurils and Sakhalin. This bird winters in South-East Asia, more rarely in Australia. Its breeding biology and diet closely resembles those of other Stints.

The following two *Calidris* species are registered as vagrants: the **Least Sandpiper** (*C. minutilla*) in Chukotka Peninsula and the **White-rumped Sandpiper** (*C. fuscicollis*) in Franz Joseph Land.

Among the common and widespread species of Stints are **Temminck's Stint** (*Calidris temminckii*) (Plate 34 and Fig. 49) and the **Dunlin** (*C. alpina*) (Fig. 50). Both species have cross-country distribution, the first being associated with tundra habitat and the second living also in bogs covering huge expanses of the temperate forest zone.

The eastern Siberian tundras are home for several Stint species, including **Baird's Sandpiper** (*Calidris bairdii*) (Plate 34) which apart from the Chukotka peninsula also breeds in American tundras, and the **Rock Sandpiper** (*C. ptilocnemis*) (Plate 34) which breeds only in the Chukotka peninsula in Russia and in Alaska in the USA. The **Western Sandpiper** (*C. mauri*) (Plate 35) has the same distribution as the previous species. The **Semipalmated Sandpiper** (*C. pusillus*) was registered in 1986 as a breeding bird in Chukotka Peninsula next to Alaska. From the Yamal peninsula in the west to the Chukotka in the east it is possible to see the prominiscuous **Pectoral Sandpiper** (*C. melanotos*) (Plate 35) while the **Curlew Sandpiper** (*C. ferruginea*) (Plate 34), a true Arctic bird, breeds in the northernmost parts of the tundra, including the Taimyr peninsula. Taimyr serves as home for another species, namely the **Purple Sandpiper** (*C. maritima*) which in Russia is also found in the westernmost sector of the Russian Arctic, in the Kola peninsula.

The **Sharp-tailed Sandpiper** (*Calidris acuminata*) (Plate 34) is a Russian endemic. This uncommon species breeds only on the tundras of Yakutia. From there, the Sharptail migrates to wintering grounds in South-East Asia, Indonesia, New Guinea and Australia, adults and young birds choosing surprisingly different routes. The old birds migrate through the continent passing Lake Baikal on their way, while those on their first migration gather on the shores of the sea of Okhotsk and then fly southwards along the coasts of the Pacific. The breeding biology closely resembles that of other sandpipers.

Two of the largest species of sandpipers are the **Great Knot** (*Calidris tenuirostris*) (Plate 35) and the **Red Knot** (*C. canutus*). The first species is another endemic of Russia which breeds in mountainous tundra in East Siberia up to the Chukotka peninsula. The breeding biology of this restricted species is largely unknown and only two nests have ever been discovered. The Great Knot breeds in dry areas of mountainous tundra covered by pebbles and sparse vegetation. The clutch consists of four eggs. After breeding, the birds tend to fly directly to the coasts and migrate to their wintering quarters in South Asia and northern Australia. The Knot, as the Curlew Sandpiper, is a species of high Arctic latitudes. In Russia, it has sparse distribution in the Taimyr peninsula and on the Arctic islands. Like the Great Knot, it favours gravel-covered slopes or hills which carry little vegetation.

The distribution range of the **Sanderling** (*Calidris alba*), another largely high Arctic species, covers several areas in Russia between the Yenisey and Lena river deltas. The **Buff-breasted Sandpiper** (*Tryngites subruficollis*), an American species some time ago regarded as vagrant in Russia, was found breeding on Wrangel Island. The **Broad-billed Sandpiper** (*Limicola falcinellus*) is much less gregarious than *Calidris* species, particularly during the autumn migration. It breeds in Scandinavia, the Kola and Yamal peninsulas, and in several parts of the Central and Eastern Siberian tundras. It has characteristically patchy distribution in Russia and is regarded as an uncommon and insufficiently studied species.

The subfamily Scolopacinae which includes the well known snipe tribe, has several exotic species in Russia along with the more common ones. It starts with the **Jack Snipe** (*Lymnocryptes minima*) which is an uncommon species inhabiting open mud-swamps with sparse grass in the sub-arctic and boreal latitudes. The breeding season starts in April-May, the nest is placed on the ground in short vegetation and sometimes may be surrounded by water. Incubation, apparently by the female only, takes about 24 days. The Jack Snipe winters in Western Europe, south Asia and Africa.

The genus *Gallinago*, or the true snipes, has six species in Russia, all of which breed. The well known **Common Snipe** (*G. gallinago*) enjoys wide distribution throughout the country and is common in suitable habitats. **The**

Fig. 51 *Swinhoe's Snipe (*Gallinago megala) *in central Ussuriland.*
Photo Y. Shibnev

Japanese Snipe (*G. harwickii*) is a Far Eastern species which inhabits the wet meadows of the southern part of Ussuriland, the Sakhalin and Kuril Islands.

In damp woodland glades and marshy forest edges; in the meadows of Ussuriland and in some areas of western Siberia and the Transbaikal region, you may hear a rushing sound almost like a jet aircraft and then see a small bird flying at some height and from time to time making a steep dive. This is **Swinhoe's Snipe** (*Gallinago megala*) (Fig. 51). Displaying snipe may be heard following their spring arrival in late April. They nest on the ground, on a moss cushion, or in a tussock of sedge. A clutch of four eggs is laid from late May. The wintering grounds of this snipe cover South-East Asia and Australia.

The **Pintail Snipe** (*Gallinago stenura*) (Plate 35) is a solitary nester whose breeding range covers large areas of Siberia. The habitat of this bird is different from that of the Common Snipe and includes drier places such as low hills, dry bogs and alpine tundra with stones. It is uncommon throughout its range. Its breeding biology resembles that of other snipes. The Pintail Snipe winters in the south of Asia.

One of the most secretive birds in the whole of Russia is the **Solitary Snipe** (*Gallinago solitaria*). It is quite widely distributed in the mountain ranges of Central Asia and Siberia but little is known about its way of life. The first nests were discovered in the Altai mountains, in the Katun range. We visited these places in 1985 and were lucky enough to encounter this fascinating bird. The Katun range in Altai is certainly most majestic and impressive, and at altitudes of 2000-3000 metres the display calls of Solitary Snipe may be heard. The birds do not take into consideration the weather and call even during the thunderstorms which are by no means rare in Altai. Their calls, which are not produced with the feathers like other snipes, are quite strong but melancholic and are mostly heard at night. After they call, the birds dive down and the sound of a jet aircraft engine is produced by their tail feathers. Their nests are on the ground on the mountain slopes, covered by varied but usually very thick vegetation. The usual clutch consists of four eggs. Next to nothing is known about this unusual bird's breeding biology. Its wintering quarters, usually by the shores of mountain streams, are on the mountains of Central Asia, where it is solitary for the harsh time of the year.

Populations of **Great Snipe** (*Gallinago media*) which is better known in the west, have been declining recently in most places due to the destruction of its habitats. This generally solitary bird is known for its spring courtship displays, very different from those of other snipes, when the male birds gather on the ground in the forest meadow and pose spectacularly, fight with other males for territories, and copulate.

Boreal and temperate forests with extensive humidity, cool shade but not wet terrain are home for the well-known **Eurasian Woodcock** (*Scolopax rusticola*) the breeding range of which covers huge expanses throughout Russia not only in the lowland taiga zone but also in the mountains of Central Asia.

There are six curlew species (*Numenius*) in Russia, large and impressive wading birds, five of which are breeding and one extinct. The **Eskimo Curlew** (*N. borealis*) was last recorded in the Anadyr river delta in the extreme north-east of Russia in the last century.

Endemic to Russia is the **Little Curlew** (*Numenius minutus*) which has two main breeding areas in eastern Siberia. The western area covers the north-east of the Krasnoyarsk region and north-west Yakutia while the eastern one incorporates the middle reaches of the Yana and Indigirka rivers. The Little Curlew favours the slopes and foothills of low mountains, particularly where a forest has been burned and the grass vegetation is flourishing. The main breeding grounds lie in hardly accessible areas and are quite safe even though the bird is included in the Russian Red Data Book. Overall numbers are estimated at roughly 5,000 birds. The nests are built in dry areas with low vegetation cover, usually on moss. The clutch of four eggs is laid at the end of May or beginning of June, and the chicks hatch by the end of June. At the nest birds are very aggressive towards intruders and may even attack a human. The food consists of a variety of insects and other invertebrates, also of different berries. The wintering grounds of the Little Whimbrel include Australia, Tasmania and New Zealand.

Probably the rarest bird in Europe is the **Slender-billed Curlew** (*Numenius tenuirostris*). Endemic to Russia, it is included in the Russian Red Data Book as Category I – under threat of extinction. The presumed breeding range covers the area of Western Siberia between the Ural mountains and the Ob' river valley. The data on nests was collected from the Tar and Barnaul regions more than 65 years ago and since then no nests have been found. A special group was set up by the Russian Ornithological Society in order to discover present breeding grounds and to create a nature reserve there, with no success up to now. Encouragingly, the birds are seen during migration including on the Crimea peninsula where a group of 48 birds was seen in 1975, the largest number recorded in Russia in recent times. The wintering grounds are on the western coasts of the Mediterranean. The total number is estimated at 1,000 birds, probably less. These birds nest in solitary pairs or in a small colonies with nest 2-15m apart. The arrival at the breeding grounds is in mid-May, and by the end of this month the clutch of four eggs is usually completed. The autumn migration starts in July and ends in October. Arrival at wintering grounds in Morocco takes place not earlier than December.

The best known species of this genus is probably the **Western Curlew** (*Numenius arquata*), a large bird, sparsely distributed in the wetlands from Western Europe to the Transbaikal region. Recently it has been recorded breeding on agricultural fields in Russia.

Raised bogs in Ussuriland and the Amur region are home for a distinctive and interesting species of curlew – the **Far Eastern Curlew** (*Numenius madagascariensis*) (Plate 36), the full extent of whose range is still not established. It has a patchy distribution and is quite common locally. Far Eastern Curlews arrive to breed in early April and reach quite high densities on some raised bogs, forming colonies of five to eight, or less commonly ten to fifteen pairs. Solitary breeding also takes place. The total breeding population of the Khanka lowland is about 50 pairs. Apart from Ussuriland and the Amur region, the Russian range embraces Kamchatka, and a number of localities in Eastern Siberia. The species nests outside Russia in China and Korea. The wintering grounds include the Philippines, Indonesia and Australia.

The **Whimbrel** (*Numenius phaeopus*) has very sporadic distribution in Russia from north of European Russia and the Baltic States to Eastern Siberia. It is common locally and inhabits different types of wetlands from forest tundra to the forest steppe.

Among rather common and well-studied species in Russia are both species of godwits (*Limosa*). The **Black-tailed Godwit** (*L. limosa*) (Fig. 52) has its

Fig. 52 *Black-tailed Godwit* (Limosa limosa) *in Lithuania. Photo H. Sakalauskas*

main breeding range from the western borders to the River Ob' basin, with many patches to the east. In Ussuriland, the specific subspecies (?) *L. l. melanuroides* inhabits the raised bogs in the forests, often together with the Far Eastern Curlew. The breeding range of the **Bar-tailed Godwit** (*L. lapponica*), which is primarily a tundra species, extends to the Eurasian tundras as well as to Alaska. The **Long-billed Dowitcher** (*Limnodromus scolopaceus*) is mostly an American species with an extension of its breeding range to Chukotka and Eastern Siberia.

Among the most intriguing and rarest of the Russian waders is the **Asiatic Dowitcher** (*Limnodromus semipalmatus*). This bird has a highly fragmented distribution and is included in the Russian Red Data Book. The Asiatic Dowitcher is clearly a relict species, settling to breed on the shores of rivers and lakes mostly in the steppe zone. The separated breeding areas are in Western Siberia around Barnaul, in the Transbaikal region on the river Argun and in the Khanka lowland in Ussuriland. These sites are thousands of kilometres apart. In the Russian part of Lake Khanka (part of the lake lies in China), the Dowitchers nest only on the eastern side where they occupy the low-lying marshy inundation zone between the rivers which empty into the lake. The species is colonial and tends to nest close to or in gull and tern colonies. Numbers of dowitchers depend on many different factors, the major ones being the level of the lake, the weather conditions in a particular year, and the breeding success of the previous year. In years with very low water levels at Khanka, the dowitcher population reaches

Fig. 53 *Common Pratincole* (Glareola pratincola). *Photo P. Romanov*

100-150 pairs. These birds arrive on their breeding grounds from about mid-May and the peak display period is from then up to the start of laying, near the end of the month. The breeding season is protracted and the dates vary between years. Asiatic Dowitcher are like most waders in being ground-nesters, but unusual in that they lay only two eggs. Their nests are sometimes plundered by magpies and other predators.

The latest records from Khanka occur during the last days of August. Outside Russia, this species is distributed in Mongolia and north-east China. It winters in India, South-East Asia and Indonesia.

The family Glareolidae is represented in Russia by three species of pratincole and the **Cream-coloured Courser** (*Cursorius cursor*). The latter is on the northern edge of its distribution in Russia and occurs mainly in the very south where the border of Iran, Afghanistan and Russia meet and where the Badkhyz nature reserve was set up. Its numbers differ significantly from year to year and in some years coursers do not appear at all.

Both the **Common Pratincole** (*Glareola pratincola*) (Plate 36 and Fig. 53) and **Black-winged Pratincole** (*G. nordmanni*) (Plate 36) are widespread in the country's steppes and deserts. Their behaviour and biology are very similar. They are vivacious, restless birds, sociable and noisy, and are most often seen flying like swallows. Pratincoles have long and narrow wings and a deeply forked tail. In flight, they are somewhat reminiscent of tern and differ markedly from the more compactly built typical waders or shorebirds.

Pratincoles are migratory, wintering in Africa. The earliest birds are back at their breeding grounds by mid-April and departure takes place in August or September. Typical habitat, where both species are common, is open clay or salt flats with a cover of short grass or Saltwort Salsoa, and birds favour sites near water. Colonies of 10-20, sometimes several hundred, pairs are formed. Quite often, the two pratincoles nest together with other species such as White-tailed Plovers (*Chettusia leucura*), Common Redshanks (*Tringa totanus*), and Pied Avocets (*Recurvirostra avosetta*). The pratincole's nest is a simple scrape. Laying begins in May, the normal clutch being four (3-5) eggs. Flocks, reaching a considerable size in August, are formed when the young fledge. Pratincoles feed mainly on insects which they hunt especially in the mornings and in the evenings. The hottest hours of the day are spent idling by water.

The **Oriental Pratincole** (*Glareola maldivarum*) is on the edge of its northern distribution in Russia. Its main breeding grounds lie in Mongolia and South Asia. In Russia, it breeds locally in the Transbaikal region, around the Torey Lake system and by the River Argun. There is a possibility of breeding in the Khanka lowland in Ussuriland.

The Skuas (Stercoraridae), a compact group of gull-related sea birds have four species in Russia, three of which breed and the **Great Skua** (*Stercorarius skua*) is a vagrant species recorded in the Barents and Baltic Seas.

The remaining three species, the **Pomarine Skua** (*Stercorarius pomarinus*) (Plate 37), the **Arctic Skua** (*S. parasiticus*) (Plate 37) and the **Long-tailed Skua** (*S. longicaudus*) (Plate 37) all enjoy circumpolar distribution in tundras of Eurasia and America. The most northerly species is the Pomarine Skua which does not even breed in Scandinavia. Numbers of this bird are uneven through its breeding range while the other two species are quite common.

Next is the Gull family (Laridae), a group of highly successful and adaptive birds distributed around the world. There are 34 (32) species in Russia, 32 of which breed and two (the Iceland Gull (*Larus glaucoides*) and Saunders's Gull (*L. saundersi*)) of which are vagrants. Two numbers are given because the latest research by Dr L. Stepanyan suggests that the **Herring Gull** (*L. argentatus*) should be separated into three species because of a number of factors including reproductive isolation. This decision still is not final. The proposed species are as follows: the Herring Gull (*L. argentatus*) inhabiting the area between the Baltic and Barents Seas; *L. heuglini*, with its breeding range covering Arctic and sub-Arctic coastal and inland areas between Kola and Chukotka peninsulas; and the **Eastern Herring Gull** (*L. cachinnans*) (Plate 39), inhabiting the southern waters of Russia from the Black sea to Lake Khanka in Ussuriland.

The **Great Black-headed Gull** (*Larus ichthyaetus*) (Plate 37) is one of Russia's and the world's largest and most attractive gulls. In size, it approaches the Glaucous and Great Black-backed Gull. It has a typically fragmented distribution, breeding sites being in many cases separated by hundreds of miles. The breeding range extends from the northern Crimean region east to Mongolia. As the main breeding colonies are located in Russia and the world population is not large (Russia has about 20-25,000 pairs), the Great Black-headed Gull is listed in the Russian Red Data Book. It nests in colonies of several hundred pairs, sometimes more, always on islands, quite often several kilometres from the shore. This species almost always nests together with Herring Gulls which settle on the edge of the colony. Laying starts in late March or early April and there are usually three (1-3) eggs, which are incubated by both sexes for a period of 25-29 days. These large gulls feed mainly on fish, less commonly on insects or small rodents.

The unique member of the family is the **Relict Gull** (*Larus relictus*) (Plate 37 & 38). This bird nests in several locations which are widely separated: Lake Barun-Torey in the Transbaikal region and Lake Alakol in eastern Kazakhstan. Breeding has also been confirmed in Mongolia, with the possibility of breeding in China as well. The story of this bird's discovery is facinating one. It was first described in 1931 as a subspecies of the Mediterranean Black-headed Gull. Some ornithologists considered it to be a hybrid between the Mediterranean and Great Black-headed Gull. Clarification came only in 1963, because until that time no one knew where these gulls were breeding. Then the first colony was discovered at Lake Barun-Torey and the birds in question were found to be a completely independent species, the Relict Gull.

The Relict Gull has proved to be very rare. Up to now, three places where it breeds have been discovered. The author was fortunate enough to visit Lake Alakol in eastern Kazakhstan, not far from the border with China, to see and photograph this exceptionally rare and exciting bird. It should perhaps be mentioned that both the lakes where the Relict Gulls nest are known for their very strong winds. Wild storms and gales are a regular feature of the summer and some of the small islands are submerged. At Alakol, such weather is due first and foremost to the geographical location. This large lake (about 100 km in length) lies right at the entrance to the so-called Dzungarian Gate, a very low-lying area borded in the west by the mighty Dzungar Alatau range (which marks the edge of the Tien Shan mountain region) and in the east by the start of the Altai mountain land – the low Tarbagatai mountains. It is not difficult to imagine the fierce gales that can tunnel through the Dzungarian Gate – and from both sides!

Yet it is in this bleak and hostile place that the Relict Gulls have chosen to breed. They nest on various islands, changing from year to year, but Sredniy (Middle) Island, lying about 30 km from the shore, is the main site. Lake Alakol has many other breeding birds – large colonies of Great Black-headed Gulls, Caspian Terns, Gull-billed Terns, cormorants and others. When we visited

Alakol, we were delighted to see that some Relict Gulls had chosen to nest on a small sandy island only about one kilometre from the shore. It is impossible to get to Sredniy Island without a large launch.

It is fortunate that visits by humans are in fact a rare exception – the localities are very remote and both are protected. The total population of Relict Gulls in Russia is put at 1,500–1,800 breeding pairs, but sharp fluctuations in numbers between years are characteristic of the species. At Alakol, for example, the breeding population varies between 30 and 1,200 breeding pairs! Numbers are limited by the restricted breeding range, the high egg and chick mortality during storm surges, and the loss of chicks in cold, wet years. A further contributory factor is peculiarities of the diet. During the breeding season, the gulls feed mainly on insects – adult chironomid gnats, numbers of which are very much dependent on how wet the area is where the gulls nest. As the lake recedes, the food-supply diminishes and the ecological capacity of the area is also very much reduced.

The Relict Gull is a docile, rather quiet bird, unlike most of its relatives, and has a somewhat melancholy look. It is to be hoped that this apparent sadness does not presage disaster for this strange and it would appear virtually defenceless gull – especially when the gulls as a family are otherwise so well known for their plasticity, adaptability, great vigour and energy.

Colonies of Relict Gulls are very dense, with an average distance between the nests of 0.45 m. Egg-laying starts at the begining of May. The clutch consists of two to three eggs which are incubated by both sexes for 24-26 days. The fledging period is about 45 days. The wintering grounds of this species cover the coasts of South-East Asia.

The **Mediterranean Gull** (*Larus melanocephalus*) (Plate 38 and Fig. 54) is regarded as a symbol of the Black Sea. Its rather restricted breeding range covers the eastern Mediterranean region, and the wintering grounds are in the same area. It has also started to nest in small numbers in the colonies of the Black-headed Gull (*L. ridibundus*). The Mediterranean Gulls nest in large and very dense colonies, often together with Slender-billed Gulls (*L. genei*) and Sandwich Terns (*Sterna sanvicensis*). If frequently disturbed when breeding, the gulls may destroy their eggs and desert the colony. On small islands, where the various gulls and terns nest together, mixed colonies tend to have separate pockets of each species. A general view across such a colony shows up this pattern very clearly: in one place a dense colony of Sandwich Terns, further on a rosy-pink haze of Slender-billed Gulls, then a forest of jet-black heads belonging to the Mediterranean Gulls. These are truly wonderful places which may be visited when the chicks are being ringed.

Mediterranean Gulls start nesting in late April or early May. The nest is made of dry grass and usually lined with a few feathers. One to three eggs

Fig. 54 *Mediterranean Gulls (*Larus melanocephalus*) in Sivash Bay, South Ukraine. Photo A. Knystautas*

are laid, the usual number being three. After hatching, the chicks leave the nest once their down is dry and hide among the dense grassy vegetation. The gulls feed on small fish, marine invertebrates and also terrestrial arthropods which are collected on arable fields up to 70-80 km from the colony.

The **Little Gull** (*Larus minutus*) (Plate 38) is common locally and is unevenly distributed in Russia from the western borders to Lake Baikal in the east. As well as elsewhere, the **Black-headed Gull** (*L. ridibundus*) is expanding and growing in numbers. Its breeding range now covers most of the territory of Russia, excluding the most northerly parts.

The **Brown-headed Gull** (*Larus brunnicephalus*) (Plate 38) is a true mountain species whose breeding range covers the Tibetan highlands. In Russia, it now nests only on Lake Karakul in the Eastern Pamir mountains. About 300 pairs nest on the islands in the lake which is 4,000 m above sea level. Brown-headed Gulls winter on the coasts of South and South-East Asia. They first breed at two years old. Dense colonies of 100-200 pairs are formed and the gulls usually nest together with Bar-headed Geese (*Anser indicus*) and Tibetan Common Terns (*Sterna hirundo tibetana*). Nests are located in open places and among stones. Nesting starts in late May. Two to three eggs are laid, the peak laying period being mid-June. Brown-headed Gulls feed mainly on aquatic invertebrates as well as small fish.

An elegant and beautiful bird, the **Slender-billed Gull** (*Larus genei*) (Plate 38 and Fig. 55) is distributed in the Black Sea region, the Sea of Azov, the

Fig. 55 *Slender-billed Gull* (Larus genei) *in Sivash Bay, South Ukraine. Photo A. Knystautas*

Caspian Sea and in several large lakes in Kazakhstan. During the breeding season, they haunt sea coasts and saline or brackish lakes, where they form large colonies. A shallow depression with rudimentary lining serves as the nest and the two to three eggs are incubated by both sexes. Small fish and various invertebrates make up the diet. Birds make long foraging flights from the colony, visiting steppes, arable and other fields to collect insects. After hatching, flocks of Slenderbills can be seen flying inland to collect food for their young and returning to the colony in the evening. The main food in the breeding season is grasshoppers and locusts.

The **Lesser Black-backed Gull** (*Larus fuscus*), widely distributed in Western Europe, breeds in Russia in Estonia, Karelia and on the shores of the White and Barents Seas.

The marine coasts and islands of the Pacific, from the Bering Sea in the north to the Hokkaido in the south are home of the **Slaty-backed Gull** (*Larus schistisagus*) (Plate 39). This oceanic gull nests in colonies on the rocks and cliffs along the coasts and is common in suitable places. The **Glaucous-winged Gull** (*L. glaucescens*) breeds along the shores of the extreme north-east of Russia, also in the Kamchatka peninsula and on the Commander Islands. Its breeding range extends into Alaska and the western coasts of Canada and in the USA south to the state of Washington. The **Iceland Gull** (*L. glaucoides*) is a vagrant species to Russia and was recorded on the Novaya Zemlia (New Land) Islands.

The **Glaucous Gull** (*Larus hyperboreus*) (Plate 39) is one of the largest

Fig. 56 Black-legged Kittiwakes (Rissa tridactyla) and Guillemots on the Barents Sea Islands. Photo L.Veisman

and most impressive gulls. It is an arctic species, being distributed in coastal tundras and islands from the Kanin peninsula east to the Bering Straits. It also breeds in Spitzbergen, Greenland, Newfoundland and Arctic America.

The **Great Black-backed Gull** (*Larus marinus*), a typical marine species of gull, is on the edge of its distribution in Russia. It breeds in the Baltic Sea along the coasts and islands of Estonia and on the coasts of the Barents Sea.

The **Common Gull** (*Larus canus*) enjoys extremely wide distribution in Russia, covering most of the country's territory, avoiding desert and mountain areas as well as high arctic latitudes. Another Far Eastern gull species, together with the Slaty-backed Gull, is the **Black-tailed Gull** (*L. crassirostris*) (Plate 39), which in Russia breeds in the Bay of Peter the Great, on the Kuril and Sakhalin Islands. It is common in sea ports and in human habitats, collecting possible food from the garbage. It particularly favours the fish factories in the Far East, in the Vladivostok region. It breeds in colonies and in solitary pairs on marine islands. The clutch is laid in May, consisting of two to three eggs. Outside Russia, this species breeds in the sea of Japan, along the coasts of Korea and China. Winter is spent within the breeding range.

Sabine's Gull (*Xema sabini*) is generally a high Arctic breeder but also appears in the sub-Arctic areas. It settles not far from the coasts and often breeds on islands. It prefers marshy tracts of flat tundra, breeding in Russia in the Taimyr peninsula, in Yakutia and in Chukotka. This bird has patchy circumpolar distribution.

Black-legged Kittiwakes (*Rissa tridactyla*) (Fig. 56) are a characteristic

Fig 57 *Ross's Gull (*Rhodostethia rosea*) in the Kolyma Delta. Photo V. Flint*

and numerous species of seabird, and form colonies from the Barents Sea to Kamchatka and the Commander Islands. Outside the breeding season kittiwakes occur in flocks in the littoral zone, but often wander far from the coast. They nest in huge colonies on inaccessible sheer mainland or inland cliffs, building nests of seaweed, grass and feathers on a ledge or rock projection. Two to three eggs are laid from mid-May and the chicks fledge when fully feathered. Black-legged Kittiwakes eat mainly small fish, also fewer marine invertebrates.

The Commander Islands in the Pacific are the home of the **Red-legged Kittiwake** (*Rissa brevirostris*), a rather scarce gull whose habits and biology are akin to those of its Black-legged cousin.

Ross's Gull (*Rhodostethia rosea*) (Plate 40 and Fig. 57), the jewel of the Arctic, is included in the Russian Red Data Book, but in Category V which embraces those species now considered out of danger. There are now reckoned to be at least 50,000 breeding pairs. Numbers in the breeding range fluctuate between years, depending on the spring weather conditions.

Ross's Gull is a bird of the lake-studded lowlands of East Siberia, in the sub-zone of typical tundra. Its main breeding range lies between the estuaries of the Omoloy and Kolyma rivers. Isolated breeding has been recorded elsewhere in Russia, including on Taimyr and in the Chaun lowlands; also outside the country in Greenland, islands in the Canadian Arctic and Hudson Bay. This splendid bird winters by unfrozen parts of the Bering Sea and the northern Arctic Ocean. The gulls roam about, keeping to open water patches

Fig. 58 *Breeding colony of Ivory Gulls (*Pagophila eburnea) *in Franz Joseph Land. Photo P. Tomkovich*

with ice-floes. Hitherto, man's economic activity has had virtually no impact on Ross's Gull's habitats.

The gulls nest in the marshy plains of true tundra and in the northern part of the wooded tundra zone with its multitude of lakes. They first breed when at least three years old. Typically, small colonies (several up to several tens of pairs) are formed, though solitary nesting in not uncommon. Nests are built on islets of moss and sedge and their nearest neighbours are usually several tens of metres apart. Laying begins in early to mid-June and the clutch of is of one to three eggs. Incubation takes 21-23 days.

The **Ivory Gull** (*Pagophila eburnea*) (Fig. 58) is called the Phantom of the polar ice floe. These truly high Arctic species nest in Russia on Franz Joseph Land, on the Severnaya Zemlia (Northern Land) islands and on Uedenenya Island in the Kara Sea.

This bird is rare and colonies, which are formed on the stony slopes of the islands, rarely exceed ten to fifteen pairs. A marked decrease has been recorded in several parts of its breeding range since the last century. The Ivory Gull is included in Russia's Red Data Book.

There are ten breeding species of terns (Sterninae) in Russia. The so-called black terns of the genus *Chlidonias* are represented by common and widespread species such as the **Black Tern** (*C. niger*) (Fig. 59) and the **White-winged Black Tern** (*C. leucoptera*) (Plate 40). The **Whiskered Tern** (*C. hybrida*) has patchy distribution in the south of Russia,being more common in Central Asia.

The **Gull-billed Tern** (*Gelochelidon nilotica*) (Plate 40) is also patchily

Fig. 59 *Black Tern* (Chlidonias niger) *in the Nemunas River Delta, Lithuania. Photo A. Knystautas*

distributed in the south of Russia and frequents mostly large saline lakes and seashores. It often forms mixed colonies with other gulls and terns.

The largest representative of terns breeding in Russia is the **Caspian Tern** (*Hydroprogne caspia*) (Plate 40). It has an easy, powerful flight; when fishing, it flies with bill pointed down, often hovering to search for prey in the water below. Though quite extensive, the Caspian Tern's breeding range is highly fragmented. In Russia, this migratory spieces nests on sand or shingle beaches on the coast or by lakes. The typically small colonies are usually separated from other species; solitary pairs are less common. A shallow pit in the sand or shells, usually without any kind of lining, serves as the nest. One to three eggs are incubated by both sexes for a period of 20-22 days and the young fledge at 30-35 days. Flocks are formed in August and the birds then start to disperse from the breeding grounds. Caspian Terns feed mainly on small fish, also invertebrates, and sometimes on the eggs and chicks of other birds.

The **Sandwich Tern** (*Sterna sanvicensis*) (Plate 40) is another large species of tern, only the Caspian being larger. A good fieldmark is the bi-coloured bill – black with a yellow tip. This migratory species lives on coasts and islands in and outside the breeding season. It nests in large colonies, often together with Common and Little Terns and Slender-billed Gulls. The nest itself is no more than a shallow depression in the sand or shells. One or two, less commonly three, eggs are laid, usually in late May or early June.

Fig. 60 *Arctic Tern (*Sterna paradisaea*) at Matsalu, Estonia. Photo A. Knystautas*

Both sexes incubate, starting with the first egg, and the period is 22-23 days. Fish, caught by plunge-diving, are the main food.

The **Common Tern** (*Sterna hirundo*) has four subspecies in Russia and is distributed along the shores of very different water bodies from medium-sized inland lakes to sea islands, both in lowlands and high mountains. In Pamir it breeds at an altitude of 4,000 m. This species is common throughout its range.

The tern of the tundra is the **Arctic Tern** (*Sterna paradisaea*) (Fig. 60) which has a circumpolar distribution. Arctic Terns are well known for their remarkable long-distance migrations which involve a journey to the winter quarters and back of 20,000 or even 30,000 km. In respect of diet, breeding and other aspects of its biology, the Arctic Tern has much in common with other representatives of the genus *Sterna*.

The Kamchatka peninsula and Sakhalin Island are home of the **Aleutian Tern** (*Sterna aleutica*). It breeds on coastal marshes and tundras, on river deltas, estuaries and islands. On Sakhalin Island there are estimated to be between 750 and 1000 breeding pairs, and in Kamchatka around 3,000. The overall population of Russia is put at about 4,000 breeding pairs. The Aleutian Terns breed in solitary pairs, small or large colonies of up to 500 pairs. The distances between two neighbouring nests are about 10 m. Breeding starts only in mid-June. The full clutch is two eggs, incubation period is 26-27 days. The main diet consists of small fish and aquatic invertebrates.

The **Little Tern** (*Sterna albifrons*) (Fig. 61) is found along the shores of rivers, lakes and seas of European Russia, some areas in Western Siberia,

Transcaucasus and Central Asia. In some parts of European Russia a marked decrease in numbers has been reported in recent years. This is particularly obvious in places with increasing human pressure, e.g. in Lithuania. The breeding biology and food are much the same as in other species of terns of the genus *Sterna*.

The auks (Family Alcidae) is a group of small to moderately large birds, primarily seabirds, represented in Russia by 20 species, 18 of which breed and two of which are vagrants. This group can easily be divided into two; those species which are primarily "western", characteristic of the Atlantic coasts and islands; and those which are "eastern", and inhabit the Pacific.

In Russia, **Little Auks** (*Alle alle*) are found only on the north island of Novaya Zemlia and Franz Joseph Land. Little Auks are a numerous dispersive species which nest in huge colonies on talus slopes, both close to the water and quite far inland. A single egg is laid in a cavity under rocks from mid-June and no nest is made.

The **Razorbill** (*Alca torda*) is a common representative of the colonial Alcids and is found only in the western part of the Russian Arctic. This species usually nests in small groups together with other auks. The nest is sited in a cavity or crevice on a steep cliff and the single egg is laid on a rudimentary platform of small stones and seaweed from the end of May. Like other auks, Razorbills eat small fish.

154

Perhaps the most typical birds of the seabird colonies are the guillemots – the **Common Guillemot** (*Uria aalge*) and **Brünnich's Guillemot** (*Uria lomvia*). In many parts of the range, which in Russia extends along coast and islands from the Barents Sea to the south of the Far East, these two species occur together. The non-breeding season is spent at open sea.

There are three species of black guillemots or tysties (*Cepphus*) in Russia. In the Arctic the **Black Guillemot** (*C. grylle*) is found; it breeds in loose colonies and forms flocks outside the breeding season. The nest is sited in a crevice or cavity amongst boulders and scree and the clutch of two eggs is laid in June on a bed of small stones. The **Pigeon Guillemot** (*C. columba*) and the **Spectacled Guillemot** (*C. carbo*) (Plate 41) have a similar biology. They are less common than the Black Guillemot and are found on coasts and islands of the Far East seas and Pacific Ocean.

The **Marbled Murrelet** (*Brachyramphus marmoratus*) inhabits Kamchatka, the coasts of the Sea of Okhotsk and Sakhalin Island, and the western coasts and islands of North America. As with the Marbled Murrelet, only several nests of **Kittlitz's Murrelet** (*B. brevirostris*) have been recorded in Russia. The nest of the latter species was discovered on the tree in a sparse larchwood. The Marbled Murrelet breeds on the rocks of coastal mountains above the tree line. Both species are uncommon and poorly studied.

The **Ancient Murrelet** (*Synthliboramphus antiquus*) (Plate 41), an uncommon species, breeds on coasts and islands in the Sea of Okhotsk, the Sea of Japan and also the Pacific Ocean. It nests in colonies, using crevices and cavities among boulders and rock scree. The two eggs are laid in June on the bare ground – no nest is made. Murrelets eat marine invertebrates and small fish.

The **Japanese Murrelet** (*Synthliboramphus wumizusume*), as well as **Cassin's Auklet** (*Ptychoramphus aleuticus*) are recorded in Russia as vagrants.

The genus *Aethia* has three representatives in Russia. All three are birds of bizarre and striking appearance and unusual habits. They haunt coastal cliffs and rocks. The **Crested Auklet** (*A. cristatella*) is unevenly distributed in Chukotka, on the Commander and Kuril Islands, and in Sakhalin. These birds spend the winter on open water far out to sea. They nest in cliff crevices and scree slopes, and in cavities among rocks, often forming large colonies. A single egg is laid in June or July. The birds dive to great depths to obtain their staple diet of marine invertebrates.

The **Whiskered Auklet** (*Aethia pygmaea*) is found on the Kuril and Commander Islands and many smaller islands in the Far East. This species is noticeably smaller than the Crested Auklet (which is about pigeon-sized), but its biology is similar.

The **Least Auklet** (*Aethia pusilla*) is restricted in Russia to the coasts of

Chukotka. It is an amazing little bird, smaller even than a starling, restless, noisy and not at all shy. Its biology resembles that of other auklets.

Common along the coasts of Chukotka, Kamchatka and Commander Islands is the **Parakeet Auklet** (*Cyclorrhynchus psittacula*). In winter this species moves out to open waters. It forms small colonies during the breeding season and the nest-site is in a crevice under rocks. A single egg is laid from mid-June. The diet consists of marine crustaceans.

The **Rhinoceros Auklet** (*Cerorhinca monocerata*) is a colonial species found in the south of the Russian Far East and on the Kuril Islands. It nests on gentle slopes with well-developed soil covert into which it digs a burrow 2-3 m long for breeding purposes.

Birds of singular and striking appearance, mainly due to their bill colour and shape, are the **Atlantic Puffin** (*Fratercula arctica*), **Horned Puffin** (*F. corniculata*) (Plate 41) and **Tufted Puffin** (*Lunda cirrhata*). The Atlantic Puffin is found in the western part of the Russian Arctic, while Horned and Tufted Puffins nest along the mainland coast and on islands from Chukotka south to Ussuriland. Both Atlantic and Tufted Puffin nest in self-made burrows, but the Horned Puffin lays its single egg in a rock crevice.

SANDGROUSES AND PIGEONS – ORDER COLUMBIFORMES

This order has 17 species in Russia with two families represented. The sandgrouses (Pteroclidae) have four breeding species while the true pigeons (Columbidae) has thirteen, eleven of which are breeders and two are vagrants.

The **Black-bellied** and **Pin-tailed Sandgrouses** (*Pterocles orientalis* and *P. alchata*) (Plate 42) both inhabit the arid lands of Russian Central Asia. The Black-bellied Sandgrouse gives preference to the stone and clay covered deserts and semi-deserts while the Pin-tailed settles mostly on sand deserts. The biology of those species is quite similar. Both are migratory and spend the winter in south-west Asia, some individuals remaining in the very south of Russia. The nests are on the ground in the small pit with no lining, and the normal clutches consist of two to three eggs. The sandgrouses have very characteristic flight and voices which makes them easy to identify. Both species are quite common in suitable habitats.

Pallas's Sandgrouse (*Syrrhaptes paradoxus*) (Plate 42) is a truly Central Asian species, which occurs in Russia, Mongolia and China. It is less common than the two previous species even though it sometimes nests in the same habitat as the Black-bellied Sandgrouse. This species inhabits arid semi-deserts and deserts with sparse vegetation and numerous stones. It avoids drifting sands. The breeding season starts early compared with the previous species and clutches can be found even in March. Mid-April is the usual time for the chicks to hatch. The female sits very tightly on the nest and allows humans nearly to touch her, but only once. If you return, a bird becomes more and more shy. The clutch consists of two to three eggs and the incubation period is about 28 days. When flying, it makes a far-carrying humming or whistling sound with its wings. The diet consists mostly of seeds of different plants. Pallas's Sandgrouse is known for the great fluctuations in numbers and eruptions in some years. This happened mostly in the last century with the last significant one in 1908. Since then, eruptions into Europe have become rarer, with only a few birds each time outside Russia.

The rarest of the Russian Sandgrouses and included in the Red Data Book of Russia is the **Tibetan Sandgrouse** (*Syrrhaptes tibetanus*). At present, it inhabits only the mountain deserts in Eastern Pamir, at an altitudes of about 4,000 m. The main distribution range is outside the country. This bird breeds up to 4,800 m altitude. In recent decades a sharp decline in numbers has been reported and it is believed that there are no more than 300 birds living in the Pamirs. The species is gregarious, but by the end of May pairs occupy their territories and start nesting. As in other sandgrouses, the nest is a simple scrape on the ground with no lining. The clutch consists of three eggs which are incubated by both sexes for 20-24 days. The chicks hatch by the end of June. The food consists mainly of green parts of plants in summer and of their seed in winter.

The true pigeons (Columbidae) has two vagrant species in Russia, both recorded in the Far East. They are the **Japanese Wood Pigeon** (*Columba janthina*) and the **Red-collared Dove** (*Streptopelia tranquebarica*).

The **Wood Pigeon** (*Columba palumbus*) is common through its range in Russia which includes the forests of European Russia, Siberia, Transcaucasus and Central Asia. There are two separate subspecies which inhabit the forests in the Central Asian mountains (*C. p. iranica* – the Kopet Dag mountains, and *C. p. casiotis* – Tien-Shan, Pamir and Alai systems).

Nearly the same area is inhabited by the **Stock Dove** (*Columba oenas*), much rarer in Russia, which also has a separate subspecies in the mountains of Central Asia (*C. o. yarkandensis*). The **Rock Dove** (*C. livia*) lives in the wild state in many mountain ranges of Russia, being gradually replaced in Transbaikal region by the **Eastern Rock Dove** (*Columba rupestris*) which is very easily recognised in flight by the clear white colour on its tail.

Eversmann's Dove (*Columba eversmanni*) (Plate 43 and Fig. 62) is worth special mention since this species is still poorly known. It inhabits sparse forest of Central Asia and Kazakhstan, and sometimes settles in the villages, by the banks of the rivers and canyons. This bird resembles the Rock Dove but can be distinguished by its more delicate structure and smaller size. It is particularly obvious in flight. The breeding season starts in late April-early

Fig. 62 *Eversmann's Dove (*Columba eversmanni*) in the Ili River Valley, East Kazakhstan. Photo A. Knystautas*

May, and the nests are situated in the tree holes, burrows in the river banks and canyons, and rock crevices. The clutch, as is typical for all pigeons, consists of two white eggs. These birds tend to breed in loose colonies. It winters in Iran, Afghanistan and northern India.

The rarest and most exotic of Russian pigeons is the **Snow Pigeon** (*Columba leuconota*) which inhabits some of the high mountain ranges of Central Asia. The usual altitudes for this bird are between 3,000 and 5,000 m. It nests in solitary pairs or in small colonies on steep rocks. Two eggs are laid in May-June. In Russia only several nesting records were made. This species is included in the Russian Red Data Book.

The genus *Streptopelia* is represented by four breeding species and one vagrant already mentioned above. Among the common and well known birds are the **Collared Dove** (*S. decaocto*) which dramatically expanded its breeding range in European Russia in recent decades, and the **Turtle Dove** (*S. turtur*), which inhabits forests of different types as well as separate groups of trees in arable fields from the western borders to Central Asia and Western Siberia. It readily settles in the mountains as well.

The **Rufous Turtle Dove** (*Streptopelia orientalis*) (Plate 43) is common and widespread over the large part of Asia. It is a typical inhabitant of mixed and broad-leaved Ussuri forests as well as mountain woods of Central Asia. Like other doves, this species builds a loose and flimsy nest of thin twigs usually not very high up in a bush or tree, a nest which seems barely capable of supporting the clutch of two white eggs. Rufous Turtle Doves feed on seeds, while the chicks are given the well-known regurgitated "pigeon milk" of partially digested seeds. Departure usually takes place at the end of October.

The distribution of the **Laughing Dove** (*Streptopelia senegalensis*) (Plate 43) is closely related to different types of human inhabitance in Central Asia, and it is not found outside it, in truly wild sites. It is sedentary and starts to breed very early in spring, building nests on the trees as well as in the buildings, e.g. on balconies. These birds form a very characteristic feature of big Central Asian cities like Tashkent or Alma-Ata, and their gentle voices can be heard everywhere.

The **Japanese Green Pigeon** (*Sphenurus sieboldii*) breeds on the southern islands of Kurils, particularly on Kunashir. Breeding is not considered to be proved but ornithologists who visited the Kurils are convinced that this bird is by no means a rarity here during the breeding season.

CUCKOOS – ORDER CUCULIFORMES

The cuckoos is essentially a tropical group of birds and has six representatives in Russia, five of which breed and one (the **Great Spotted Cuckoo**, *Clamator glandarius*) is vagrant. All five breeding species can be traced in Ussuriland. They are one of the great delights of the Ussuri taiga. Choose a good spot in the "Cedar Valley" nature reserve and you may hear the calls of four different species!

Most mysterious of the Ussuri cuckoos is the **Fugitive Hawk Cuckoo** (*Hierrococcyx fugax*) which differs in appearance from the other species significantly and is placed in a separate genus. This is quite a rare bird, slightly commoner in only a few places. It is secretive and very wary, betraying its presence only by its loud, penetrating disyllabic call which is unlike that of other cuckoos. Fugitive Hawk Cuckoos call in all weathers (even in a thunderstorm) and at any time of the day and night. The species most often parasitised is the Blue-and-White Flycatcher (*Cyanoptila cyanomelana*).

In the summer of 1982, we were fortunate enough to hear the **Indian Cuckoo** (*Cuculus micropterus*) in the "Cedar Valley" nature reserve where has been no previous breeding-season records. Our exotic discovery was made in remote mixed wood in the central part of the reserve. With Siberian Chipmunks (*Eutamias sibirica*) whistling all around, we were finding it difficult to concentrate on the birds. Suddenly, from the tree-tops, there came an unfamiliar 4-syllabic call, clearly belonging to some kind of cuckoo. It was indeed an Indian Cuckoo, the fifth of the reserve's cuckoo species. The bird was heard again in the same place a month later. Indian Cuckoos are commoner in the light deciduous woods of the Amur region, in the valley of the Ussuri River. Their biology is little known, but Shrikes (*Lanius*) are reported to be their most frequent hosts.

The **Eurasian Cuckoo** (*Cuculus canorus*) is also common in Ussuriland, but here it favours river valleys, and water meadows, avoiding the dense taiga. This species is extremely widespread in Russia and it is really hard to find a habitat where its characteristic voice cannot be heard, be it in the middle of the sand desert or high up in the mountains. In Lithuania, the first call of a cuckoo in spring (it usually arrives here by the end of April) is associated with financial welfare. If at the moment of the first call someone has some change in their pocket, they are supposed to become rich; if not, poor. Among the hosts of Eurasian Cuckoos are a number of different passerines which naturally vary a great deal in such a huge country.

The **Oriental Cuckoo** (*Cuculus saturatus*) (Plate 43) is widespread throughout the taiga regions of Russia as far as the Far East. Indeed, it is the most common cuckoo species in Ussuriland. In river valleys or in the mountains, in fine or dull weather when almost all other birds are silent, you will hear its muffled "poo-poo-poo", which resembles the calls of a Hoopoe (*Upupa epops*). The first returning birds are seen, or more likely heard, from the first half of May. Like many other cuckoos, the Oriental spends most of its time in the canopy and is thus difficult to see. The main hosts of this species are *Phylloscopus* warblers, especially the Eastern Crowned Leaf Warbler (*P. coronatus*) which is very common throughout its range. We also have found chicks in the nests of the Pale-legged Leaf Warbler (*P. tenellipes*).

From the end of May, the distinctive call of the **Little Cuckoo** (*Cuculus poliocephalus*) – something like "vot-toot-to-tetyukhe" – is heard in the southern part of Ussuriland. This cuckoo is mostly found in broad-leaved riverain forest alternating with more open areas such as meadows with patches of scrub. The Little Cuckoo is more conspicuous than its relatives and can often be seen flying from one group of trees to another. In some places, several males may be heard calling together excitedly. The main host is the Chinese Bush Warbler (*Horeites diphone*), a bird of tall-grass meadows with dense scrub. Outside Russia, the Little Cuckoo ranges through China, Japan and South-East Asia.

Watching and listening to cuckoos in Ussuriland is always interesting. They are difficult to study, leading a secretive life among the tree-tops and attracting your attention only by their calls, but this only increases the fascination exerted by these amazing birds. Many more interesting facts about them still await discovery.

OWLS – ORDER STRIGIFORMES

Two families of owls with 18 breeding species altogether are recorded in Russia. There are no vagrant species. The family of typical owls (Strigidae) is represented by 17 species and the family of barn owls (Tytonidae) – by one.

The **Snowy Owl** (*Nyctea scandiaca*) (Plate 44) has long been considered as one of the symbols of the Arctic. This is a large, generally white-plumaged owl which is to some extent resident but mainly a dispersive species. The Holarctic distribution embraces coasts and islands in the northern Arctic Ocean and tundra. During their dispersive movements, which are sometimes on a grand scale, Snowy Owls reach southern parts of Russia and some countries of Western Europe. They nest on both flatter and more mountainous parts of the tundra. Numbers are uneven across the vast range and there is some evidence to suggest that there is a general decline. Departure from the tundra takes place between September and November and the return migration to the breeding grounds is in April or May.

The nest is a simple scrape usually on a hill or at least dry ground, as snow will still be lying when the female starts laying in mid- to late May. Five to eight eggs are normally laid, but in a bad years only three to four, or in optimal years up to eleven or even thirteen. Incubation is by the female alone, starting with the first eggs so that hatching is asynchronous and there is a considerable age difference between the young of a brood. During an incubation period lasting 32-34 days, the male regularly provides for his mate. The young owls fledge at about 50-55 days.

Snowy Owls are not strictly nocturnal, their hunting flights taking place in the morning and evening. They tend to sit on the ground and rarely perch in trees. Rather wary, they can fly fast when the need arises. The main prey is various rodents, and the numbers of eggs laid as well as general numbers of Snowy Owls breeding are closely associated with prey numbers in a particular year.

The **Northern Eagle Owl** (*Bubo bubo*) (Plate 44) is extremely widely distributed in Russia in nearly all possible habitats. The number of subspecies breeding in Russia speaks for itself – there are 11 altogether. In all places the Eagle Owl is uncommon and a marked decline has been reported in recent decades.

Where the larger rivers flow through mixed taiga forests of the Far East, the enigmatic and little known **Blakiston's Fish Owl** (*Ketupa blakistoni*) (Plate 44 and Fig. 63), can be found. It is a large bird, the size of an Eagle Owl, with a very peculiar biology, many aspects of which had not been studied until recently. Blakiston's Fish Owl is rare throughout its range. Especially favoured are places dissected by many channels, springs that do not freeze in winter, backwaters and creeks. These owls are sedentary, a

Fig. 63
*Blakiston's Fish
Owl chick (*Ketupa
blakistoni*) in the
Bikin River Valley,
central Ussuriland.
Photo* Y. *Shibnev*

pair remaining in its chosen territory for life. Only in the hardest winters, when springs and river shallows freeze over, are they forced to move in search of new feeding grounds, where five to six owls then sometimes gather. Fish Owls do not breed before their third year of life.

Courtship activity is at its peak in the second half of February. It is restricted to the nesting territory and ends in May, while the non-breeding immatures will call almost all year round from various places within their hunting area or home-range. Fish Owls have a double hooting "hoo-hooo" and a whistle; pair members perform a hooting duet. The nest is situated high up in a tree cavity. Of two nests found in the middle Bikin valley, one was on the top of a dead, broken off poplar at a height of 18 m and the other 12 m up an old ash tree. An Asian Black Bear (*Selenarctos tibetanus*) hibernated in the latter tree-hole in 1978, and at first the owls did not nest there because the cavity was deep and, having such long wings, they would have found it difficult to get out. However, when a branch broke off on the other side and a new, albeit narrow, entrance was formed the owl did nest in the hole. Only one dirty-white egg is laid and incubation begins in mid-March when all around is covered in a thick layer of snow. Hatching follows in mid-April, and the young owls leave the nest hole in late May or early June. It seems that all the incubation is done by the female, the male feeding her three to five times per night. When the chick is small and the nights still frosty, the female broods her offspring almost uninterruptedly, rarely leaving the hole. The male provides for them both. In early May, the female starts to leave the nest hole for longer periods, and makes long hunting flights, usually bringing back fish. The male in contrast hunts near the nest and preys mainly on frogs. Sometimes he will start feeding the chick himself, but otherwise gives the whistling call to summon the female and then passes the prey to her. A small owl chick gives a quite whistle and short trilling "pi-pi-pi" sounds. As the chick growths, the whistle becomes louder and more insistent. In the autumn and winter Fish Owls eat mainly crayfish and small mammals.

The range of this rare owl covers Ussuriland, the Sea of Okhotsk coastal belt, Sahkalin and Kuril Islands, north-east China and Hokkaido in Japan. The total population in Russia is put at 300-400 breeding pairs and the species appears in the Russian Red Data Book.

Among common and well-studied species of owls in Russia familiar to western birdwatchers are the **Long-eared Owl** (*Asio otus*), the **Short-eared Owl** (*A. flammeus*), and the **Eurasian Scops Owl** (*Otus scops*) (Plate 44). These species are not rare in suitable habitats and neither are the northern taiga and mountain species of owls, such as the **Hawk Owl** (*Surnia ulula*) (Plate 45), the **Eurasian Pygmy Owl** (*Glaucidium passerinum*) and **Tengmalm's Owl** (*Aegolius funereus*), which have a wide distribution in the country. Common, particularly in the southern parts of Russia is the **Little Owl** (*Athene noctua*).

The **Indian Scops Owl** (*Otus sunia*) (Plate 45) is the most common owl in the south of the Russian Far East. It reaches its highest density in broad-leaved and mixed forests. This small owl arrives at its breeding grounds in early May and nests in a tree cavity, the height above the ground varying considerably. Four to six eggs are laid, but there are rarely more than three to four young in a brood. All incubation is by the female and takes 19-20 days. Both parents share in the feeding of the young, the chief prey being insects, though some small rodents are also taken. The range of the Indian Scops Owl covers the south and east of the Asian continent.

The **Pallid Scops Owl** (*Otus brucei*) breeds in Russia in riverine forests but mainly in farmlands and towns, steppe and desert lowlands, staying out of the mountains. It arrives at its breeding grounds in Central Asia in late March and leaves in September-October. By the end of April, the usual clutch of four to five eggs is laid and incubated by the female for about 28 days. The young fledge at an age of 28-30 days. The location of the wintering grounds is not clear but they are probably located in the Middle East.

The **Collared Scops Owl** (*Otus bakkamoena*) (Plate 45) inhabits the south of the Russian Far East and is rather scarce. It is dispersive or migratory, and also winters in small numbers in Russia. In winter these owls stay on fairly open hill slopes where there is an uneven snow cover which rapidly thaws. Breeding birds also haunt mainly open woods with a sparse herb layer and undergrowth. Collared Scops Owls nest in holes in trees at varying height. Like other rodent-eating owls, this species concentrates its nesting in areas where there are explosive increases in rodent populations.

The male is much smaller than the female and usually hunts 200-400 m from the nest. While the female is incubating, her mate brings her one or two small rodents per night. The female flies out to meet him, but often she does not do so straight away but keeps him waiting for 5-10 minutes. Having finished her meal the female returns to the nest after 10-15 minutes. When the young hatch, the parents bring them mice, usually decapitated, but close to fledging such prey is sometimes brought to the nest whole. The young leave the nest-hole in July, the breeding season being rather protracted.

Collared Scops Owls are not especially shy and will allow approach to within 4-5 m; they show no fear and trust completely in their wonderful camouflage. And they are indeed fiendishly difficult to see – the slanting eyes closed to a slit, long ear-tufts erect, and the whole complex plumage pattern blending perfectly with the tree, whatever species that happens to be.

When the moon rises over the hill tops and the Ussuri forest is bathed in ghostly light, the stillness of the night is broken every now and again by the calls of various species of owls. Some of them we know already, but Ussuriland is home to several exotic species belonging to the Indo-Malayan fauna. One of these is the **Brown Hawk Owl** (*Ninox scutulata*) (Plate 45) which is generally scarce, but reasonably common in some places. This is a bird of unusual appearance and is easy to tell from other owls. They return from their wintering grounds in early May. For a long time, little or nothing was known about the breeding biology of the Brown Hawk Owl, but some information has now been obtained. It is known, for example, that the nest is in a tree cavity at 10-14 m high and trees are only chosen which the birds can approach in easy flight. Three (2-4) eggs are laid in late May or early June and the fledging period is 25-27 days. It is surprising that such a relatively large owl feeds entirely on insects. The Brown Hawk Owl's range covers east and south Asia.

The **Eurasian Tawny Owl** (*Strix aluco*) is distributed in Russia in the European part of the country and in western Siberia, Caucasus and in the mountains of Central Asia. All these localities have separate subspecies, four altogether.

The **Ural Owl** (*Strix uralensis*) is not uncommon through its vast range across the forest zone of Eurasia. Any search for its nest has to be made early in the year – laying takes place in late March or early April. Ural Owls nest in holes in trees, usually quite high up. It is worth noting that you are taking a considerable risk if you decide to climb up to the nest hole. Ural Owls are extremely aggressive at the nest and can inflict very nasty wounds, puncturing or gashing the skin with their razor-sharp claws.

Breeding density is closely linked with the level of prey population; where there are large numbers of rodents, Ural Owl density is correspondingly high, nests can be as little as 1 km apart and three to four owls may be heard from one spot. Ural Owls have a hard time in years with deep snow and many then perish from starvation. There is a remarkable record of a Ural Owl, perhaps a young and inexperienced bird, attacking a Siberian Weasel (*Mustela sibirica*) and being eaten by it. Should rodents be scarce in spring, Ural Owls will take frogs and even crayfish. Dispersive movements take place in autumn.

One of the largest and most impressive of the Holarctic owls in the **Great Grey Owl** (*Strix nebulosa*) (Plate 45), a true taiga bird which is distributed throughout this zone of Russia. It is uncommon everywhere and its populations have undergone marked fluctuations in different years.

The **Barn Owl** (*Tyto alba*), of the family Tytonidae, is quite rare in Russia and is on the eastern edge of its distribution. Its habitat includes the western parts of Lithuania, Byelorussia, Ukraine and Moldavia.

NIGHTJARS – ORDER CAPRIMULGIFORMES

Family Caprimulgidae (nightjars) has three breeding species in Russia. The familiar **European Nightjar** (*Caprimulgus europaeus*) breeds in many parts of European Russia, southern Siberia and Central Asia, as well as Caucasus. It is particularly common in deserts and mountains of Central Asia, where it reaches altitudes of about 3,000 m.

The song of the **Jungle Nightjar** (*Caprimulgus indicus*) (Plate 46), if it may be called song, is a not uncommon sound in the mixed forests of central and northern Ussuriland as well as in the Amur region. This bird breeds on hill slopes, favouring forest edges, clearings, fire-affected areas and a patchwork landscape of dry copses, meadows and raised bogs with scattered trees. As in other nightjars, no nest is made, the two eggs being laid amongst the litter of the forest floor. Jungle nightjars are occasionally recorded in river valleys of the Khanka lowlands, but it is generally rare in the south of Ussuriland. The breeding range covers East and South Asia.

Desert and semi-desert habitats in Russian Central Asia are the haunt of the **Egyptian Nightjar** (*Caprimulgus aegyptius*), which also occurs in North Africa and the Near and Middle East. This species avoids mountainous terrain and stony soils. The normal nesting habitat, where the Egyptian Nightjar is not uncommon, is waterless barkhan dunes with sparse vegetation, or clay deserts with patches of wind-drifted sand. No nest is made, the two eggs being laid in a barely noticeable hollow on the ground. Laying takes place in May and the eggs hatch after 17-18 days incubation. The Egyptian Nightjar eats various insects, most of which are caught in flight. The best distinction from other nightjars is the pale golden-red and brown plumage colour.

SWIFTS AND HUMMINGBIRDS – ORDER APODIFORMES

There are five species of swift (Apodidae) in Russia and one species of hummingbird (Trochilidae), namely the **Rufous Hummingbird** (*Selasphorus rufus*) which was recorded as vagrant in the extreme north-east of the country.

The **White-throated Needle-tailed Swift** (*Hirundapus caudacuta*) is a very interesting member of the swift family from the Far East. Needletails are common only in northern and central parts of Ussuriland, and the Amur region. They can be seen here from the end of April. Flocks of 50-70 birds are an impressive sight in mid-May but it is the end of July before you will see the largest flocks of up to 200 birds. Needletails nest in trees. The clutch consists of two to three eggs. Apart from Russia, this species occurs in China, Japan, and the Himalayas.

The **House Swift** (*Apus affinis*) occurs only in the extreme south of Russia, in the Kopet Dag mountains in Turkmenistan and in southern Tadjikistan. The **Eurasian Swift** (*A. apus*) is common through its large range in Russia from the western borders to Lake Baikal.

The **Pacific Swift** (*Apus pacificus*) inhabits the eastern part of the country and is particularly common on the coasts and islands of the southern part of the Russian Far East. On some small rocky islands in the Sea of Japan any possible crevice is occupied by these birds and huge flocks of them fly around all the time, producing their characteristic sounds. The clutch is laid in June, consisting of two to three eggs, and is incubated for about 20 days by both sexes. The food, as in other swifts, consists mostly of flying insects.

The **Alpine Swift** (*Apus melba*) is closely associated with rocky mountain habitats in the south of the country. This species is scarce and unevenly distributed in the southern mountains. It returns from its wintering grounds at the end of April. The nest is in a rock crevice and two to three eggs are laid. The winter is spent in Africa and India.

ROLLERS, KINGFISHERS AND ALLIES – ORDER CORACIIFORMES

This order of rollers, kingfishers and allies has ten species in Russia altogether, six of which breed and four of which are vagrants. There are three families represented.

The family rollers (Coraciidae) has two breeding species, one of which is the **European Roller** (*Coracias garrulus*) (Plate 46). This species is distributed in European Russia where the birds breed mainly in tree holes, and in some areas of Central Asia where it is far more numerous and they nest there in the steep sides of river valleys and in the piedmont zone of desert mountains. Four to six eggs are laid in May and incubation takes 18-19 days. The chicks are born naked and helpless and will spend about a month in the nest. After fledging, the family remains near the nest for some time before dispersing. Rollers feed mainly on insects, especially large ones such as bush-crickets, various grasshoppers and beetles, these being most often captured on the ground.

One of the most exotic of Russian birds is the **Eastern Broad-billed Roller** (*Eurystomus orientalis*), (Plate 46 and Fig. 64) whose plumage betrays its tropical origins. It is found in forests along rivers and streams with adjacent open areas. An encounter with the Broadbill leaves behind an unforgettable impression: two strange birds in flight overhead occasionally give their weird rasping calls. Against the sky, their violet and blue plumage cannot be seen, but as soon as they fly lower and more rapidly past against the backdrop of the forest, all their glorious colours are revealed – red bill and legs, light-blue patches on the wings. Broadbills are quite common in suitable areas of Ussuriland and the Amur region. Arrival takes place from mid-May,

Fig. 64
*Young Eastern Broad-billed Roller (*Eurystomus orientalis*) in central Ussuriland. Photo Y. Shibnev*

and courtship displays reach their peak later in that month. The displays take various forms: pair members will sit close together on a dead branch, almost uninterruptedly giving their harsh, rasping calls. Birds also raise and lower their heads, making repeated circular movements; they frequently fly to a potential nest hole and cling there briefly, or fly up calling and perform aerial acrobatics in a display striking in its beauty and elegance.

The nest is in a hole in a tree, often very high up. Laying takes place in early June and most young Broadbills fledge in the period from late July to early August and parental feeding continues to the end of August. Broad-billed Rollers eat various large insects, mostly beetles and dragonflies. Impressive gatherings are sometimes seen in places where there is a mass hatch of the insects: up to 30 birds will hunt in the company of a few Amur Red-footed Falcons (*Falco amurensis*), this continuing until dusk is well advanced, especially over a smooth and quiet stretch of river. Broadbills depart for their wintering grounds in the first half of September. The species has a wide distribution over much of South and East Asia, the Philippines and Indonesia.

Out of five species of Kingfisher (family Alcedinidae) registered in Russia only three are breeders. Among them is the **European Kingfisher** (*Alcedo atthis*) (Plate 47) which enjoys a very wide distribution all across Russia and is common in many places, and the **Greater Pied Kingfisher** (*Ceryle lugubris*) (Plate 46) which breeds on the southern Kuril Islands of Kunashir and Shikotan. An irregular breeder in southern Ussuriland is the **Black-capped Kingfisher** (*Halcyon pileata*).

The following species are registered as vagrants: the **Lesser Pied Kingfisher** (*Ceryle rudis* – Volga Delta and Crimea Peninsula), the **White-throated Kingfisher** (*Halcyon smyrnensis* – Lenkoran Lowland in southern Azerbaidzan) and the **Ruddy Kingfisher** (*H. coromanda* – Sakhalin Island).

There are two species of bee-eaters in Russia: the **European Bee-eater** (*Merops apiaster*) which inhabits vast areas from European Russia to Central Asia and the **Blue-cheeked Bee-eater** (*M. superciliosus*) (Plate 47) which inhabits the deserts of Central Asia and Kazakhstan. Unlike the European species, the Blue-cheeked Bee-eater sometimes makes its nest burrows in nearly flat surfaces. Habitat-wise these species are isolated in Central Asia.

HOOPOES – ORDER UPUPIFORMES

The **Hoopoe** (*Upupa epops*) is the sole member of this order found in Russia. It breeds from the western borders to the Transbaikal region in the east. In European Russia and in most of its Siberian distribution range it is not a very common bird. This situation is different in Central Asian states where this species is very characteristic of the local fauna. Out of 8 subspecies in the world, Russia is inhabited by just one, the nominal race.

WOODPECKERS – ORDER PICIFORMES

There are thirteen species of woodpecker in Russia out of which twelve are breeders and one species, the **Scaly-bellied Woodpecker** (*Picus squamatus*) is believed to be extinct due to habitat destruction along the desert rivers in southern Turkmenistan and Uzbekistan.

Well-known woodpecker species include the **Great Spotted Woodpecker** (*Dendrocopos major*) (Plate 47), **Lesser Spotted Woodpecker** (*D. minor*), **Middle Spotted Woodpecker** (*D. medius*), **Green Woodpecker** (*Picus viridis*), and **Northern Wryneck** (*Jynx torquilla*). Amongst the more sought-after birds is the **Black Woodpecker** (*Dryocopus martius*) (Plate 47), a species distributed across the taiga belt of Russia all the way to the Far East. This impressive bird is neither common nor rare and breeds mostly in aged woods with plenty of fallen trees and debris. Usually they prefer coniferous forests both in the mountains and on the plains. They usually mate for one breeding season and start to work on an impressive hole in a tree by the end of March – beginning of April. The clutch consists of three to six eggs which are incubated by both parents for 12 to 14 days. These birds are sedentary and do not migrate.

The **Grey-headed Woodpecker** (*Picus canus*) is sparsely distributed from the western borders of Russia and the Ukraine all the way to the Far East. Besides inhabiting taiga forests they also breed in riverine forests in the southern parts of their breeding range. Their nest hole is made in a soft deciduous tree and by the end of April a clutch of six to nine eggs is laid. After 24 to 28 days the young leave the nest hole and start to roam around the breeding area together with their parents.

Two species of woodpecker are associated with southern areas of this country. These include the **Syrian Woodpecker** (*Dendrocopos syriacus*), populations of which expanded dramatically during recent decades and now it not only inhabits parks and riverine forests in Trans-Caucasus but also breeds in southern Ukraine and Russia. The **White-winged Woodpecker** (*D. leucopterus*) (Plate 47 and Fig. 65) is mostly a desert species but sometimes also occurs on mountain slopes. It can be found in Turkmenistan, Uzbekistan, Kirghistan and Kazakhstan, mostly in small woods in the middle of the deserts. Often nesting holes are made in saxaul trees and the breeding biology closely resembles that of the Great Spotted Woodpecker.

White-backed Woodpeckers (*Dendrocopos leucotos*), the largest among our Spotted Woodpeckers, are very difficult to see. They breed across mixed and coniferous forest zones of Russia and occupy enormous breeding areas where they lead a very secretive and mostly silent life during the breeding season. By the end of April the nesting hole is finished and the clutch of three to five eggs is laid. The incubation lasts only 10 to 11 days but the young stay in the hole for 24 to 28 days. As in most cases, both parents take care of the young.

Fig. 65
*White-winged
Woodpecker*
(Dendrocopos
leucopterus) *in
Repetek Nature
Reserve,
Turkmenistan.*
Photo H. Sakalauskas

The **Rufous-bellied Woodpecker** (*Dendrocopos hyberythrus*) has been registered many times in southern Ussuriland and the author was fortunate enough to see this bird several times there. There is hardly any doubt that this species is breeding there, favouring open Mongolian oak woods in the lowlands.

Two specific woodpeckers inhabit Ussuriland, particularly its southern part. Reasonably common is the **Japanese Pygmy Woodpecker** (*Dendrocopos kizuki*) (Plate 48) which leads a sedentary life in mixed and broad-leaved forests, gardens and forest edges. Nest holes are made in already dead and rotten tree trunks, like those of the Lesser Spotted Woodpecker. In winter, when snow is plentiful in many parts of Ussuriland, it is usual to see this attractive little bird looking for insect larvae inside the huge dead umbrella-shaped plants along the forest edges. The **Grey-headed Pygmy Woodpecker** (*D. canicapillus*) (Plate 48) occurs in Ussuriland on the edge of its distribution range and is rare across this country.

There is a popular joke that the **Three-toed Woodpecker** (*Picoides tridactylus*), (Plate 48) is a non-existent species specially invented to tease birdwatchers. As the collection material proves, the species does exist, and occupies the gloomy coniferous forests across the taiga belt of Russia. Isolated breeding populations are located in a number of mountain ranges in Europe and Asia including the Tien Shan. In March they are already active in their breeding area and start to built their nesting hole. The clutch consists of three to five eggs and breeding lasts 11 to 14 days. Out of all the Russian woodpeckers, this is the true taiga species.

PASSERINES – ORDER PASSERIFORMES

This largest order of the world's birdlife is represented in Russia by 366 species out of the 816 total (44%). This is a far lower percentage than the world's figures where passerines comprise about 5500 out of nearly 9000 species (61%). This is explained by the northerly location of the country and the lack of tropical and equatorial zones in Russia which contribute the majority of the ornithological fauna of the world.

Swallows (Hirundinidae)

The swallow family has ten species in Russia. This includes well-known and common species such as the **Barn Swallow** (*Hirundo rustica*) which can be found in nearly every corner of the world's largest country. The **Sand Martin** (*Riparia riparia*) (Plate 48) also enjoys an extensive distribution in Russia where there are three subspecies. The **African Sand Martin** (*R. paludicola*) breeds in a very isolated area in Tadzikistan and is on the verge of its distribution range.

The **House Martin** (*Delichon urbica*) is split into two separate species. The eastern race which breeds east of Lake Baikal is now regarded in Russia as the **Eastern House Martin** (*D. dasypus*). The same species inhabits the Himalayas. The House Martin chooses to breed mostly in the cities and villages but in many mountain ranges it behaves as a completely unurbanized species and builds its nest on inaccessible rocks and crags. The same breeding pattern is characteristic of the **Crag Martin** (*Ptyonoprogne rupestris*). This species occurs only in the mountains and canyons and breeds along the southern borders from Great Caucasus to the mountains of southern Siberia. Its nest is built on the rock and this species often forms small breeding colonies on suitable sites. By the end of May a clutch of three to five eggs is laid and incubated by both parents for 13 to 15 days. After a comparatively long stay in the nest, 23 to 27 days, the young embark on their first journey. As with other swallows and martins, the Crag Martin feeds on insects which are caught in the air.

There are two more species of the genus *Hirundo* in Russia. One is the **Needle-tailed Swallow** (*H. smithii*) occuring in small isolated areas in the south of Tadzikistan. The other, more common and widely distributed, is the **Red-rumped Swallow** (*H. daurica*) (Plate 48). This species actually occurs along the southern frontiers of Russia all the way to the Far East. It favours mostly urbanized areas, villages and towns, mostly along the mountain slopes, and does not usually occur in the desert areas of Central Asia. This species breeds in separate pairs and appears on the breeding grounds by the end of April. The nest is comparatively large and takes a long time to build. It resembles the nest of the House Martin but is large and has a long entrance sleeve. A clutch of three to six eggs is laid by the end of May and normally two broods are reared a year. Incubation, by both parents, takes 12 to 16 days and after about 21 days the young leave the nest.

Two vagrant swallow species, the **Tree Sparrow** (*Tachycineta bicolor*) and the **American Cliff Sparrow** (*Petrochelidon pyrrhonota*) are registered as vagrants, both on Wrangel Island in the Chuktchi Sea.

Larks (Alaudidae)

The lark family not only has an impressive 16 species in Russia, it also includes two attractive endemics, namely the **Black Lark** (*Melanocorypha yeltoniensis*) (Plate 50) and the **White-winged Lark** (*M. leucoptera*). Both these species are distributed in the steppes of southern Russia and Kazakhstan. The Black Lark is a nomadic species and changes breeding sites very often. This species is now disappearing completely from the areas where it was not only common but abundant, such as the huge Zaisan Lowland.

The Black Lark is usually more common than the White-winged but essentially occupies the same breeding sites. During their spring display flights Black Larks present a very unusual sight. Even though the flight pattern – a slowing down of the wing movements – resembles that of other *Melanocorypha* species, the colour is distinctive. Completely black smallish birds flying in an incredible way and singing from all around leaves an unbelieveable impression. The display starts by the end of March and the nest is built in a pit on the ground. By the end of April a clutch of four to five eggs is laid and incubated by the female only for 15 to 16 days. The young are fed by both parents. The White-winged Lark's breeding pattern is very similar.

The **Skylark** (*Alauda arvensis*) is a widely distributed and very common bird across Russia. The **Japanese Skylark** (*Alauda japonica*) is regarded by many as a subspecies of the Skylark; however, in Russia it stands as a full species, and inhabits the Kuril Islands and possibly the southern parts of Sakhalin Island. The **Crested Lark** (*Galerida cristata*) (Plate 49) is also common across Russia, although it is mostly restricted to the southern parts of the country. Southern slopes of the Kopet-Dag Mountains in Turkmenistan are inhabited by the uncommon **Desert Lark** (*Ammomanes deserti*). Western parts of Russia, Byelorussia and Ukraine as well as the Baltic States are home for the **Wood Lark** (*Lullula arborea*).

The **Short-toed Larks** (*Calandrella*) are represented by four species in Russia. The **Short-toed Lark** (*C. cinerea*) (Plate 49) is common in steppes and semi-deserts across southern Russia whereas the **Lesser Short-toed Lark** (*C. rufescens*) (Plate 49) favours deserts proper, particularly the sand deserts of Central Asia. **Hume's Short-toed Lark** (*C. acutirostris*) is the rarest of all four species and breeds in very small numbers in the Karatau mountains and on the slopes of Tien Shan as well as in the Western Pamirs. The **Mongolian Short-toed Lark** (*C. cheleensis*) breeds in salty desert areas, usually in the vicinity of water, from eastern Kazakhstan to the borders with Mongolia in the Transbaikal region.

Most impressive of all the Russian larks are the species of the genus *Melanocorypha* to which the previously described Black and White-winged Larks belong. Apart from these two, there are three more species of this genus in this country. They are the **Calandra Lark** (*M. calandra*) (Plate 49), the **Bimaculated Lark** (*M. bimaculata*) (Plate 50), and the **Mongolian Lark** (*M. mongolica*). The widest distribution in Russia is enjoyed by the Calandra Lark which breeds from the western borders of Ukraine to the borders with China in the east. The Bimaculated Lark (*M. bimaculata*) is mostly distributed in the semi-deserts as well as the mountains of Central Asia and southern Siberia, whereas the Mongolian Lark lives in the steppes of Tuva and the Transbaikal region. All these birds are reasonably common and their breeding biology is similar.

Central Asia is also inhabited by the **Oriental Skylark** (*Alauda gulgula*) which resembles the Skylark in many ways. This species breeds in very arid areas, mostly stony semi-deserts, and is rather unevenly distributed. In April it is possible to hear the characteristic song of this species in its breeding grounds. The nest is built on the ground and the clutch, laid at the end of April, consists of three to five eggs incubated by the female only. The young stay in the nest for about ten days.

The **Shore Lark** (*Eremophila alpestris*) (Plate 50) occupies two completely different habitats in Russia – tundra in the north, and a number of mountain ranges across the southern frontiers. Most of the mountain ranges have their own specific subspecies which differ a great deal, mostly in the intensity of colour. There are areas in places like the Eastern Pamir Mountains where the Shore Lark is the only visible bird at altitudes of about 4500 m. The time of arrival at their breeding grounds varies, but most birds in the mountain appear in May. The nest is built in a tiny pit in the ground where the clutch of three to six eggs is laid. Normally two broods are reared a year.

Wagtail & Pipits (Motacillidae)

The wagtail and pipit family is represented in Russia by 21 species (10 pipits and 11 wagtails), out of which 20 species are breeders and the **Japanese Pied Wagtail** (*Motacilla grandis*) was recorded several times in the south of the Russian Far East.

Richard's Pipit (*Anthus richardii*) (Plate 51) inhabits open landscapes, usually rich and wet meadows of southern Siberia and Eastern Kazakhstan. It is common in suitable areas and arrives at its breeding grounds by

Fig. 66 *Meadow Pipit* (Anthus pratensis) *in the St. Petersburg area. Photo A. Sokolov*

mid-May. The nest is located on the ground and is usually well covered by the neighbouring vegetation. In June, four to six eggs are laid and incubated by the female only for about 13 to 14 days. Like other pipits and wagtails, Richard's Pipit feeds on various insects.

Blyth's Pipit (*Anthus godlewskii*) breeds in southern Siberia east of the Altai mountains and in the Transbaikal region and Tuva, penetrating into Mongolia and China. It favours stony mountain slopes and meadows, arriving at its breeding places by the beginning of May. The nest is made on the ground and is well camouflaged. The clutch consists of three to five eggs and the female starts incubation, which lasts 12 to 14 days, by the end of May. Normally one clutch a year is laid.

The **Tawny Pipit** (*Anthus campestris*) is distributed in Russia from its western borders to the Sayan mountains in southern Siberia. It has three subspecies in this country and inhabits areas as diverse as deserts and mountains, always giving preference to dry, arid landscapes.

Well known species such as the **Tree Pipit** (*Anthus trivialis*) and **Meadow Pipit** (*A. pratensis*) (Fig. 66) are widely distributed and common in Russia.

A separate group of pipits is closely related to tundra habitats, namely the **Red-throated Pipit** (*Anthus cervinus*) and **Pechora Pipit** (*A. gustavi*). The first is a very common species in the tundras of Russia all across this geographical zone. The Pechora Pipit is sparce and unevenly distributed from the valley of the Pechora River to the Chukotka Peninsula in the Far East. A different and quite distinct subspecies *A. g.* (?) *menzbieri* inhabits the valley of Lake Khanka in southern Ussuriland, thousands of miles away from the main breeding range.

Two closely related species, the **Olive-backed Pipit** (*Anthus hodgsoni*) (Plate 51) and the **Buff-bellied Pipit** (*A. rubescens*) (Plate 51), inhabit huge expanses of Siberia and the Far East. The Arctic coast of the Kola Peninsula and numerous mountain ranges in the south are inhabited by four subspecies of the **Water Pipit** (*A. spinoletta*). In the mountains this is a true alpine species rarely descending lower than 2500 m.

Wagtails essentially occupy similar habitats to pipits, particularly those of the Yellow Wagtail grouping. The species-subspecies problem in both White and Yellow Wagtails presents a great difficulty to ornithologists and is a matter of study and continuous interest. Here we follow the division accepted by Russian ornithologists where the **White Wagtail** (*Motacilla alba*) is divided into three species within Russia and Yellow Wagtail into four. The White Wagtail proper inhabits European Russia and large parts of Siberia and the Arctic areas. The **Masked Wagtail** (*M. personata*) (Plate 52) is found mostly in Central Asia whereas the **Kamchatka Wagtail** (*M. lugens*) (Plate 52) inhabits the coatline and islands off the Far Eastern seas and the Pacific.

The **Yellow Wagtail** is a common breeder in huge expanses of wet meadows of European Russia and Siberia. Apart from *Motacilla flava*, the following species are separated: *M. taivana* (Plate 51), living in Eastern Siberia and the southern Far East of Russia, *M. lutea*, inhabiting northern Kazakhstan and southern parts of Western Siberia, and the **Black-headed Wagtail** (*M. felgedd*), closely associated with the wet meadows and salt water basins in Central Asia.

The **Citrine Wagtail** (*Motacilla citreola*) (Plate 52) is known for its expansion westwards. Some years ago they were recorded as breeders in Moscow region, and now several pairs breed even in Lithuania. The breeding sites of this attractive species are generally wet and rich meadows both in the valleys and in the mountains. It also breeds in the huge expanses of the Siberian Arctic, in proper tundra habitats. It has four subspecies in Russia. The **Grey Wagtail** (*M. cinerea*) is a common and characteristic species in many mountain ranges in Russia, closely associated ecologically with mountain streams.

The **Forest Wagtail** (*Dendronanthus indicus*) (Plate 52) looks completely different and lives in completely different habitats. This species inhabits dense woods on the mountain slopes along the river valleys in Ussuriland. It also breeds in Korea and North-east China. Preference is given to woods of Mongolian Oak (*Quercus mongolica*), which are rather uniform and poor in other bird species. Forest Wagtails appear in May, when the vegetation is in bloom and forests are already rich in insects. The nest is built on the tree at varied heights, but most usually at about 3 m above the ground. The clutch consists of four to five eggs.

Shrikes (Laniidae)

The shrike family has a total of 12 attractive species in Russia, 11 of which are breeders and one, the **Masked Shrike** (*Lanius nubicus*) is vagrant.

Two species of shrike are found in the Far East only. The **Bull-headed Shrike** (*Lanius bucephalus*) (Plate 53) inhabits southern Ussuriland and the Kuril Islands whereas the **Tiger Shrike** (*L. tigrinus*) lives only in the very south of Ussuriland, penetrating into China. Like other shrikes, those two species inhabit bushy areas and forest edges and avoid dense, continuous forests. All shrikes build their nests in trees or bushes, usually not high above the ground (about 2-3 m). The nest is a strong and massive structure of small twigs, grass and sometimes feathers. The clutch normally consists of three to six eggs and is incubated by the female only. At this time the male brings her food. Incubation takes about 15 days, and young stay in the nest for about 14 to 16 days. The food is varied and consists mostly of different insects, sometimes small lizards and even rodents. All shrikes nest in solitary pairs and arrive at their breeding grounds reasonably late when insects are already abundant.

An interesting group of shrikes are those closely related to the **Red-backed Shrike** (*Lanius collurio*) which inhabits a large part of European Russia, western and southern Siberia. The Red-backed Shrike has recently been split

Fig. 67 *Long-tailed Shrike (*Lanius schach*) in the western Tien Shan Mountains. Photo A. Knystautas*

into two species; the **Isabelline Shrike** (*L. isabellinus*) (Plate 53) which has five subspecies and breeds along the southern frontiers of Russia and the CIS, and the **Brown Shrike** (*L. cristatus*) (Plate 53), which inhabits vast areas of Siberia and the Far East.

In the very south of the country, on the borders with Iran and Afghanistan, limited numbers of the **Bay-backed Shrike** (*Lanius vittatus*) can be found breeding in pistachio woods. In Trans Caucasus, the **Red-headed Shrike** (*L. senator*) is reasonably common.

While travelling along the roads in Central Asia, the attention of keen birdwatchers may be attracted by a rather large and beautiful shrike, the **Long-tailed Shrike** (*Lanius schach*) (Fig. 67). This species is closely associated with human habitation, and breeds mostly in small villages where there are plenty of trees, particularly poplars, around. They arrive at their breeding sites in Central Asia by the end of April and immediately become visible and noisy. The nest is usually made in a poplar and is often quite high off the ground. Normally only one brood per season is reared, but if the first attempt fails, they will try to breed again. The young stay in the nest for about 17 to 19 days, and are fed by both parents.

The next grouping of shrikes, consisting of three species in Russia, are the so-called Grey Shrikes. The well known species are the **Great Grey** (*Lanius excubitor*) (Fig. 68) and **Lesser Grey Shrikes** (*L. minor*) (Plate 53).

Fig. 68 *Desert subspecies of the Great Grey Shrike (*Lanius excubitor*) in the Sary Ishikotrau Desert, Kazakhstan. Photo A. Knystautas/O. Belialov*

The Great Grey Shrike has seven subspecies in Russia, some of which, like the desert one (*L. e. palidirostris*) are quite specific.

The southern part of Ussuriland is inhabited by the uncommon **Chinese Great Grey Shrike** (*Lanius sphenocercus*). It is on the edge of its northern distribution here. This impressive species which is actually larger than the Great Grey Shrike, inhabits forest edges and groups of tall trees along river valleys. They arrive in Ussuriland to breed in late April.

Orioles (Oriolidae)

The essentially tropical oriole family has two species in Russia. The **Golden Oriole** (*Oriolus oriolus*) is distributed in large areas of European Russia and Central Asia, where there is a different subspecies with even brighter plumage: *O. o. kundoo*. This beautiful bird is very common in Central Asia where it is far more visible than in European Russia and the rest of Europe.

The **Black-naped Oriole** (*Oriolus chinensis*) (Plate 54) is larger and brighter than its European counterpart. In Russia, it inhabits bright woods along the river valleys in Ussuriland and the Amur region to which it adds much life by its spectacular flights and colours as well as its restless voice. They appear on their breeding grounds only in the second half of May and announce their arrival by piercing calls and display flights. The Black-naped Oriole is a solitary breeder, but in suitable areas their populations can reach large numbers and sometimes the false impression can be given that they are breeding in sparce colonies. Their nests, as those of the Golden Oriole, are a classical oriole nest on a tree branch far from the trunk and usually high above the ground. The clutch, laid in June, consists of three to four eggs and is incubated by both parents for about a fortnight. The young stay in the nest for 13 to 15 days. They are fed on various insects by both male and female.

Starlings (Sturnidae)

The starling family is related to the orioles and in Russia is represented by eight species. Six species are breeders and the **Chinese Starling** (*Sturnia sinensis*) and the **Black-headed Starling** (*Sturnus podagorum*) are vagrants in Ussuriland and Central Asia respectively. Three species of starling are to be found in the Far East, mainly Ussuriland. The **Grey Starling** (*Sternus cineraceus*) is very common and is a clear substitute for the **European Starling** (*Sturnus vulgaris*) in the Far East. The **Daurian Starling** (*Sturnia sturnina*) (Plate 54) is rarer and breeds along the forest edges and in the villages in southern parts of Ussuriland. The **Violet-backed Starling** (*Sturnia philippensis*) is an occasional breeder on the islands in the Bay of Peter the Great.

The **Rose-coloured Starling** (*Sternus roseus*) (Plate 54), a notorious colonial breeder of southern steppes and mountain slopes, particularly in

Central Asia, is a very beautiful member of this family. Its colonies sometimes reach unprecedented numbers of tens of thousands of pairs. They are usually placed between the rocks on huge screes in lower parts of the mountains, ravines and gorges, as well as under roofs of huge agricultural buildings such as farms. Building takes place from early May and egg laying starts in mid-May. The clutch consists of three to nine, most usually five to six eggs which are incubated by both parents for 11 to 14 days. The young stay in the nest for 14 to 19 days fed by both parents. Rose-coloured Starlings feed mostly on insects and are notorious for eating huge numbers of the Migratory Locust (*Locusta migratoria*), a very voracious insect.

The most aggressive of all our starlings is the **Indian Myna** (*Acridotheres tristis*). During the past 50 years they have occupied huge areas of Central Asia. In places where the Common Starling was once the dominant species in this ecological niche mynas now roam as the sole owners. The success of the myna in Central Asia is nearly inseparable from the progress of man, but after occupying lowlands with human settlement mynas turned to the mountains and now breed on inaccessible rocks at considerable altitudes. The birds are sedentary and spend their winter around the breeding grounds – this probably keeps them from moving even further north where they could not possibly survive the harsh winters. The nest is built in a tree hole, under roofs of different buildings or in rock crevices. They nest all season round, starting from March. The clutch consists of three to six eggs and is incubated by both parents for about a fortnight. The young stay in the nest for 24 to 27 days and are fed by both male and female.

Crows (Corvidae)

The crow family has 17 species in Russia, 16 of which are proved breeders, and **Henderson's Ground Jay** (*Podoces hendersoni*) is probably breeding in the Zaisan Lowland and in Tuva.

The **Siberian Jay** (*Perisoreus infaustus*) (Plate 55) is a true taiga species, closely associated with the cold coniferous forests which cover immense areas of Russia. This attractive species spends winter and summer in the forests where the temperature differences between seasons can reach about 70 degrees centigrade. The nest is built close to the trunk of a tree and by the end of May a clutch of three to six eggs is laid and incubated by both parents for 18 to 20 days. Both male and female take care of the young and they stay in the nest for up to 23 days.

The **Eurasian Jay** (*Garrulus glandarius*) is widespread from the western borders all the way to the Far East. Crimea and Caucasus have their own specific subspecies. Out of a total of 35 subspecies in the world, Russia has five.

The **Azure-winged Magpie** (*Cyanopica cyana*) (Plate 55) is an unusually

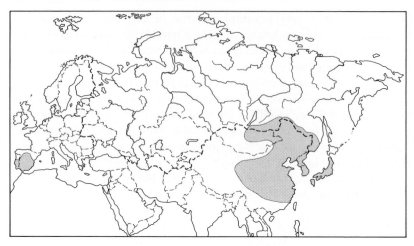

Fig. 69 *Distribution of the Azure-winged Magpie (*Cyanopica cyana*).*

beautiful representative of the corvids. In Russia, this species can be found breeding from the Trans Baikal region to the south of Ussuriland (Fig. 69). Another widespread species is the **Black-billed Magpie** (*Pica pica*); it is very hard to imagine a place in Russia where you will not see or hear this bird, be it high in the mountains or deep in a desert.

An species endemic to this country is the **Pander's Ground Jay** (*Podoces panderi*) (Plate 55). This unusual bird lives in the deserts of Central Asia, in two separate areas in the Karakum desert and in the Sary Ishikotrau Desert south of Lake Balkhash. Two different subspecies inhabit these areas. The Ground Jay does not migrate and spends the winter roaming the desert. By March they are already visiting their breeding sites, looking for a suitable place to build a nest. It is believed that this species mates for life. In April the clutch of four to five eggs is laid and incubated by the female only for 16 to 19 days. There is only one brood per season. The young are fed by both parents and after leaving the nest the whole family start to travel widely in the desert in search of food which mostly comprises different insects. In winter, their food becomes increasingly plant-based.

The **Spotted Nutcracker** (*Nucifraga caryocatactes*) like the Siberian Jay, is a true taiga species of corvid. But unlike the Siberian Jay, the Spotted Nutcracker is found not only in lowland taiga forests but also in coniferous woods of different mountain ranges. The adaptations of this species to the harsh winter is incredible – they manage to save and store on the forest floor a huge number of different seeds, particularly the so-called cedar nut, or seeds of the Siiberian Pine tree. How they manage to find all they have

Fig. 70
Red-billed Chough
(Pyrrhocorax
pyrrhocorax)
*in the Tien Shan
Mountains.*
Photo O. Belialov

stored under the thick layer of snow is a mystery. Nutcrackers are known for their spontaneous fluctuations in numbers; during a successful breeding year many birds migrate far away from their breeding areas and reach distant countries. Breeding starts very early (by March) when there is a lot of snow around; a nest is built on a fir tree normally 3 to 5 m above the ground. The clutch of two to five eggs is laid by the end of March-beginning of April and incubated by the female only for 17 to 19 days. After 21 to 28 days the young leave the nest.

Two spectacular species of corvid inhabit the numerous mountain ranges of Russia – the **Red-billed Chough** (*Pyrrhocorax pyrrhocorax*) (Plate 56 and Fig. 70) and the **Alpine Chough** (*P. graculus*). Their ranges essentially overlap and very often they form mixed flocks to look for food together. In Russia, they are essentially alpine and do not breed in lowland areas or on sea cliffs as they do in Britain. Both species are colonial breeders and their nests are situated on inaccessible rocks usually at considerable altitudes. There are two subspecies of Red-billed Chough (out of a total of seven) and two subspecies of Alpine Chough (out of a total of two).

The **Western Jackdaw** (*Corvus monedula*) is very common throughout Russia and is split into two species. Areas east of Lake Baikal are inhabited by the **Daurian Jackdaw** (*C. dauuricus*), which has a lot more white in its plumage.

Other species of the genus *Corvus* in Russia include the very common **Rook** (*C. frugilegus*), whose range is expanding; the **Hooded Crow** (*C. cornix*), and the **Carrion Crow** (*C. corone*) (Plate 56), the last two forms being regarded as separate species in this country. The Far East is inhabited by the **Jungle Crow** (*C. macrorhynchos*) (Plate 56) which is a substitute for the Carrion Crow in many areas like Ussuriland.

The **Common Raven** (*Corvus corax*) has also been split into two species in Russia; in the Russian deserts the **Desert Raven** (*C. ruficollis*) (Plate 56) may be found, which is more brownish in colour. The raven enjoys a very wide distribution in Russia and can be found from the Arctic areas all the way to the high mountains of Central Asia, where it is represented by the subspecies *C. c. tibetanus*.

Waxwings (Bombycillidae)

The waxwing family has three species in Russia. One is the well-known and common **Bohemian Waxwing** (*Bombycilla garrulus*) (Plate 57) which is a taiga bird, appearing in large flocks during the winter months in more southerly areas. Endemic to Russia, the **Japanese Waxwing** (*B. japonica*) is an uncommon breeder found only in the Amur region of the Far East. This secretive bird arrives there in May and starts building its nest (of which only several have ever been discovered) in a tree. By the beginning of June four to six eggs are laid which are incubated by the female only. There is one brood per season. This species needs more study to discover its breeding biology and distribution. The third waxwing, a rare and secretive member this family, can occasionally be found in the very south of the CIS on the borders with Iran and Afghanistan, along the valleys of the desert rivers. This is the **Grey Hypocolius** (*Hypocolius ampelinus*).

Minivets (Campephagidae)

The tropical minivet family has only one species in Russia, namely the **Ashy Minivet** (*Pericrocotus divaricatus*) (Plate 57). This attractive bird breeds in Ussuriland and the Amur region of the Far East. They breed in solitary pairs and in small groups choosing groups of huge trees by the forest edges. They arrive at their breeding grounds in May and immediatedly start to busy themselves with breeding. The tiny and beautiful nest is usually built high up on a horizontal tree branch and four to five eggs are laid. Both parents take care of the young and normally rear one brood per season.

Bulbuls (Pycnonotidae)

Another tropical family, the bulbuls (Pycnonotidae), is represented in Russia by two species. One, the **Chestnut-eared Bulbul** (*Mycroscelis amaurotis*), is believed to be breeding on the Kunashir Island in Kurils, the other, the **White-cheeked Bulbul** (*Pycnonotus leucogenys*), is vagrant in the Piandz Valley in Central Asia.

Dippers (Cinclidae)

An ornithological joke says that Russia holds 50 per cent of the world's dipper species. This is actually true, even though there are only two dipper species in Russia altogether. The well-known **White-throated Dipper** (*Cinclus cinclus*) (Plate 57) is widespread but is mostly restricted to the mountain ranges and mountain streams rather than lowland rivers. Six distinct subspecies breed in the north of European Russia, the Ural mountains, Caucasus and Trans Caucasus, the Carpathians, Central Asian mountains, and the Altai and Sayan ranges in southern Siberia. The **Brown Dipper** (*Cinclus pallasi*) (Plate 57) occurs in the Central Asian mountains where it actually competes with the White-throated Dipper for suitable breeding sites. The Brown Dipper appears to end up in larger and quieter rivers than its white-bellied counterpart. The Brown Dipper extends to the Far East where it breeds in crystal-clear rivers in Ussuriland and even on the Kuril Islands. The breeding biology of the two does not differ a great deal. Everybody is aware of the incredible feeding pattern of dippers. In March, birds are already active on their breeding sites and start nest-building between the rocks, tree roots and branches just above the water, under bridges etc. The clutch consists of three to six eggs and normally two broods a year are reared. The young stay in the nest for about 21 to 24 days.

Wrens (Troglodytidae)

We will not go to the lengths of describing the breeding biology of the **Northern Wren** (*Troglodytes troglodytes*) in Russia where, as in the rest of Eurasia, it is the only representative of an American family (Troglodytidae) with 60-odd members. There are nine subspecies of this wren in Russia and we found it breeding in Central Asia at up to 3500 m altitude. It is really difficult to name an area in Russia where the wren cannot be found.

Accentors (Prunellidae)

In contrast to the previous family of wrens, the accentors (Prunellidae) are extremely well represented in Russia. Out of a world total of 13, Russia has eight breeding species. The first small group of the sub-genus *Laiscopus* contains two attractive species – the **Alpine Accentor** (*Prunella collaris*) (Plate 58) and the **Himalayan Accentor** (*P. himalayana*) (Plate 58). The Alpine Accentor breeds in most mountain ranges of Russia's southern frontiers. Starting from the Carpathians, through Caucasus, Central Asian mountains, Altai and Sayan it reaches the Pacific Coast of the Sea of Japan where it breeds on the cliffs along the shores and on the rocky islands. The Himalayan Accentor is restricted to the alpine and sub-alpine belts of the mountains of Central Asia and southern Siberia. As other accentors, it breeds in solitary pairs along the rocky mountain slopes particularly favouring the screes. Normally there is one brood per season, and the nest is built in May among the rocks. A clutch of four to six eggs is laid in June, and incubated by both parents for about 14 to 15 days. Young stay in the nest for 14 to 16 days and are fed by both parents on insects.

Far more common in suitable sites is the **Brown Accentor** (*Prunella fulvescens*) (Plate 58). Its breeding range in this country is restricted to the high mountains of Central Asia, southern Siberia and the Transbaikal region. This species favours open mountain slopes in sub-alpine and alpine zones covered by sparce vegetation, for example creeping juniper trees, and sometimes breeds together with the Himalayan Accentor on screes with no vegetation cover at all. This species demonstrates an incredible adaptation to the high altitudes and manages to rear three broods per season by sharing parental responsibilities even between different breeding pairs – the same was demonstrated with the Dunnock in Britain. The nest is a well-concealed structure usually placed under a rock. The first clutch is in May and consists of four to five eggs; these are incubated for 10 to 12 days, and it takes the same time for the young to leave the nest. The food consists of different insects, and out of the breeding season the Brown Accentor adopts a more vegetarian diet.

On the borders of Armenia and Turkey it is possible to see the rather rare **Radde's Accentor** (*Prunella ocularis*). Vast expanses of the Siberian forests are inhabited by the endemic **Siberian Accentor** (*P. montanella*) (Plate 58) which like the Dunnock is an essentially a forest bird. It is reasonably common in its range and the breeding biology is very much like other accentors. The nest is placed on a small tree (fir or larch) or in a small bush.

Two separate areas serve as a breeding range of the **Black-throated Accentor** (*Prunella atrogularis*). One small and restricted area is in the north of European Russia, on the foothills of the Ural mountains, and a much more significant one is in the mountains of Central Asia. Ecologically, the Black-throated Accentor demonstrates a clear connection with the coniferous forests of the mountains and avoids areas above it, favoured by its possible rival the Brown Accentor. The nest is made on fir trees, sometimes unusually high for an accentor. In suitable sites it is a rather common bird and its spring songs heard upon its arrival in May add much to the spring atmosphere of the majestic forests of Tien Shan Spruce.

Two more species of Russian accentors are the **Dunnock** (*Prunella modularis*) and the **Japanese Accentor** (*P. rubida*). The Dunnock is common, but is not at all urbanized in Russia; on the contrary, it breeds deep in the mixed woods giving preference to young firs for breeding. The Japanese Accentor inhabits the mountain slopes above the tree line in Sakhalin and Kuril Islands in the Far East.

Warblers (Sylviidae)

The warbler family is represented extensively in Russia, with 62 species registered to date, including a great number of exciting birds like various Grasshopper Warblers and Leaf Warblers. Fifty-eight species are breeders and four vagrants. Among the vagrants of this family are the **Large-billed Bush Warbler** (*Bradypterus major*), registered in the Eastern Pamir mountains; the **Olive-tree Warbler** (*Hippolais olivetorum*), which possibly breeds in the very south of Turkmenistan; the **Subalpine Warbler** (*Sylvia cantillans*), registered near Odessa, Ukraine, and **Bonelli's Warbler** (*Phylloscoipus bonelli*), registered near Lvov, Ukraine.

The **Short-tailed Bush Warbler** (*Urosphena squameiceps*) (Plate 59) is restricted in its distribution to Ussuriland, Korea and north-east China. This tiny bird inhabits large forests on the mountain slopes and in river valleys often far away from the forest edge. They favour places with many fallen trees and debris where they subsequently build their nests. Like other warblers, they breed in solitary pairs and are territorial, arriving in Ussuriland in the first half of May. By the end of May a clutch containing five to seven eggs is laid. Both parents take care of the young which leave the nest when about 10 to 12 days old.

The **Japanese Bush Warbler** (*Horeites diphone*) (Plate 59) is yet another warbler specific to the Far East. This bird is also restricted to Ussuriland, Sakhalin and the Kuril Islands, Japan, Korea and north-east China and is a representative of the Chinese faunal type. To breed, they choose a completely different habitat from that of the Short-tailed Bush Warbler. They favour open slopes of low mountains covered with very thick if not impassable vegetation. Their characteristic song can be heard in these places from the end of April. The nest is the leaf-warbler type with a side entrance and in May four to five eggs are laid. Normally two broods per season are reared. Incubation is by the female only and takes 13 to 14 days. Both parents take care of the young which leave the nest when about two weeks old.

Cetti's Warbler (*Cettia cetti*) (Plate 59) is a well-known and widely distributed species which in Russia breeds on extensive areas of Caucasus, southern Russia and Central Asia.

The genus *Bradypterus* is known for the great secrecy of its representatives and the difficulties in finding and studying them. Two species are registered as breeders in Russia, namely the **Spotted Bush Warbler** (*B. thoracicus*), which is quite common in suitable areas in southern Siberia and the Transbaikal region, and the **Chinese Bush Warbler** (*B. tacsanowskius*) (Plate 59) which was discovered breeding in the Transbaikal region and has also been recorded in Ussuri River Valley and Lake Khanka.

The **Japanese Marsh Warbler** (*Megalurus pryeri*) was recorded several times during the breeding season in Lake Khanka in Ussuriland; this included singing males.

The complex and exciting genus *Locustella*, or Grasshopper Warblers has nine species represented in Russia. **Gray's Grasshopper Warbler** (*L. fasciolata*) (Plate 59) is the largest in this group and is reasonably common eastwards of the Ob' river valley all the way to the Far East. Arriving in the breeding grounds as late as early June, this species favours bushy areas along the river valleys. Their song is very characteristic and has no similarities to those of other Grasshopper Warblers breeding in Europe. The nest is built on the ground, as in other representatives of this genus. A clutch consists of three to four eggs incubated for about 15 days. The young leave the nest when about two weeks old. A very closely related species, **Stepanyan's Grasshopper Warbler** (*L. amnicola*) is described from the Sakhalin Islands.

All three species of European Grasshopper Warblers are reasonably common and widespread in Russia but none of them actually penetrates deep into eastern Siberia and the Far East. They are the **Grasshopper Warbler** (*Locustella naevia*), **Savi's Warbler** (*L. luscinioides*) and the **River Warbler** (*L. fluviatilis*).

Pallas's Grasshopper Warbler (*Locustella certhiola*) (Plate 60) is essentially a Siberian species breeding on numerous wetlands and tussocky grasslands all the way to the Far East. This attractive bird is characterized by its specific song accompanied by a display flight unusual for this genus. On suitable wet grassland it is possible to hear up to ten males displaying at the same time and this certainly leaves an unforgettable impression. The nest is incredibly well camouflaged under the grass and a clutch of four to six eggs is laid by early June. Incubation is by the female only and takes about 12 days.

Middendorff's Grasshopper Warbler (*Locustella ochotensis*) (Plate 60) is a true Far Eastern species and inhabits wet grasslands and reedbeds of the Far Eastern coast of Russia, the Kamchatka Peninsula. A closely related species was recently described from the islands in the Bay of Peter the Great (southern Ussuriland), namely **Styan's Grasshopper Warbler** (*L. pleskei*). It is characterised first and foremost by the fact that is does not breed on the continent, only on islands along the coast, where it can be found on steep and densely covered slopes.

The **Lanceolated Warbler** (*Locustella lanceolata*) (Plate 60) is the smallest of Russian Grasshopper Warblers and is reasonably common in huge expanses of Siberia and the Far East. This species inhabits grasslands, not necessarily the wet ones. By mid-May it is possible to hear its simple song which resembles the sound of a grasshopper. The nest is a well camouflaged structure on the ground. A clutch consists usually of five eggs which are

Fig. 71
Reed Warbler
(Acrocephalus
scirpaceus) *in
Lithuania. Photo
A. Knystautas*

incubated by the female only for about 12 days. It takes the same time or sometimes less for the young to leave the nest.

The genus *Lusciniola* is represented in Russia by the **Moustached Warbler** (*L. melanopogon*). This attractive and secretive bird is sparcely and unevenly distributed from the Danube Delta along the large deltas and other water basins across the Caucasus region all the way to Lake Balkhash and Lake Alakol in Eastern Kazakhstan. Its favourite habitat is wet meadows with sparce bushes and the occasional reedbed, where it normally arrives at the end of April. Nest-building is in May, and by the end of that month a clutch of four to six eggs is laid and incubated for 11 to 12 days. As other warblers, the Moustached Warbler feeds on different insects.

The genus of true reed warblers (*Acrocephalus*) is represented in this country by nine species distributed in most parts of the country, excluding high arctic areas and mountains. Several species are common and well known in Europe as well, such as the **Reed Warbler** (*Acrocephalus scirpaceus*) (Fig. 71), the **Marsh Warbler** (*A. palustris*) (Fig. 72) and the **Great Reed Warbler** (*A. arundinaceus*). In Russia, the latter species is split into two and the birds inhabiting southern parts of its range within this country, particularly in Central Asia, are called **Clamorous Reed Warblers** (*A. stentoreus*). Very common in Russia is the **Sedge Warbler** (*A. schoeno- baenus*), which is distributed up to Western Siberia.

Fig. 72 *Marsh Warbler (Acrocephalus palustris) in Lithuania. Photo A. Knystautas*

Rare and declining in Russia as elsewhere is the **Aquatic Warbler** (*Acrocephalus paludicola*). In Russia it breeds only in European areas, and mostly in the west. Records of breeding are coming from the Danube Delta, southern Ukraine, and Lithuania.

The **Black-browed Reed Warbler** (*Acrocephalus bistrigiceps*) (Plate 60) is an incredibly common and typical bird of the Far East. It is particularly numerous in Ussuriland, where the chorus of its joyful song resounds in May from every meadow, grassland, and reedbed. It is essentially a grassland bird and does not require reeds for breeding. A nest is made in the typical way for all reed warblers in the form of a deep cup. By the end of May the laying starts and a normal clutch consists of four to six eggs. Incubation takes 13 to 14 days.

The **Paddyfield Warbler** (*Acrocephalus agricola*) (Fig. 73) is distributed along the shores of southern water basins in Russia starting at the Danube Delta and going across Central Asia all the way to the Far East, where it is represented at Lake Khanka by the very specific subspecies *A.a.tangorum* which has a larger and more massive nest and a quite different song.

Blyth's Reed Warbler (*Acrocephalus dumetorum*) is a common breeder across gardens, forest edges and grasslands from the Baltic Sea all the way to Eastern Siberia. It is a common bird which arrives at its breeding grounds in May. It builds a nest in small bushes and grass and lays four to six eggs in June. Their breeding biology is very much in line with that of other small

Fig. 73 *Different subspecies of Paddyfield Warbler* (Acrocephalus agricola). *Left:* A. a. septima, *Sivash Bay, South Ukraine, photo A. Knystautas. Right:* A. a. tangorum, *Lake Khanka, Ussuriland, photo Y. Shibnev*

Acrocephalus species. Their field identification is a real challenge for birdwatchers.

Closely related to reed warblers but nevetheless separated into a different genus is the **Thick-billed Warbler** (*Phragmaticola aedon*) (Plate 60). It breeds in southern Siberia and the Far East and is reasonably common in suitable areas. Its favourite habitat is bushy areas within the forest or on the forest edge. The nest is built in a bush usually about 2 m above the ground. Laying takes place by mid-June and a clutch consists of three to five eggs.

The genus *Hippolais* has six species in Russia, five of which are breeders and the **Olive-tree Warbler** (*Hippolais olivetorum*) is a vagrant. All species inhabit the European part of Russia, Caucausus and Central Asia, some penetrating into Western Siberia. There are no *Hippolais* species in Eastern Siberia and the Far East which is easily understandable bearing in mind the Mediterranean roots of this group.

The **Icterine Warbler** (*Hippolais icterina*) is a common bird in European Russia and its lively, loud song is often heard from the tree tops in parks and light mixed and deciduous woodland areas.

The **Booted Warbler** (*Hippolais caligata*) normally breeds only in Russia

189

and Mongolia. It has been split recently into two species, the **Southern Booted Warbler** (*H. rama*) inhabiting the deserts of Central Asia and penetrating into India and Pakistan.

All other species are characteristic to the southern parts of Central Asia. Both **Upcher's Warbler** (*Hippolais languida*) (Plate 61) and the **Olivaceous Warbler** (*H. pallida*) inhabit groups of trees and bushy areas in the deserts and mountain foothills in Central Asia.

Out of the genus *Sylvia* it is probably worth singling out the following species: Hume's Lesser Whitethroat (*S. althaea*), the Desert Warbler (*S. nana*), the Orphean Warbler (*S. hortensis*) and Ménétérie's Warbler (*S. mystacea*). The rest of the *Sylvia* species are very well known and include the **Blackcap** (*S. atricapilla*), the **Garden Warbler** (*S. borin*), the **Barred Warbler** (*S. nisoria*), the **Whitethroat** (*S. communis*) and the **Lesser Whitethroat** (*S. curruca*) (Plate 61). One species, the **Subalpine Warbler** (*S. cantillans*) is vagrant.

Hume's Lesser Whitethroat (*Sylvia althaea*) (Plate 61) became separated from the Lesser Whitethroat for a number of reasons, which included reproductive isolation. In the same areas of Central Asia where mountain slopes are inhabited by Hume's Lesser Whitethroat, the surrounding lowlands have several specific subspecies of the Lesser Whitethroat such as *S. c. hallimodendri*. The song is entirely different from that heard in Europe, but the breeding biology is very similar.

The **Desert Warbler** (*Sylvia nana*) (Plate 62) inhabits deserts of Central Asia where it is reasonably common in suitable areas. Russia has the nominal race *S. n. nana* which is distributed from the Volga Delta east to Lake Alakol in Eastern Kazakhstan. By mid-April they are usually back at their breeding grounds and can be heard singing. The nest is built low in a bush and a clutch consists of four to five, rarely six eggs. They are incubated by both parents for 12 to 13 days and the young stay in the nest for 11 to 12 days.

The **Orphean Warbler** (*Sylvia hortensis*) (Plate 61) breeds in the mountains of Central Asia, favouring slopes sparcely covered by different bushes. It arrives on the breeding grounds in late April and by the end of May singing is at its peak. As usual, the nest is built in a bush, most commonly in Lonicera, and four to five eggs are laid and incubated for about 13 to 14 days. The young stay in the nest about the same time. This species feeds mostly on insects, and during the non-breeding period will also eat berries.

Ménétérie's Warbler (*Sylvia mystacea*) (Plate 62) is on the edge of its distribution around the southern part of the Caspian Sea. Here it breeds in bushy areas of river valleys. The male is rather spectacular with a red band around its eye and white "moustache". The breeding biology is similar to

Fig. 74 *Wood Warbler (*Phylloscopus sibilatrix*) in the St. Petersburg region. Photo A. Sokolov*

most other *Sylvia* species. Normally, two broods a year are reared.

The genus *Phylloscopus* – leaf warblers – is represented extensively in Russia and is one of the favourite groups of passerines among western birdwatchers. There are 18 species of leaf warblers in Russia out of which 16 are breeders and two vagrants (**Bonelli's Warbler** (*Phylloscopus bonelli*) and **Brooks's Willow Warbler** (*P. subviridis*)).

The **Chiffchaff** (*Phylloscopus collybita*) enjoys a wide distribution in Russia and has been split into two species, the **Mountain Chiffcaff** (*P. lorenzii*) inhabiting Caucasus and Trans Caucasus and having a notably different call and song. The same goes for the southern Siberian subspecies *P. c. tristis* which is still regarded as a subspecies even though its song is completely different from that of the ordinary Chiffchaff. Very common and widely distributed in Russia is the **Willow Warbler** (*P. trochilus*). The **Wood Warbler** (*P. sibilatrix*) (Fig. 74) inhabits mixed and deciduous forests from the western borders to the Altai Mountains in southern Siberia.

The **Greenish Warbler** (*P. trochiloides*) (Plate 62) is yet another species which has been split into two in Russia. The ordinary Greenish Warbler inhabits vast expanses of Russian woods in Europe and Siberia, whereas the **Green Warbler** (*P. nitidus*) lives in the forests of Caucasus.

Mountain slopes of the Alai system in Central Asia are inhabited by the uncommon **Plain Willow Warbler** (*Phylloscopus neglectus*). Another species restricted to the mountains of Central Asia but having a somewhat wider distribution is the **Sulphur-bellied Warbler** (*P. griseolus*) (Plate 63). Like other species of warbler, this bird is monogamous and breeds in solitary pairs high up in the mountains favouring bushes among the rock and scree, particularly creeping juniper trees. They arrive at the beginning of May and start building a typical leaf-warbler-type nest structure with a side entrance in the bush close to the ground. The nest is usually masterfully hidden and by the end of May four to five eggs are laid which are incubated by the female only for 14 to 17 days. The young stay in the nest for 15 to 17 days fed by both parents. Together with the Radde's and Dusky Warblers the Sulphur-belllied Warbler belongs to the sub-genus *Herbivocula*.

The **Arctic Warbler** (*P. borealis*) (Plate 62) is common all across boreal forests of Russia from the Scandinavian borders to the Far East. This species breeds in bushy areas and by forest edges and its breeding biology is similar to that of other smaller leaf warblers. The clutch consists of five to six eggs normally laid in the second half of June, and incubated by the female only for 12 to 13 days. The incubation time is shorter than for example, the Sulphur-bellied Warbler. The young stay in the nest for 13 to 14 days fed by both parents. The food as in other leaf warblers consists of insects.

The Far East has its own set of leaf warblers, the **Pale-legged Leaf Warbler** (*Phylloscopus tenellipes*) (Plate 63) being one of them. This secretive species was poorly studied until recently; the first nest was only discovered in 1966. It breeds in the south of the Russian Far East mostly along the river valleys deep in the woods where there is plenty of debris and fallen trees. Its nest is hidden under the ground, amongst decaying roots and leaves and is impossible to see. Sometimes they nest in steep rocks along the rivers and build their nest in a rock crevice which of course makes it much easier to find. Otherwise the breeding biology is very much in line with other similar species. On the Sakhalin island another species (?) was split from the Pale-legged Leaf Warbler and called *P. borealoides* (the **Japanese Pale-legged Willow Warbler**). It has a completely different song, but it has not yet been put into the official Russian bird list.

Another very common and typical species of the Ussuri forests is the **Crowned Leaf Warbler** (*Phylloscopus coronatus*) (Fig. 75). It is a substitute for the Willow Warbler or Chiffchaff in Europe. A closely related species, the **Large Crowned Willow Warbler** (*P. occipitalis*), inhabits parts of Central Asia and the Himalayas.

One of the smallest species in this genus is the **Yellow-browed Warbler** (*Phylloscopus inornatus*) which has two major breeding areas – Siberia and Central Asia. The nominal subspecies inhabits vast expanses of the Siberian woods whereas *P. i. humei* breeds in the mountains of Altai and Sayan, Tien

Fig. 75 *Crowned Leaf Warbler* (Phylloscopus coronatus) *in south Ussuriland. Photo A. Knystautas/ Y. Shibnev*

Shan and Pamir. Since the song of the latter is almost completely different some people are inclined to believe that it could be singled out as a separate species, **Hume's Yellow-browed Warbler** (*P. humei*). Another extremely small *Phylloscopus* species is **Pallas's Leaf Warbler** (*P. proregulus*) which breeds in the coniferous woods of East Asia and is a regular winter visitor to Western Europe.

The subgenus *Herbivocula* includes the three largest species of Russian leaf warblers. We have already discussed the Sulphur-bellied Warbler which breeds in the mountains of Central Asia. Two other species breed in Siberia and the Far East – **Radde's Bush Warbler** (*Phylloscopus schwarzii*) (Plate 63) and the **Dusky Warbler** (*P. fuscatus*) (Plate 63). The latter is distributed much further north than Radde's Warbler and is found breeding in places like the Kamchatka Peninsula.

A very specific inhabitant of the deserts of Central Asia belongs to the warbler family and is the only representative of the genus *Scotocerca* in Russia. This species, the **Streaked Scrub Warbler** (*S. inquieta*), leads a partially sedentary life despite the somewhat cold winters in the deserts of Central Asia. For breeding, it chooses sand deserts with bushy areas and builds its nest close to the ground. By its form the nest resembles that of a leaf warbler with a side entrance. In May, four to six eggs are laid and incubated for 14 to 15 days. The young stay in the nest for a fortnight fed by both parents.

Goldcrests (Regulidae)

The goldcrest family has three breeding species and one vagrant in Russia. The most common and widely distributed is the **Goldcrest** (*Regulus regulus*) which breeds in coniferous forests from the western borders all the way to the Transbaikal region, Amur region and Ussuriland. It also breeds in montane forests of Central Asia. The **Firecrest** (*R. ignicapillus*) is uncommon in Russia and is restricted to the westernmost areas including Crimea and the Black Sea coast of Caucasus. The American **Ruby-crowned Kinglet** (*Regulus calendula*) is vagrant to the Arctic Far East of Russia.

The most unusual of all three breeders is of course **Severtzov's Tit Warbler** (*Leptopoecile sophiae*) (Plate 64) which inhabits the mountains of Central Asia. It is a very attractive little bird but very difficult to see since it keeps moving all the time. It inhabits the sub-alpine belt of the mountains where it breeds in Turkestanic Juniper trees or Tien Shan Spruces normally around 2-3 m above the ground. They appear on the breeding grounds during the second half of April. The nest, round with a side entrance, is normally finished by the end of May. A clutch consists of four to six eggs and is incubated by both parents for about 13 days. Both parents also take care of the young. A drastic and probably natural fluctuation in numbers is a common phenomenon in this species.

Drongos (Dicruridae)

The tropical drongo family has two species in Russia both of which are vagrants. They are the **Black Drongo** (*Dicrurus macrocercus*) and the **Hair-crested Drongo** (*D. hottentotus*). Both have been recorded in Ussuriland.

Flycatchers (Muscicapidae)

An extensive flycatcher family is divided into five smaller units – sub-families – in Russia. This helps to sort out the large number of quite different birds such as the Little Forktail or Paradise Flycatcher. The first sub-family, Monarchinae, is represented by two essentially tropical species, one of which breeds and the other, the **Black Paradise Flycatcher** (*Terpsiphone atrocaudata*), is vagrant to Ussuriland. The **Asian Paradise Flycatcher** (*T. paradisi*) (Plate 64) has two breeding areas in this country. The Central Asian mountains are one of their strongholds, and they are much rarer in Ussuriland, in Khanka Lowland and along the Ussuri River Valley. They arrive at the breeding grounds in May and start building their delicate nest on a tree branch, very often above the water. By the end of May – beginning of June a clutch of four to five eggs is laid and incubated by both parents for about 15 days. The young are fed on different insects. The concentration of this species in suitable habitats, namely in the deciduous woods along the mountain rivers, may reach considerable numbers, sometimes outnumbering all other passerine species in this particular habitat, as in the Karatau mountains in Kazakhstan.

The Subfamily Muscicapinae (true flycatchers) has 12 breeding species in Russia. Among the most common and well-known are the **Pied Flycatcher** (*Ficedula hyploleuca*) and the **Spotted Flycatcher** (*Muscicapa striata*) (Plate 65). The **White-collared Flycatcher** (*Ficedula albicollis*) breeds in southern parts of Russia and in Caucasus, choosing tree holes and artificial nest-boxes for breeding, like the Pied Flycatcher. The **Red-breasted Flycatcher** (*Ficedula parva*) enjoys a very wide distribution in Russia, being a reasonably common though quite secretive bird from the western borders all the way to the Far East where it breeds in the Kamchatka Peninsula.

The Russian Far East has the whole host of attractive and beautiful flycatcher species. One of the most common is the **Yellow-rumped Fly-catcher** (*Ficedula zanthopygia*) (Plate 65) which favours mixed and deciduous woods of Ussuriland and the Amur region. It breeds in the tree holes as well as in artificial nest boxes and arrives at its breeding grounds in Russia in May. Normally they rear one brood a year and a clutch consists of four to seven eggs incubated by the female only for 12 to 14 days. The young stay in the nest for 13 to 15 days and are fed on insects by both parents. The **Narcissus Flycatcher** (*Ficedula narcissina*) lives in similar habitats on the islands of Sakhalin, Kunashir and Shikotan.

The **Mugimaki Flycatcher** (*Ficedula mugimaki*) is a true taiga species which lives in coniferous forests of Siberia and the Far East. This species builds its nest in a tree, unlike other species of the same genus. In June, four to eight eggs are laid and incubated by the female for about 13 days.

An unusually beautiful member of the flycatcher family lives in the very south of Ussuriland. The **Blue-and-White Flycatcher**'s (*Cyanoptila cyanomelana*) (Plate 65) breeding range is restricted to north-east China, Korea, Japan and Ussuriland. It breeds on the steep rocky slopes in montane woods where the rocks are wet and mossy and the atmosphere quiet and foggy. The loud song resembles the main part of a Redwing's song and is heard on the breeding grounds from May. A nest is built out of moss in a rock crevice and four to six eggs are laid and incubated by the female only for about 14 days. Both parents take care of the young.

As well as the Spotted Flycatcher, the genus *Muscicapa* has four more species in Russia. In the mountains of Central Asia it is possible to see the uncommon **Rufous-tailed Flycatcher** (*M. ruficauda*) which usually breeds in the gardens of the mountain villages. The **Brown Flycatcher** (*M. latirostris*) (Plate 65) is a forest species distributed in Siberia and the Far East. Its nest is built on a tree branch and is an unusually beautiful structure decorated with lichens. A clutch of four to five eggs is laid by the end of May. There is one brood per season, and a clutch is incubated by the female only for 14 days. The young stay in the nest for 15 to 16 days being fed by both parents.

The **Siberian Flycatcher** (*Muscicapa sibirica*) is yet another forest species which breeds in the forests of Siberia and the Far East. Its breeding area is divided into two major regions – Siberia from the Ob' River Valley to the Kamchatka Peninsula in the Far East, and the Himalayas. The **Grey-streaked Flycatcher** (*M. griseisticta*) is an uncommon and poorly studied species mostly restricted to the larch woods in Ussuriland and Eastern Siberia.

The thrushes and allies (Turdinae) are the largest subfamily in the Flycatcher family. This group has not only a great number of very exciting species but also contains a great number of probably the most beautiful of the Palearctic passerines, such as the Redstarts.

The genus *Saxicola* has four breeding species in Russia. Common in European Russia is the **Whinchat** (*Saxicola rubetra*), and the **Stonechat** (*S. torquata*) (Fig. 76) has an extensive distribution and a number of distinctive subspecies in Russia. It breeds in the mountains of the south, in the Arctic North as well as in the Far East.

An elusive and rare species is **Hodgson's Bushchat** (*Saxicola insignis*) which breeds in very small numbers on the borders between Russia and Mongolia and nowhere else. This species breeds in suitable areas in very sparce colonies of four to six pairs and favours open dry mountain slopes

Fig. 76   *A male Stonechat (*Saxicola (torquata) maura*). Photo H. Sakalauskas*

at altitudes of about 1000 m. The nests are built on the ground and a clutch of four to five eggs is laid. Incubation is by the female only.

The **Pied Stonechat** (*Saxicola caprata*) is a species of the Central Asian lowlands where it usually breeds not far from water basins like rivers and lakes as well as in human habitation. It is reasonably common in suitable areas and in breeding biology resembles other stonechats. It arrives at its breeding grounds by the end of April. A clutch consists of three to five eggs which are incubated by the female for 13 to 14 days. The young stay in the nest for 11 to 14 days.

The genus *Oenanthe* (Wheatears) has eight species in Russia all of which breed. The widest distribution is enjoyed by the common **Northern Wheatear** (*O. oenanthe*) (Fig. 77) which breeds nearly everywhere in Russia, even in the Arctic regions extending to Alaska. Amazingly, in all of this huge area there is only one subspecies even though the colour variation from north to south is significant.

Most of the other species belong to the so-called black-and-white wheatear group and breed mostly in southern Russia, Caucasus and Central Asia. The **Pied Wheater** (*Oenanthe pleschanka*) is one of the most common southern wheatears in Russia. Like most of the other species, it chooses to breed on the rocky dry slopes of low mountain ridges and also rocky lowlands where it builds its nest among the rocks and crevices. They arrive

Fig. 77 *Northern Wheatear* (Oenanthe oenanthe) *in the Altai Mountains. Photo A. Blazys*

early, sometimes at the end of March, and start breeding in April. A clutch of four to six eggs is laid and incubated by the female for 13 to 14 days. There is normally one brood per season. The young stay in the nest for 13 to 15 days. As with other wheatears, the Pied Wheatear feeds mostly on insects.

The **Black-eared Wheatear** (*Onenanthe hispanica*) breeds in this country in Trans Caucasus and in Central Asia, mostly the western part. **Finsch's Wheatear** (*O. finschii*) inhabits arid stony areas in the south of Central Asia, by the Oxus (Syr Darja) River Valley and the foothills of the Alai system. By the borders with Afghanistan it is possible to see the **Variable Wheatear** (*O. picata*) which becomes more numerous in the Western Pamir mountains.

Western Pamir is also host for the **Red-tailed Wheatear** (*Oenanthe xanthoprymna*) (Plate 66) which does not have the characteristic black-and-white pattern of the previous species. This bird also breeds in Trans Caucasus.

Deserts are home for the **Desert Wheatear** (*Oenanthe deserti*) (Plate 66). This bird breeds in the deserts of Central Asia and in dry semi-deserts and even steppes in the Altai region. A specific subspecies inhabits the mountain desert of Eastern Pamir at an altitude of about 4000 m.

Yet another species typical of deserts and dry steppes is the **Isabelline Wheatear** (*Oenanthe isabellina*) (Plate 66). In Central Asia, particularly in the sand deserts, this bird is one of the most common and its vigorous diplay flights and accompanying songs may be seen and heard everywhere. In these places Isabelline Wheatears find a very suitable companion – the Great Gerbil (*Rhombomys opimus*) which breeds in colonies in nearly every little valley between the sandy hills – the barkhans. Their burrows serve as ideal nesting sites for wheatears. Even though the species is monogamous, it gives an impression that in suitable sites one pair breeds in the close vicinity of another and the chorus of songs makes you feel as if you are in the middle of a wheatear colony. The wheatears arrive in May and start their display songs before building a nest in a burrow or under the rocks. In the second half of April some pairs already have eggs which number four to seven in a clutch. They are incubated by the female for about 15 days. The young start their shy appearances from the burrow when 13 to 16 days old.

The sole representative of its genus in Russia is the **Rufous Bush Chat** (*Cercotrichas galactotes*) (Plate 66). It is essentially a desert bird, favouring sand deserts with extensive bushy areas, in the Central Asian deserts of Kara Kum and Kyzyl Kum. These chats are strictly territorial. From the end of April males produce their lovely songs and display flights when their beautiful tail feathers are shown in full. They build a nest in a bush usually close to the trunk and low to the ground. In May, two to five eggs are laid and incubated by the female only for about 14 days. There are normally two clutches per season. The young stay in the nest for 15 to 17 days.

The genus *Monticola* (Rock Thrushes) has two breeding species in Russia; the **Rock Thrush** (*M. saxatilis*) and the **Blue Rock Thrush** (*M. solitarius*), both of which are well known. The first species inhabits mountain ranges at different altitudes in Caucasus, Crimea and Central Asia. The Blue Rock Thrush prefers more arid areas of the mountains in the same areas and is usually less common than the first species. It also extends its range all the way to the Far East, where a specific and very different subspecies (*M. s. philippensis*) breeds on the coast and rocky islands of the sea of Japan.

Closely related to the previous genus is the genus *Petrophila* which is represented in Russia by the **White-throated Rock Thrush** (*Petrophila gularis*), a beautiful, uncommon and secretive bird of the Transbaikal region and the Far East. They breed in large forests and forested mountain slopes, usually one pair far away from another. Their beautiful and somewhat melancholic song can be heard in the misty evening in Ussuriland from mid-May. The nest is built on the ground and is usually well hidden. In June four to six eggs are laid. The breeding biology has not yet been studied in any detail.

Nobody can really be indifferent to redstarts, let alone keen birders. The genus *Phoenicurus* is represented in Russia by a whole plethora of impressive species such as Guldenstadt's or Eversmann's Redstarts. In total there are six proper redstarts in Russia and two related species. All six are breeders.

The **Common Redstart** (*Phoenicurus phoenicurus*) is widespread from the western borders as far as Western Siberia and Central Asia (the Tien Shan mountains). The only redstart which does not actally have a red tail is the **Blue-headed Redstart** (*P. caeruleocephalus*) (Plate 66), a very beautiful bird with restricted distribution. It breeds in the montane coniferous forests of Tien Shan and is penetrating slightly into the Alai system in Central Asia. By the beginning of April the woods of Tien Shan Spruce resound with the beautiful songs of this bird and the impressive sight of males fighting for territories leaves an unforgettable impression. Nests are built under tree branches, rocks or in rock crevices and in the beginning of May, the female lays three to five eggs, incubating them for about 13 to 15 days. Both parents take care of the young even though the female is more active in this process. The young stay in the nest for about 15 to 17 days. Normally this species rears two broods per season.

The **Black Redstart** (*Phoenicurus ochruros*) (Plate 67) has several very distinctive subspecies in Russia and is distributed from the western borders all along the southern mountain ranges. In the European part of Russia, as in most parts of Europe, it is restricted to areas of human habitation, whereas in Caucasus and Central Asia it is a truly alpine species and rarely nests below 3000 m. In these places the Black Redstart seems somewhat more exotic

Fig. 78
Daurian Redstart
(Phoenicurus
auroreus) *in South
Ussuriland.*
Photo Y. *Shibnev*

and attractive, and the subspecies with the red belly like *P. o. rufiventris* look more beautiful on the snowy rocks of the Central Asian mountains.

Eversmann's Redstart (*Phoenicurus erythronotus*) (Plate 67) is a very beautiful bird restricted to the mountains of Central Asia and southern Siberia. It breeds in the subalpine belt of the mountains and in montane woods of Altai. The males are really spectacular birds and their spring songs are a delight. Nest-building takes place in May and the nests are built in different sites such as rock crevices, under fallen trees etc. The clutch consists of five to six eggs which are incubated by the female only for about 14 days. Normally there are two clutches per season. The young stay in the nest for about 16 days; they are fed by both parents mainly on different insects.

Southern Siberia and the Far East are inhabited by the **Daurian Redstart** (*Phoenicurus auroreus*) (Plate 67 and Fig. 78). This reasonably common species breeds in the woods and human habitation of Siberia and is not associated with the mountains. It serves to some extent as a substitute for the Common Redstart in Siberia where the latter does not occur. The breeding sites are also similar to those of the Common Redstart – under the roofs of buildings, in tree holes and artificial nest boxes.

The most impressive of all species of this genus is **Güldenstädt's Redstart** (*Phoenicurus erythrogaster*) (Plate 67). This is an extremely beautiful bird restricted to truly alpine habitats in Caucasus and Central Asia. The nominal subspecies inhabits Caucasus and the subspecies *P. e. grandis* breeds in the mountains of Central Asia. It also penetrates into the mountains of Southern Siberia. The breeding sites are well above the tree line, over 3000 m, and are hostile and cold parts of the mountains full of rock and scree. In May it is possible to see this incredible bird feeding on the snow among the rocks. They raise only one brood per year and in May they start building a nest in the rock crevice. A clutch consists of three to five eggs and is incubated by the female only. The young stay in the nest for about 18 days.

A close relative of the redstarts is the **River Chat** (*Chaimarrornis leucocephalus*). This species is restricted in Russia to the torrential mountain streams of the Western Pamir mountains. Another species of the group is the **Plumbeous Water Redstart** (*Rhyacornis fuliginosus*) which has been registered in Pamir as vagrant.

The **European Robin** (*Erithacus rubecula*) is common and widespread, and, unlike in the UK, is not attracted by human settlements but lives deep in the mixed woods. The **Japanese Robin** (*Luscinia akahige*) (Plate 68) is on the northern boundary of its distribution and can be found breeding in the Kuril Islands and the southern part of Sakhalin Island.

The best singers of the Russian birds belong to the this genus *Luscinia*, the nightingales. There are eight species of this genus in this country, all of which are breeders. The **Nightingale** (*L. megarhynchos*) (Fig. 79) is very widely distributed in southern parts of Russia and in Central Asia which has a much paler subspecies, *L. m. hafizi*. The **Thrush Nightingale** (*Luscinia luscinia*) is a common bird and undoubtedly the best singer in European Russia and some parts of southern Siberia.

Both species of the subgenus *Calliope* (rubythroats) are known for their beauty. The **Siberian Rubythroat** (*Luscinia calliope*) is found is huge areas of Siberia and the Far East both in the mountains and lowlands. It is a common bird in suitable habitats; sparce woods and forest edges, bushy river valleys. It arrives at its breeding grounds in mid-May or even later when the harsh Siberian winter gives way to the warmth of the spring. They build a nest on the ground resembling in its form that of a leaf warbler, with a side entrance. In June, four to six eggs are laid and are incubated by the female for about 14 days. The **Himalayan Rubythroat** (*Luscinia pectoralis*) (Plate 68) epitomizes the mountains of central Asia. This gorgeous bird lives in solitary pairs sometimes rather close to each other in the subalpine belt of the Central Asian mountains. They appear in their breeding grounds by the end of April and males start to sing usually from the top of a turkestanic juniper tree. The nest is built on the ground inside the bushes and is quite impossible to see. The entrance is from the side. At the end of May three to five eggs are laid and are incubated by the female only for 13-15

Fig. 79 *The much paler subspecies of the Nightingale* (Luscinia megarhyn-chos hafizi*) in the Ili River Valley, Kazakhstan. Photo V. Morozov*

days. Normally there is one clutch per season, more rarely two. The young stay in the nest for about 16 days fed by both parents with various insects.

Among the more widespread and common species across Russia is the **Bluethroat** (*Luscinia svecica*) which has a number of distinct subspecies (seven in Russia out of eight or nine altogether). The **Siberian Blue Robin** (*L. cyane*) (Plate 68) is known for the striking beauty of the males. There are two subspecies, one of which inhabits the Transbaikal region and the Far East, the other lives in the south of Western Siberia. They breed in deciduous and mixed forests, favouring edges and river valleys. They appear on their breeding sites in May, when the males announce their arrival by loud melodious songs. The nest is built on the ground and is very well concealed under vegetation, usually near a dead tree or small but steep bank of a stream. In June, four to six eggs are laid and incubated by the female for about 14 days.

Swinhoe's Robin (*Luscinia sibilans*) inhabits taiga forests of southern Siberia and the Far East. This species is rather uncommon and unevenly distributed, and unlike the previously described species of *Luscinia* builds its nest on a dead tree trunk, or in a tree crevice etc. but not on the ground.

One of the most attractive birds of taiga forests is the **Red-flanked Bluetail** (*Tarsiger cyanurus*) (Plate 68) which breeds from the western borders with Scandinavia all across this endless sea of conifers and mixed forests to the Far

Fig. 80 *Male White-throated Robin* (Irania gutturalis) *in the western Tien Shan Mountains. Photo A. Knystautas*

East. Usually the pairs are well separated, but, with a bit of luck, one may find them. They appear on the breeding grounds by the end of April – beginning of May. The nest is built on the ground or very low above it. At the end of May at the earliest a clutch of five to seven eggs is laid and is incubated by the female for about 14 days. Normally there are two clutches per season.

The southern parts of Trans Caucasus and the mountains of Central Asia are inhabited by another attractive member of this group, namely the **White-throated Robin** (*Irania gutturalis*) (Plate 68 and Fig. 80). For breeding, these beautiful birds choose dry mountain slopes at altitudes of 1000-2200 m, sometimes higher. The spectacular spring displays which may be seen and heard after their arrival in the breeding grounds at the end of April are incredibly beautiful. The males show their display flights and sing while flying, chasing each other, and courting a female. A nest is built in a bush or small tree normally 1-2 m above the ground. At the end of May, a clutch of four to five eggs is laid and incubated by the female for about 15 days. Both parents take care of the young.

An American group of thrushes of the genus *Catharus* is represented by two species – the **Grey-cheeked Thrush** (*C. minimus*) is a breeder in the Chukotka Peninsula close to Alaska, while **Swainson's Thrush** (*C. ustulatus*) has been recorded as a vagrant in Ussuriland. Another American species of this group, the **Varied Thrush** (*Ixoreus naevius*), has been recorded as vagrant on Wrangel Island.

Identifying thrushes proper is a real challenge in Russia, particularly the Siberian species. There are 15 species of *Turdus* (14 breeders and one vagrant (*T. cardis*, the **Japanese Grey Thrush**)) and two species of *Zoothera* thrushes (both breed).

The **Pale Thrush** (*Turdus pallidus*) is a typical *Turdus* species which breeds in East Asia, including coniferous and mixed forests of the Amur region and Ussuriland. They arrive at the breeding grounds by the end of April and start building nests on a tree or bush; as is usual for thrushes, these are bulky and heavy structures, easily visible to predators. At the end of May, four to five eggs are laid and are incubated by the female for 13 to 14 days. Normally this species rears two broods a year, as do most of the others. The young stay in the nest for about 13 to 15 days fed by both parents on various invertebrates. In autumn, the diet consists mostly of plant material like berries.

Other Far Eastern species of thrushes incude the **Red-billed Thrush** (*Turdus chrysolaus*) which breeds only on the islands of Sakhalin and Kurils; the **Eye-browed Thrush** (*T. obscurus*), appearing in the taiga forests across southern Siberia and the Far East; and the **Grey-backed Thrush** (*T. hortulorum*) (Plate 69) which is the most common species and the best singer in the Amur region and Ussuriland.

Recently split species which breed in the heart of the Siberian woods are the **Black-throated Thrush** (*T. atrogullaris*) (Plate 69) and the **Red-throated Thrush** (*T. ruficollis*). The latter enjoys a more easterly distribution and breeds around Lake Baikal, and in the south of Central and Southern Siberia. Its westernmost outpost is Teletskoye Lake in the Eastern Altai mountains. The first species actually breeds in European Russia as well as in the Kama River basin, and penetrates all the way to Lake Baikal. Both species breed in mountain and lowland forests.

Another species of thrush split into two is **Naumann's Thrush** (*T. naumanni*). Its western form is now regarded as the **Dusky Thrush** (*T. eunomus*) (Plate 69). Both are native to Siberia and breed even in the most northern forests in the world. Naumann's Thrush appears to the east of the Yenisey River all the way to the Sea of Okhotsk. The second species breeds from the Pur River valley to Kamchatka Peninsula, and in a number of places its habitat overlaps with Naumann's Thrush, and limited hybridization takes place.

Five species of thrush are very well known in the west and all are common and widespread in Russia as well. Notably, not a single one of them actually penetrates to Eastern Siberia and the Far East, which is occupied by a number of specific species described above and below. These well-known species are the **Fieldfare** (*Turdus pilaris*), the **Blackbird** (*T. merula*), the **Song Thrush** (*T. philomelos*), the **Mistle Thrush** (*T. viscivorus*) and the **Redwing** (*T. iliacus*).

The mountains of Caucasus, the Carpathians and an isolated part of the Kola Peninsula in the north are inhabited by the **Ring Ouzel** (*Turdus torquatus*) which in Caucasus breeds up to the alpine belt and is seen together with choughs, alpine coughs and water pipits.

The genus *Zoothera* is represented by two impressive thrushes – **White's Thrush** (*Z. dauma*) (Plate 69) and the **Siberian Ground Thrush** (*Z. sibirica*). White's Thrush is an uncommon and unevenly distributed bird found from the woods of the Tien Shan mountains in the west all the way across Siberia to the Far East and Ussuriland. The Siberian Ground Thrush breeds from the Yenisey River in the west all the way to the Far East. It chooses mixed forests on the mountain slopes and arrives at its breeding grounds in May. The nest is built in a tree, preferably a fir, and a clutch of four to five eggs is laid and incubated by the female for about 14 days. The young stay in the nest for 12 to 14 days fed by both parents.

The mountains of Central Asia are home for a very large and impressive thrush – the **Blue Whistling Thrush** (*Myiophoneus caeruleus*) (Plate 69). This species is closely associated with mountain streams and always breeds close to the water. It particularly favours waterfalls and its strong song may be heard very far away despite the roar of the waterfall. In Russian, this bird is called a bird of a dream because of its deep violet-blue colour and its song. Its nest is always built on a rock near the water and is a massive and bulky structure. In May, three to five eggs are laid and incubated by the female. There is one brood per season.

The last subfamily of flycatchers is the forktails (Enicurinae) which has a single representative in this country, the **Little Forktail** (*Microcichla scouleri*) (Plate 70) which breeds on the mountain streams in Central Asia. This incredible little bird is even more vigorous than the dippers and often builds a nest behind the stream of a waterfall. Waterfalls are their favourite places, and they form an inseparable part of this habitat in the Central Asian mountains along with two dipper species, the Blue Whistling Thrush, the River Chat and the Grey Wagtail.

Babblers (Timaliidae)

This family has only one species in this country which is the **Himalayan Streaked Laughing-Thrush** (*Garrulax lineatus*). This bird is reasonably common on mountain slopes covered with sparce bushes, mostly in the Alai system of Central Asia. They breed in bushes and small trees and the clutch consists of two to four eggs, usually three. The biology is still poorly studied and this species is on the edge of its northern distribution here.

Fig. 81 *Female Bearded Tit (*Panurus biarmicus*) in the Ili River Valley, Kazakhstan. Photo V. Morozov*

Parrotbills (Paradoxonithidae)

The family Paradoxonithidae (Parrotbills) is represented by three species. One of them is the well-known **Bearded Tit** (*Panurus biarmicus*) (Plate 70 and Fig. 81) which is a common bird in suitable habitats in this country. Both other species occur only in the south of Ussuriland in the Far East. One is **Polivanov's Parrotbill** (*Paradoxornis polivanovi*) (Plate 70) one of the rarest birds in Russia. It breeds only in the reedbeds of the huge Lake Khanka and numbers about 700 surviving individuals. They lead a sedentary life, so any disruption of their territory may lead to their complete extinction. The incredible form of their bills is designed to cut even large reeds in search of insects. They build a nest on the reeds in the same way as reed warblers, and in mid-May lay a clutch of four to five eggs. Incubation lasts 12 days and the young leave the nest when they are 11 to 12 days old and start to roam around in the reeds even though they are not yet able to fly.

The **Vinous-throated Parrotbill** (*Suthora webbiana*) (Plate 70) breeds in bushy forest edges, rich grasslands with tall grass and reedbeds. It is an unevenly distributed and uncommon bird which arrives in southern Ussuriland at the end of May. The nest is built in the grass, reeds and bushes low to the ground and in the end of May a clutch of five to six eggs is laid.

Long-tailed tits (Aegithalidae)

This family has one species in Russia; the **Long-tailed Tit** (*Aegithalos caudatus*). There are four subspecies in Russia which occur from the western borders all the way to the Far East.

Tits (Paridae)

The tit family (Paridae) consists of two subfamilies in Russia, one of which is the penduline tits (Remizinae). There are two species in this subfamily, both belonging to the genus *Remiz*. The well-known **Penduline Tit** (*R. pendulinus*) occurs in many parts of Russia and also has a number of subspecies including the black-headed *R. p. coronatus*, occuring in Central Asia. The nest building pattern of the Penduline Tit is quite unique and very well known. In places where this bird is very common, like the enormous reedbeds of the Volga Delta, their nests are visible in many places.

The **Reed Penduline Tit** (*Remiz macronyx*) has been split from the Penduline Tit and there are three subspecies in Russia. Its nest is built mostly in reeds and this species occurs around the Caspian Sea and in Central Asia.

The subfamily of tits proper (Parinae) has 17 species in Russia all of which are breeders. There is a number of species which are well known in the rest of Europe and common in Russia as well, like the **Marsh Tit** (*Parus palustris*), the **Willow Tit** (*P. montanus*) (Fig. 82), the **Blue Tit** (*Parus*

Fig. 82 *Willow Tit (*Parus montanus*) in the St. Petersburg region. Photo A. Sokolov*

caeruleus), the **Great Tit** (*P. major*), the **Coal Tit** (*P. ater*), and the **Crested Tit** (*P. cristatus*).

The montane forests of the Tien Shan mountains in Central Asia are inhabited by the **Songar Tit** (*Parus songarus*) (Plate 71) which in breeding biology and life style closely resembles the Willow Tit. Its distribution range is very limited.

Two species of the same group of tits (subgenus *Poecile*) inhabit Trans Caucaus. Both breed on the border zones. In Armenia it is possible to see the **Sombre Tit** (*Parus lugubris*), and in the Talysh Mountains in Azerbaidzan the **Iranian Sombre Tit** (*P. hyrcanus*).

One species of tit is a true taiga breeder, closely associated with the cold coniferous forests of Siberia. This is the **Siberian Tit** (*Parus cinctus*) (Plate 71) which is distributed from the Scandinavian borders all the way across the taiga zone to the Far East. It also breeds in the montane forests of southern Siberia. Siberian Tits start breeding in May and their breeding biology is very much like that of other tits in the same group. The nest is built in a tree hole which the birds design themselves in a rotten tree trunk, and a clutch of seven to nine eggs is laid and incubated by the female for 13 to 16 days. Normally there is one clutch per season, more rarely two. The young stay in the nest for 17 to 20 days fed by both parents on insects.

An interesting species of tit breeds in the mountains of Central Asia. It is the **Rufous-naped Tit** (*Parus rufonuchalis*) (Plate 71) which is closely associated with the sparce woods of Turkestanic juniper trees locally called archa. Appearing at their breeding sites by the end of April, they choose a nesting place, this may be a rock crevice or a hole in a juniper tree. Sometimes they breed in artificial nest boxes. The clutch, which is laid in May, consists of four to five eggs. Both parents take care of the young and after leaving the nest the whole family wander around in these enchanted woods producing their unmistakeable, melancholic calls.

On the northern edge of its distribution is the **Varied Tit** (*Parus varius*). In Russia, it breeds only on the Kuril Islands, its main breeding grounds being in Japan and China.

Two extremely attractive and closely related species of tits inhabit mostly southern parts of Russia. The **Azure Tit** (*Parus cyanus*) (Plate 72 and Fig. 83) enjoys a wide distribution range from southern parts of European Russia all the way to the Far East. There are five subspecies altogether all of which occur in Russia. The Western Tien Shan Mountains and the Alai system in Central Asia are inhabited by the **Yellow-breasted Azure Tit** (*P. flavipectus*) (Plate 72) which breeds in the montane woods as well as gardens on the mountain slopes. They start breeding in May and choose a tree hole for nesting or build their nest under the roof of a building. A clutch consists of

Fig. 83 *Azure Tit (Parus cyanus) in the Tien Shan Mountains. Photo V. Morozov*

6 to 11 eggs which are incubated by the female only for about 13 to 14 days. The young stay in the nest for 16 to 17 days.

The **Great Tit** (*Parus major*) has been split into four different species in Russia. This is based on a number of research studies and analysis of collection material together with thorough field studies. The Great Tit proper inhabits huge areas of Russia and is common from the western borders all the way to the Far East. Central Asian mountain slopes and deserts are inhabited by two species – the **Grey Tit** (*P. cinereus*) and the **Turkestan Tit** (*P. bokharensis*) (Plate 72). This is primarily a desert bird, whereas the Grey Tit breeds in the Kopet Dag mountains on the border with Iran. Ussuriland is inhabited by *Parus minor* (Fig. 84) which has limited hybridization with the Great Tit in the Amur region.

Nuthatches (Sittidae)

The Nuthatch family (Sittidae) has five species in Russia all of which are breeders. The **Eurasian Nuthatch** (*Sitta europaea*) enjoys a very wide distribution in Russia all the way to the Far East. It has great variation in colour in this huge breeding range and forms ten subspecies (out of a world

Fig. 84
Parus minor (?)
in Ussuriland.
Photo Y. Shibnev

total of 30). The **Rock Nuthatch** (*S. neumayer*) inhabits rocky areas in Trans Caucasus whereas the **Eastern Rock Nuthatch** (*S. tephronota*) (Plate 73) lives in the mountains of Central Asia. These birds, even though not very common, add a lot of life to the mountain slopes. They are always busy and noisy even when most of the birds are silent, as on lazy summer afternoons. They choose to breed in dry, rocky areas and canyons where they start breeding as early as March. They build a nest out of clay with a small corridor as the entrance and lay six to eight eggs. These are incubated by the female only for about 14 to 15 days. The young are fed on different insects by both parents and stay in the nest for 20 to 25 days. It is a sedentary species, and its migrations are usually only altitudinal.

Krüper's Nuthatch (*Sitta krueperi*) inhabits the western side of the Great Caucasus mountains where it breeds in the majestic forests of Caucasus Fir trees. They lead a sedentary life and in spring start their display calls which are absolutely unmistakeable and very harsh, which makes it difficult to believe that they are coming from such a sweet and beautiful little bird. It is generally an uncommon bird, common only locally. The very south of Ussuriland (Shufan Plateau) is inhabited by the **Chinese Nuthatch** (*S. villosa*) which is rare in these places and is on the edge of its northern distribution.

Treecreepers (Certhiidae)

The Treecreeper family (Certhiidae) has four species in Russia all of which are breeders. It has two subfamilies, the Tichodrominae, or wallcreepers, and treecreepers proper, the Certhiinae. The first subfamily contains the most impressive, elusive and sought-after species – the **Wallcreeper** (*Tichodroma muraria*). This uncommon and unevenly distributed bird occurs in all the major mountain ranges in the south of Russia, starting from Caucasus and penetrating into Central Asia.

Three species of Treecreepers include the well-known **Common Treecreeper** (*Certhia familiaris*) which is common and widespread in Russia, the **Short-toed Treecreeper** (*C. brachydactyla*), which occurs only in the western parts of the country and is an uncommon bird here, and the **Himalayan Treecreeper** (*C. himalayana*) which is a rare bird of the Pamir Mountains, sometimes occuring in the Tien Shan and Alai systems.

White-eyes (Zosteropidae)

The tropical White-eye family (Zosteropidae) has two breeding species in Russia. Generally limited to north-east China, Korea and Ussuriland is the **Chestnut-flanked White-eye** (*Zosterops erythropleura*) (Plate 73). It is reasonably common in Ussuriland but is very difficult to see and observe. They arrive from their wintering grounds in the second half of May when spring is established. Their nest is built at different heights in a tree and a clutch of two to four eggs is laid in June. Incubation lasts 11 to 12 days and the young leave the nest when 11 days old.

Another breeding species of White-eye is the **Japanese White-eye** (*Zosterops japonica*) which is found in small numbers in the southern Kuril Islands.

Wood Warblers (Parulidae)

The American Wood Warbler family (Parulidae) is represented in Russia by two vagrant species – the **Yellow-rumped Warbler** (*Dendroica coronata*), found on Wrangel Island and the **Northern Waterthrush** (*Seiurus noveboracensis*) in Chukotka Peninsula.

Sparrows (Passeridae)

The sparrow family (Passeridae) is represented by twelve species, out of which ten are breeders, one is a possible breeder (the **Pale Rock Sparrow** – *Petronia brachydactyla*) and one is vagrant in Central Asia (**Meinertzhagen's Snow Finch** – *Montifringilla theresae*).

We will not stop to describe in detail the **House Sparrow** (*Passer domesticus*) or the **Tree Sparrow** (*P. montanus*) both of which are common across the whole of Russia. The House Sparrow has been split into two species; the **Indian Sparrow** (*P. indicus*) inhabits Central Asia along with the House Sparrow but is migratory and the House Sparrow is sedentary. Central Asia is inhabited by another species of the same genus, the **Spanish Sparrow** (*P. hispaniolensis*) (Plate 74) which is exceedingly common and breeds in huge colonies, sometimes mixed with House and Indian Sparrows.

The deserts of Central Asia are home for two species of sparrow which are closely tied to this habitat and not found elsewhere. They are the **Saxaul Sparrow** (*P. ammodendri*) (Plate 74) and the **Desert Sparrow** (*P. simplex*) (Plate 74). The Saxaul Sparrow is limited in distribution to the deserts of Central Asia. There are two subspecies in Russia out of four altogether. They breed in colonies sometimes mixed with other sparrows, in tree holes and under the roofs of buildings. A clutch consists of four to six eggs and is incubated by the female for 12 to 14 days. The young stay in the nest for 13 to 15 days fed by both parents on different insects and seeds. The Desert Sparrow breeds locally in the Kara Kum Desert where it is rare and included in the Russian Red Data Book. They breed in solitary pairs building a bulky nest on a saxaul or desert acacia tree.

The **Cinnamon Sparrow** (*Passer rutilans*) inhabits the islands of Sakhalin and Kurils in the Far East, and is at the northern edge of its distribution. It breeds in tree holes mostly at forest edges.

Other species of the family belong to different genuses, like the well-known **Streaked Rock Sparrow** (*Petronia petronia*) and the **White-winged Snow Finch** (*Montifringilla nivalis*) a typical alpine species. Both breed in the mountains of Caucasus, Central Asia and southern Siberia. Both are reasonably common in suitable habitats but are never abundant.

The Transbaikal region is inhabited by **Pierre David's Sparrow** (*Pyrgilauda davidiana*). This species is common locally and arrives at its breeding grounds by the end of April. From mid-May, a clutch of five to six eggs is laid and is incubated by the female only. The species is still poorly studied.

American Blackbirds (Icteridae)

This family is represented in Russia by one vagrant species recorded in Chukotka Peninsula; the **Rusty Blackbird** (*Euphagus carolinus*).

Finches (Fringillidae)

The huge finch families have a number of spectacular species in Russia. Two species of the genus *Fringilla* breed in Russia, namely the **Chaffinch** (*F. coelebs*) which is the most common species of bird in the forests and parks of European Russia, and the more northerly **Brambling** (*F. montifringilla*) (Plate 75) which is a true taiga breeder found all the way to the Far East.

The genus *Chloris* is represented by two species as well; the common and well-known **Western Greenfinch** (*C. chloris*) which is widespread in Russia,

Fig. 85
*Twite (*Acanthus
flavirostris*) in the
Altai Mountains.
Photo A. Blazys*

and its eastern counterpart, the **Chinese Greenfinch** (*C. sinica*) (Plate 75). The **Red-fronted Serin** (*Serinus pusillus*) (Plate 75), is a very beautiful species which breeds in the mountains of Central Asia and Caucasus. The **European Serin** (*S. serinus*) occupied western parts of Russia, Ukraine, Byelorussia and the Baltic States in the past decades. Very common and widespread in coniferous woodland is the **Siskin** (*Spinus spinus*).

The **European Goldfinch** (*Carduelis carduelis*) breeds in European Russia and southern Siberia. In Central Asia it has been separated into a different and rather distinct species, the **Grey-headed Goldfinch** (*C. caniceps*) (Plate 75) which breeds in the mountains as well as lowlands.

The **Linnet** (*Acanthis cannabina*) is a common and widespread bird in Russia, found from its western borders to the Yenisei river valley in the east. Separate subspecies inhabit Crimea and Caucasus as well as Central Asia.

The **Twite** (*Acanthis flavirostris*) (Fig. 85) has a patchy distibution range, and occurs mostly across mountainous areas in southern parts of the country, for example Altai.

Tundra areas are inhabited by two species of finch, namely the **Redpoll** (*Acanthis flammea*) (Plate 75) which is more common and more widely distributed than the **Arctic Redpoll** (*A. hornemanni*) which tends to breed in more northerly areas. Both species build nests on small bushes and start breeding in June. A clutch of four to six eggs is laid, and incubated by the female only for 11-12 days. The young leave the nest when 11-14 days old, and feed on delicate seeds and small insects.

Three or four species of Rosy finches, an interesting and anatomically specific group of birds, inhabit mountainous areas in Russia. The **Rosy Finch** (*Lecosticte arctoa*) has been split in Russia into two, the **American Rosy Finch** (*L. tephrocotis*) inhabiting the Commander Islands in the Pacific. **Brandt's Rosy Finch** (*L. brandtii*) is mostly associated with the high mountains of Central Asia and is found at altitudes of 4000 m in the Pamirs. In Tien Shan these birds can be seen somewhat lower, but rarely below 3000 m. They breed in colonies on the mountain slopes, prefering those facing south, and build their nests under stones and rocks where three to four eggs are laid in mid-June or later, depending on altitude. In the Altai mountains, this species can be found much lower, around 2000 m, and is easier to see. **Hodgson's Rosy Finch** (*L. nemoricola*) (Plate 76) is a common bird of the sub-alpine altitudes of Central Asian and Southern Siberian mountains. As other species of the genus, it breeds in scattered colonies, building nests under rocks, and travels far to collect food for its young. The young are fed only about once every 2-3 hours and food is brought in special 'sacks' in the throat which enable the adult bird to carry substantial numbers of seeds in one go.

The **Crimson-winged Finch** (*Rhodopechys sanguinea*) (Plate 76) is an attractive mountain bird which inhabits the uplands of Trans Caucasus and Central Asia. Uncommon everywhere, this species is difficult to see. Only about ten nests have been discovered in the Tien Shan mountains, most of them in the famous Aksu Dzabagly Nature Reserve in Kazakhstan. Like Rosy Finches, this species can carry large quantities of food for its young in one go, and feeds them once every 2-3 hours. Nests are situated under rocks or grass tussocks, normally between 2000-3000 m above sea level in the mountains. Egg laying takes place in May and the clutch consists of four to five eggs.

There are two species of Trumpeter finch (*Bucanetes*) in Russia, which inhabit dry arid areas in Central Asia, Kazakhstan and Southern Siberia. The **Trumpeter Finch** (*B. githagineus*) lives in Trans Caucasus and western parts of Central Asia whereas the **Mongolian Trumpeter Finch** (*B. mongolicus*) (Plate 76) is found in Eastern Kazakhstan and the Altai mountains. Both species are uncommon and difficult to see. They build their nests in rock crevices on dry slopes and in canyons and from the end of April a clutch containing three to five eggs is laid. Incubation is by both parents for 14-16 days. There are one or two normal clutches per season. Their food consists of different seeds, but the young are fed mainly on insects.

The **Black-billed Desert Finch** (*Rhodospiza obsoleta*) (Fig. 86) inhabits sandy deserts in Central Asia and Kazakhstan where it breeds on saxaul and acacia bushes, building an attractive nest usually close to the trunk. This species breeds in single pairs and starts breeding in April. A clutch consists of two to seven eggs and is incubated by both birds for about 14

Fig. 86
*Black-billed
Desert Finch (*Rhodospiza obsoleta*)
in Repetek Nature
Reserve,
Turkmenistan.
Photo H.
Sakalauskas*

days. There are two normal clutches per season. Both parents take care of the young which stay in the nest for about a fortnight.

The **Scarlet Rosefinch** (*Carpodacus erythrinus*) is a widespread and common bird in Russia in very varied habitats ranging from rich wet meadows with sparce bushes in temperate Russia to bush thickets in the mountains of Central Asia.

Other species of this genus in Russia include the endemic **Pallas's Rosefinch** (*Carpodacus roseus*) (Plate 76) which breeds in Siberia and is an unevenly distributed bird favouring forest edges and bushy areas. Of course, the most exciting species of the genus *Carpodacus* are the true mountain breeders which live mostly in the mountains of Central Asia. One of the most impressive is the **Great Rosefinch** (*C. rubicilla*) (Plate 77) which inhabits both high altitudes in Caucasus and the Central Asian mountains as well as Altai (there are different subspecies in Caucasus and Central Asia). It rarely descends below 3000 m and can be seen in the valleys during the depths of the winter. Its breeding habitat is rocks and scree in the alpine belt of the mountains. The nest is built in a rock crevice and is often inaccessible. There is one brood per season and in June three to four eggs are laid and incubated for about 16 days. Parents travel long distances to collect food for the young which, like those of many other mountain finches, are fed at significant intervals.

Two rather similar species of this genus inhabit the mountains of Central Asia, namely its subalpine belt with bushes and trees around. These are the

Red-mantled Rosefinch (*Carpodacus rhodochlamys*) (Plate 76) and the **Himalayan Red-mantled Rosefinch** (*Carpodacus grandis*). The first breeds mostly in the Tien Shan system, the other in the Gissaro-Alai mountains and the Western Pamir range.

The Tien Shan system is inhabited by another little-known and very exciting species – the **Red-breasted Rosefinch** (*Pyrrospiza punicea*). This finch is as large as the Great Rosefinch, if not larger, and differs from all *Carpodacus* species in that it is never seen lower than 3000 m altitude even in the harshest part of the high-mountain winter. This incredibly beautiful and elusive bird can sometimes be seen collecting food on the snow patches of the true alpine habitats surrounded by rocks and scree and sometimes lovely high-mountain saxifragas and primulas. But to see this bird one has to be exceedingly lucky as it is rare, and only one nest has been discovered to date. This was in the Trans Ili mountain range of Northern Tien Shan, on an inaccessible rock at an altitude of about 3200 m, and it took a team of mountaineers from the Kazakhstan capital Alma Ata to reach it.

The **Long-tailed Rosefinch** (*Uragus sibiricus*) (Plate 77) breeds across southern Siberia and the Far East. This attractive bird is reasonably common and favours river valleys with thick willow bushes and trees, forest edges and tall-grass meadows. It breeds in solitary pairs and arrives at its breeding sites in May. A nest is built in bushes and small trees and a clutch of four to six eggs are laid and incubated by both parents for 14 to 16 days. The young stay in the nest for about two weeks. Normally there is one clutch per season, and both parents take care of the young. As with other finches, the food consists mostly of plant matter, but includes some insects whilst the young are being fed.

The **Pine Grosbeak** (*Pinicola enucleator*) (Plate 77) lives in the vast expanses of the true taiga forests across Russia. It breeds in solitary pairs and is a rather uncommon bird. In winter time it appears in Western and Eastern Europe. It arrives at its breeding areas in May, and starts building its nest in a small tree, usually a fir. In June a clutch of three to five eggs is laid which is incubated by the female for about 13 to 14 days. The young stay in the nest for 14 to 16 days.

There are three species of crossbill (*Loxia*) in Russia. The **Red Crossbill** (*L. curvirostra*) is the most common and widespread species, breeding across the forests of Russia, giving preference, as all crossbills, to the coniferous woods in the lowlands as well as in the mountains. The **Parrot Crossbill** (*L. pytyopsittacus*) (Plate 77) inhabits coniferous forests from the borders with Scandinavia to the River Irtysh basin in Western Siberia. This is not a very common species and is rather difficult to see. The **White-winged**

Crossbill (*L. leucoptera*) has a very wide distribution from the western borders all the way to the Far East.

The **Northern Bullfinch** (*Pyrrhula pyrrhula*) has been divided into three separate species. Widespread from the western borders all the way to the Far East, the common and welll-know species inhabits the western parts of this huge area including European Russia, Central and Northern Siberia and reaches the shores of the Sea of Okhotsk. The other two forms, the **Grey Bullfinch** (*P. cineracea*) and *P. griseiventris*, inhabit eastern Siberia and the Far East, including Ussuriland. The real Far Eastern species is *P. griseiventris*, which has delicate peach-coloured cheeks and a grey belly. Completely grey underparts are characteristic of *P. cineracea*, which occurs from the shores of Lake Baikal to the Sea of Okhotsk.

There are four species of grosbeak in Russia which belong to three different genuses. The well known common **Hawfinch** (*Coccothraustes coccothraustes*) inhabits large areas of Russia from the western borders to the Far East, but avoids the cold and unwelcoming coniferous forests of Siberia. Two interesting species are found in in Ussuriland. The **Japanese Grosbeak** (*Eophona personata*) is an uncommon species throughout its range in Russia and is found in large, mature woods of this exciting area. Its lonely whistling song would be greeted with excitement from any birdwatcher. It arrives in Ussuriland in May and builds its nest in a tree, sometimes very high above the ground. In the first half of June, three to five eggs are laid and incubated by the female only. There is one brood per season. Much smaller and more common is the **Chinese Grosbeak** (*E. migratoria*) (Plate 77) which essentially occurs in the same areas but in quite different habitats. It usually prefers space woods of Mongolian Oak on the lowlands, and bushes along river valleys or parks. This bird arrives in Ussuriland in May and announces its arrival with indistinctive song which is a mixture of whistles. A nest is built on a tree or bush, sometimes as low as 1 m above the ground. A clutch is laid in the first half of June and consists of three to five eggs which are incubated by the female for about 15 days. The young stay in the nest for 13 to 14 days, fed by both parents.

Mountain woods of juniper trees in Central Aisa are home for another species, the **White-winged Grosbeak** (*Mycerobas carnipes*). This bird does not migrate and feeds on the berries and seeds of juiper trees throughout the year. Nest-building takes place in May and nests are placed inside juniper trees or bushes as well as on Tien Shan firs. A clutch consists of four to five eggs and is incubated by the female only for 14 to 16 days. The young stay in the nest for 13 to 14 days, fed by both parents.

Buntings (Emberizidae)

The bunting family is widely represented in Russia where it has 35 species, out of which 28 are breeders and seven vagrant. Buntings occupy all imaginable habitats and are found in Russia from the steppes and deserts to mountains and tundras in the Arctic as well as dense woods of the Far East.

Common and well known in Russia is the **Corn Bunting** (*Emberiza calandra*) which inhabits open landscapes from the western borders across southern parts of European Russia, Caucasus and Trans Caucasus to the eastern parts of Kazakhstan. The **Yellowhammer** (*E. citrinella*) is very common, distributed as far as western Siberia, the valley of the great River Ob' where it interbreeds with the **Pine Bunting** (*E. leucocephala*) which lives in wooded areas of Siberia. An isolated breeding area of the Pine Bunting is located in the mountains of Central Asia.

Rare and poorly studied in Russia is the **Japanese Grey Bunting** (*Emberiza variabilis*) which breeds in Kamchatka, on the islands of Sakhalin and Kurils. Central Asia has its own set of buntings, one of which is the exciting **White-capped Bunting** (*E. stewarti*) (Plate 78) which generally inhabits parts of the Himalayan system but is not a very common species. This bird prefers dry mountain slopes with many rocks, canyons and mountain river valleys. It arrives at its breeding ground by the end of April and males immediately announce their presence by a very simple song of five to six similar ringing sounds in sequence. A nest is built under a rock or bush, and a clutch of four to five eggs is laid and incubated by the female for 13 to 14 days. The young leave the nest when about 10 to 12 days old. They are fed by both parents on delicate seeds and different insects. Another species of bunting also inhabits Central Asia and similar dry habitats as the above species. This is the **Grey-necked Bunting** (*E. buchanani*) (Plate 80) which in some places is the most common bunting in Central Asia.

The **Rock Bunting** (*Emberiza cia*) is the most widespread mountain species and lives in the ranges of Crimea, Caucasus, Central Asia and Altai. The form which inhabits the Transbaikal region has been split, and is now called **Godlewski's Bunting** (*E. godlewskii*). Both species inhabit mountainous areas, giving preference to dry slopes.

The **Long-tailed Bunting** (*Emberiza cioides*) (Plate 78) enjoys wide distribution in Siberia and the Far East. This bird breeds by the forest edges, in rich meadows with sparce bushes and on the slopes of mountains. It arrives at its breeding sites in May and builds a nest under a bush or rock. From mid-May, a clutch of four to six eggs is laid and incubated by the female only for 12 to 14 days. There is one clutch per season and the young stay in the nest for 10 to 14 days.

Now regarded as extinct from Russian territory is **Jankowski's Bunting**

(*Emberiza jankowskii*). This elusive bird used to breed in reasonable numbers in the small piece of land to the very south of Ussuriland, in the Khasan district. All recent search parties have not brought back a single record of the bird, but there is hope that they still breed in isolated areas in Korea and north-east China.

The wetlands and meadows of the Transbaikal region and the south of the Russian Far East are home for the **Grey-Hooded Bunting** (*Emberiza fucata*). This bird is not rare and is very often seen breeding where the dominant species is the **Yellow-breasted Bunting** (*E. aureola*) (Plate 79). The latter species has a very wide distribution and in some places like the Khanka Lowland in Ussuriland breeds in incredible numbers. The well-known **Reed Bunting** (*E. schoeniclus*) is a common bird all across European Russia and Siberia forming 11 subspecies in this range (out of 16 in the world). Isolated areas of Ussuriland – Lake Khanka and Lake Khasan – are home for the **Japanese Reed Bunting** (*E. yessoensis*), an attractive and uncommon bird of the Far East. They arrive at their breeding grounds by the end of April and the males start to sing vigorously, sitting on the top of a reed or bush. A nest is built on the ground and a clutch of four to five eggs is laid and incubated by the female only for 12 to 14 days. The young stay in the nest for 10 to 13 days fed by both parents.

Outside of Russia, **Pallas's Bunting** (*Emberiza pallasi*) (Plate 78) breeds only in in the border areas of Mongolia and China. This nearly-endemic species breeds in bushy areas in lowland and mountainous tundra across Siberia. Usually they arrive at their breeding sites in the first half of June since spring in the breeding areas of this species comes very late. A nest is built on the ground and a clutch of three to five eggs is laid and incubated by the female only for 12 to 14 days. This species reaches very high Arctic areas, where there is one more species of the genus, namely the **Little Bunting** (*E. pusilla*) which is common across Arctic areas of Russia.

A species endemic to Russia is the **Yellow-browed Bunting** (*Emberiza chrysophrys*). This uncommon bird occurs in Eastern Siberia north of Lake Baikal where it breeds in bushy areas along the forest edges. It arrives at its breeding grounds in May and builds a nest on a small tree or bush. A clutch of four to five eggs is laid usually at the beginning of June and incubated by the female only for 12 to 14 days. Young stay in the nest for 10-13 days fed by both parents.

Two attractive species of buntings inhabit the woods of Ussuriland, and hardly penetrate outside this area. **Tristram's Bunting** (*Emberiza tristrami*) (Plate 79) and the **Yellow-throated Bunting** (*E. elegans*) both live in the woods, sometimes far from the edge. They both appear on the breeding grounds at the end of April-beginning of May, where snow sometimes falls in abundance.

Tristram's Buntings build nests in a small tree or bush whereas Yellow-throated Buntings place it on the ground, usually under a bush but sometimes surprisingly openly. By the end of May clutches are laid (four to five eggs in each species) and incubated by the females only for 12 to 14 days.

The **Rustic Bunting** (*Emberiza rustica*) (Plate 79) enjoys an extremely wide range in Russia, although it tends to breed in more northerly, Siberian-type woods with many conifers. For breeding they choose wet edges of the woods, rich in bushes. They arrive at the breeding grounds by the end of April-beginning of May and start building a nest on a tree or bush or on the ground. By the end of May, or in more northerly places in June, a clutch of four to six eggs is laid and incubated by the female only for 12 to 15 days. Normally there is one clutch per season.

The most common species of bunting in southern Siberia and the Far East, if not the most common bird together with the Black-browed Reed Warbler, is the **Black-faced Bunting** (*Emberiza spodocephala*) (Plate 79). These birds can be seen everywhere except the thickets deep in the woods. They appear on their breeding sites in May and start building a nest on a bush or small tree, sometimes up to 1.5 m above the ground. Usually the clutch consists of five eggs and is incubated by the female only for 12 to 14 days. The young stay in the nest for 9 to 14 days and are fed by both parents.

Contrary to the above described species, the **Chestnut Bunting** (*Emberiza rutila*) breeds deep in the woods of Ussuriland and other parts of the Russian Far East. It is not an easy bird to see and find. It is regarded as an endemic species to Russia even though there is a chance that it may breed in border areas with China, for example the Khingan Mountains. It arrives on its breeding sites in May and starts building a nest on the ground, usually under good cover. By mid-June, a clutch of four to five eggs is laid and incubated by the female only for 12 to 14 days. There is normally one clutch per season. The young stay in the nest for 10 to 13 days, fed by both parents.

Among the well-known European species is the **Ortolan Bunting** (*Emberiza hortulana*) which is a common breeder particularly in southern parts of Ukraine and Russia. The Trans Caucasus region is inhabited by the **Black-headed Bunting** (*E. melanocephala*) whereas similar open habitats in Kazakhstan and Central Asia are home to the very common **Red-headed Bunting** (*E. bruniceps*) (Plate 80). This latter species breeds in steppes, semi-deserts and mountainous areas up to 2400 m above sea level. In suitable areas it is possible to hear up to six males singing at the same time and they are certainly strikingly beautiful. They arrive at their breeding grounds by the end of April and start building a nest in a small bush or grass. From mid-May, a clutch of four to five eggs is laid and incubated by the female for 11 to 13 days. The young stay in the nest 10 to 14 days. There are normally two clutches per season.

Arctic areas across the whole of Russia are inhabited by two well-known species of bunting, namely the **Lapland Bunting** (*Calcarius lapponicus*) (Plate 80) and the **Snow Bunting** (*Plectrophenax nivalis*) (Plate 80). Interestingly, neither of these species, contrary to many other birds which breed in the arctic region, are found breeding in the mountainous tundra of the cold Siberian mountains, and are restricted to proper arctic areas only. A separate subspecies of the Snow Bunting inhabits the Commander Islands.

The following species of bunting are registered in Russia as vagrants: the **Fox Sparrow** (*Paserella iliaca* – Chukotka Peninsula and the Commander Islands); the **White-crowned Sparrow** (*Zonotrichia leucophrys* – Wrangel Island); the **Golden-crowned Sparrow** (*Z. atriacapilla* – Chukotka Peninsula and Wrangel Island); the **American Tree Sparrow** (*Spizella arborea* – Chukotka Peninsula and Wrangel Island); the **Dark-eyed Junco** (*Junco hyemalis* – Chukotka Peninsula and Wrangel Island); the **Cirl Bunting** (*Emberiza cirlus* – Crimea, Caucasus, no collection material) and **Cretzschmar's Bunting** (*E. caesia* – Caucasus).

The **Savanna Sparrow** (*Passerculus sanwichensis*), an American species which was previously regarded as vagrant to Russia, has been found as a regular breeder in the eastern part of the Chukotka Peninsula.

ORNITHOLOGY AND BIRDWATCHING IN RUSSIA

Ornithology, the scientific study of birds, a highly specialised and distinctive group of animals, occupies a special place in the system of biological sciences. Ornithology embraces all aspects of knowledge about birds, knowledge obtained by a variety of methods. This means that there is considerable overlap with sciences such as physiology, histology and biochemistry. These other spheres of scientific ornithology are chiefly the province of professional specialists, but birdwatching, discovering which birds occur where, and sometimes serious population studies are increasingly becoming a focus of interest for the huge army of amateur birdwatchers who actively pursue their hobby in many countries of the world.

Ornithological studies have a long tradition in the former Soviet Union. The diversity of natural zones and landscapes encouraged scientists to undertake large-scale faunistic investigations which began in the second half of the eighteenth century under the leadership of academician P. C. Pallas. Within a short period, a vast territory, embracing part of Siberia, the Far East and Kamtchatka had been explored ornithologically.

The first half of the nineteenth century was marked by active study of the avifaunas in various regions of the country. N. A. Severtsov (1827-1885) explored the Turkestan region and his bird studies here formed the basis of his review paper "The vertical and horizontal distribution of Turkestan animals", published in 1872. The Orenburg region was investigated by the Kazan University professor, E. A. Eversmann (1794-1866), who published his results in 1860.

The start of ecological investigations followed the publication in 1855 of Severtsiv's *Current events in the life of animals, birds and reptiles in Voronez government*. These traditions were continued and developed by A. F. Middendorff (1815-1894) who undertook a long journey through Siberia. Middendorff was the first person to put forward the hypothesis that birds orientate by using the Earth's magnetic field.

M. A. Menzbier (1855-1935) made a very important contribution to the development of ornithology in the former Soviet Union. He organized the coordination of faunistic studies which were proceeding in various regions of the country and published the results in 15 volumes: *Contributions to our knowledge of Russia's flora and fauna*. Menzbier skillfully summarised the enormous amount of accumulated data and published two handbooks with an emphasis on distribution – *The birds of Russia* and *An ornithological geography of European Russia*.

P. P. Sushkin (1868-1928) was a student of Menzbier's who became head of the department of ornithology at the Zoological Institute of the Academy of Sciences of Russia in St. Petersburg.

The Zoological Institute became a very important centre for ornithological research, and several great ornithologists, including A. Ya. Tugarinov, E. V. Kozlova, B. K. Stegman and L. A. Portenko worked there very productively at various times.

Regional bird studies developed both in the pre-war, and especially in the post-war times. A number of regional books were completed, for example the birds of Kazakhstan (6 vol.) by I. A. Dolgushin and others; those of the Ukraine by A. B. Kistyakovsky; Turkmenistan by G. P. Dementiev and A. K. Rustamov; Tadzhikistan by A. I. Ivanov and A. I. Abdusalyamov and of the north-east of Russia by L. A. Portenko and A. A. Kishchinsky.

Much important work on migration is carried out by Russian ornithologists. Studies have flourished in the post-war years thanks to the establishment of key observatories at Rybachy (former Rossiten) on the Kursiu peninsula in the Baltic Sea, in Kandalaksha by the White Sea, Oka nature reserve south of Moscow and in Astrakhan nature reserve in the Volga delta. The leading Russian migration specialist is Dr V. R. Dolnik.

The start of theoretical investigations on bird conservation sprang from the inspirational work of the famous G. P. Dementiev (1898-1969). Following in Dementiev's footsteps is the distinguished ornithologist and conservationist Dr Vladimir E. Flint, whose reputation goes far beyond the borders of the former Soviet Union. Under Dr Flint's expert guidance, work is processing on improving the Red Data Book, captive breeding of rare birds and creating new nature reserves.

Continuing the traditions of the 1920s journals *Messager ornithologique* and *Uragus*, a team of specialists has been publishing *Ornitologya* (a collection of articles, shorter communications etc.) more or less annually since 1958.

During the 1970s, a number of bodies were created which mirrored the structure of International ornithological organisations: the USSR Ornithological Society, the Soviet National section of ICPB and the Ornithological Section of the National Committee of Soviet biologists.

Applied aspects of the science have been a great stimulus to various ornithological investigations. There is a joke in Russia that the start of so-called bird strikes (aircraft collisions with birds) has provided lots of new jobs for ornithologists. Other important applied aspects are birds and agriculture, the control of animal behaviour, hunting and game management, and so on. Bearing all this in mind, USSR State Committee for Science and Technology in 1973 passed a resolution which provided for an intensification of ornithological studies in the country.

Summarising all the accumulated data on the ecology and distribution of Russian birds, the country's ornithologists are preparing *The Birds of the USSR*, a ten-volume handbook, 4 volumes of which have been published.

The wealth of factual material on bird migration has been reflected in a number of publications, including the *Proceedings of the Baltic Commission*, and volumes of collected papers entitled "Bird migration in Asia" and "Bird migration in Eastern Europe and Northern Asia". Important books cataloguing the distribution and status of Russian birds by A. I. Ivanov (1976) and L. S. Stepanyan (1975, 1978) were fundamental reference works for the editors and authors of *The Birds of the USSR*, as were the newest regional guides and handbooks.

There are about 1,000 professional ornithologists working in Russia. Listed below are the main institutes and organisations which are concerned with the study of birds.

The Zoological Institute of the Russian Academy of Sciences in St. Petersburg is a bastion of serious ornithological research on faunistics and ornithogeography, migration and population ecology. Famous ornithologists whose names are linked with the Institute include B. K. Stegmann, B. K. Yudin, E. V. Kozlova, L. A. Portenko, V. R. Dolnik, I. A. Neufeldt, R. L. Potapov, A. I. Ivanov and others.

In the Department of Vertebrate Zoology at St. Petersburg State University a group concerned with ecology and bioacoustics is headed by Yu. B. Pukinsky who formerly worked with the late A. S. Malchevsky.

In Moscow State University's Department of Biology the main fields of ornithological research are the ontogeny of avian vocal communication (G. N. Simkin), ornithogeography (R. L. Boehme), evolutionary morphology (F. Ya. Dzerzhinsky) and population ecology (I. A. Shilov). There is also the associated Zoological Museum of Moscow University where faunistics, ornithogeography and systematics are the research interest of A. A. Kuznetsov, P. S. Tomkovich and V. G. Babenko, who follow in the footsteps of G. P. Dementiev and E. P. Spangenberg.

The main ornithological investigations carried out at the Severtsov Institute of Evolutionary Morphology and Ecology of Animals (V. D. Ilyichev, E. N. Panov and others) are communication and social behaviour, also research into methods of control of animal behaviour. Also housed in the Institute's buildings is the Ringing Centre of the Russian Academy of Sciences whose Director is Dr I. N. Dobrynina. Apart from the ringing programme, the Centre organises censuses of birds and terrestrial mammals.

The Tartu Institute of Zoology and Botany of the Academy of Sciences of Estonia is researching population ecology and migration (V. Lilleleht, A. Kuresoo, R. Ma and and the late E. Kumari).

Population ecology, bird migration and orientation are the main fields of research at Salaspils near Riga, Latvia, the site of the Ornithology Laboratory in the Biological Institute of the Academy of Sciences of Latvia (the late H. A. Mihelsons, now J. Viksne and others).

In the third Baltic state, we find Lithuania's capital Vilnius, and the Institute of Zoology and Parasitology of the Academy of Sciences of Lithuania. Here bird migration and bioacoustics is being studied by various methods, including radar (M. Zalakevicius, P. Mierauskas), while P. Kurlavicius is researching the ecology of farmland birds. In Vilnius University, Dr R .R. Budrys carried out the major study on the ecology of the birds of mountain streams of Central Asia.

At Alma-Ata, the capital of Kazakhstan, the Zoological Institute of the Academy of Sciences has two laboratories where ornithological work is carried out: the ornithology laboratory (E. I. Gavrilov) and the laboratory for the conservation of rare animal species (A. F. Kovshar). Many extremely interesting bird studies have been undertaken in Kazakhstan and the republic has long and well-established traditions of ornithological research. Ornithologists there are now concentrating more and more on conservation and the establishment of new nature reserves in their republic.

The Siberian branch of the Russian Academy of Sciences has an Institute of Biology in Novosibirsk where a computerised databank of bird census material for the whole country is housed and where Yu. S. Ravkin works on the distribution of birds in Western Siberia. Formerly, the migration and ecology of individual species were studied by K. T. Yurlov.

Bird studies in the Russian Far East have deep roots and an interesting history. Several ornithologists – A. A. Nazarenko, N. M. Litvunenko, Yu. Shibaev and V. A. Nechaev – are doing important and valuable work from their base at the Institute of Biology and Soil (Far Eastern Centre of the Russian Academy of Sciences) in Vladivostok. A number of other ornithologists, notably Dr I. A. Neufeldt, have made a massive and invaluable contribution to bird studies in the Far East.

At the Institute of Ecological Problems of the North in Magadan, the main direction of study is avian ecology in tundra landscape which is being researched by A. V. Andreev, A. Ya. Kondratiev, A. V. Krechmar, and many young scientists of impressive potential.

The All-Union Research Institute for Nature Conservation and Reserve affairs in the village of Znamenskoye-Sadki near Moscow co-ordinates and carries out bird conservation work. Director of the Animal Conservation Department is Professor Vladimir E. Flint. Bird census work and animal mapping projects also come within the purview of this Institute. A separate Red Data Book laboratory has also been created, with N. A. Golovkin in charge.

In the Oka Nature reserve, the Central Ornithological Station staff (S.

G. Priklonsky, A. D. Numerov and others) work on avian ecology and operate ringing programmes. The captive breeding station for cranes and raptors are administered by Yu. Markin and V. Panchenko.

At the Zoological Institute of the Ukrainian Academy of Sciences in Kiev, ornithologists such as M. Voinstvenskiy, M. I. Golovushkin, A. M. Peklo, N. Klestov and others work on faunistics, ornithogeography, migration and the effect on the bird world of the river Dniepr barrages.

Also in Ukraine, the republic's Ornithological Station has recently been established at Melitopol where I. I. Chernichko, S. V. Vinter, V. D. Siokhin, A. I. Koshelev and others work on bird migration, rare species, and applied ornithology.

Apart from the establishments listed above, ornithological research work is carried out in all of the union republics and in almost all the country's reserves as well as at many other Institutes and Universities.

Ornithological Societies in Russia

The Russian Ornithological Society was founded at a special assembly in Moscow on 17 February 1982. The main objectives of the Society are: to promote in every way possible the study and conservation of birds in Russia; to participate actively in the development of ornithological studies in the former USSR by encouraging scientists, forestry workers, hunters as well as amateur ornithologists to tackle and resolve the theoretical and practical problems of modern ornithology; to campaign for and to play an active part in the conservation of birds and their habitats, and to work out the scientific bases for the rational use of birds. Professor V. D. Ilyichev is the elected President of the Russian Ornithological Society, and the Vice-Presidents are Professors V. E. Flint and V. R. Dolnik, Academician A. K. Rustamov and Professor E. N. Kurochkin. The scientific secretary of the Society is Dr V. A. Zubakin, and its Central Council has 55 members.

The first volume of the *Scientific Proceedings of the Russian Ornithological Society* has already appeared, as a hardback book entitled *Contemporary Problems of Ornithology*, and the second volume was published under the name *Avian Ecology and Behaviour*. The Society has set up special commissions or working groups on cranes, birds of prey, waders, gulls and allies and on colonial species.

Foreign Birdwatchers in Russia

Specialist ornithological tours of limited access to certain places, operated by Itourist and different foreign travel companies, have now been taking place annually for a number of years. Interested ornithologists from Britain, Finland and Sweden were the first to make such tours a reality.

Birdwatchers from foreign countries can now visit such ornithological hotspots as the Siberian Arctic, Central Asian mountains, Ussuriland and Kamchatka. Organised birdwatching trips now take people as far as Sakhalin Island where it is possible to find the Spotted Greenshank on its breeding grounds and even to see its fascinating nest built in a tree.

At the time of writing, most areas of the former Soviet Union are open to foreign visitors, primarily for scientists and organised groups. It is still difficult to go on your own, but usually birdwatchers go in groups and now there are plenty of exciting possibilities to explore places and birds which once were inaccessible.

Now a number of companies in Britain and elsewhere organise tours to all corners of Russia to see and experience this once forbidden land. The author himself is involved in the tourist business and travels each year to wild Russia with British birdwatchers. More information about travel possibilities may be obtained by writing to Russian Nature Tours, 57 Fore St,. Kingsbridge, Devon, TQ7 1PG.

CHECKLIST OF THE BIRDS OF RUSSIA

KEY: b – breeding species; b? – breeding probable but not yet proved;
v – vagrant; e – extinct.

1.	*Gavia stellata* – *Red-throated Diver*	b
2.	*G. arctica* – *Black-throated Diver*	b
3.	*G. pacifica* – *Pacific Diver*	b
4.	*G. immer* – *Great Northern Diver*	v
5.	*G. adamsii* – *White-billed Diver*	b
6.	*Podiceps ruficollis* – *Little Grebe*	b
7.	*P. nigricollis* – *Black-necked Grebe*	b
8.	*P. auritus* – *Slavonian Grebe*	b
9.	*P. grisegena* – *Red-necked Grebe*	b
10.	*P. cristatus* – *Great Crested Grebe*	b
11.	*Diomedea albatrus* – *Short-tailed Albatross*	v
12.	*D. immutabilis* – *Laysan Albatross*	v
13.	*D. nigripes* – *Black-footed Albatross*	v
14.	*Fulmarus glacialis* – *Northern Fulmar*	b
15.	*Pterodroma hypoleuca* – *Bonin Petrel*	v
16.	*P. inexpectata* – *Peale's Petrel*	v
17.	*P. solandri* – *Solander's Petrel*	v
18.	*Calonectris leucomelas* – *White-faced Shearwater*	b
19.	*Puffinus puffinus* – *Manx Shearwater*	v
20.	*P. carneipes* – *Pale-footed Shearwater*	v
21.	*P. griseus* – *Sooty Shearwater*	v
22.	*P. tenuirostris* – *Short-tailed Shearwater*	v
23.	*P. bulleri* – *Grey-backed Shearwater*	v
24.	*Hydrobates pelagicus* – *British Storm Petrel*	v
25.	*Oceanodroma leucorhoa* – *Leach's Storm Petrel*	b
26.	*O. monorhis* – *Swinhoe's Storm Petrel*	b
27.	*O. furcata* – *Fork-tailed Storm Petrel*	b
28.	*O. castro* – *Harcourt's Petrel*	v
29.	*Fregata ariel* – *Lesser Frigatebird*	v
30.	*Pelecanus onocrotalus* – *White Pelican*	b
31.	*P. crispus* – *Dalmation Pelican*	b
32.	*Sula bassana* – *Northern Gannet*	v
33.	*S. sula* – *Red-footed Booby*	v
34.	*Phalacrocorax carbo* – *Great Cormorant*	b
35.	*P. filamentosus* – *Temminck's Cormorant*	b
36.	*P. perspicillatus*	e
37.	*P. pelagicus* – *Pelagic Cormorant*	b
38.	*P. urile* – *Red-faced Cormorant*	b

39.	*P. aristotelis – Shag*	b
40.	*P. pygmaeus – Pygmy Cormorant*	b
41.	*Botaurus stellaris – Eurasian Bittern*	b
42.	*Ixobrychus minutus – Little Bittern*	b
43.	*I. sinensis – Chinese Little Bittern*	b
44.	*I. eurythmus – Schrenk's Bittern*	b
45.	*I. cinnamomeus – Cinnamon Bittern*	v
46.	*Nycticorax nycticorax – Black-crowned Night Heron*	b
47.	*Butorides striatus – Green-backed Heron*	b
48.	*Gorsachius goisagi – Japanese Night Heron*	v
49.	*Ardeola ralloides – Squacco Heron*	b
50.	*A. bacchus – Chinese Pond Heron*	b
51.	*Bubulcus ibis – Cattle Egret*	b
52.	*Egretta alba – Great Egret*	b
53.	*E. intermedia – Intermediate Egret*	b
54.	*E. garzetta – Little Egret*	b
55.	*E. eulophotes – Swinhoe's Egret*	b
56.	*Ardea cinerea – Grey Heron*	b
57.	*A. purpurea – Purple Heron*	b
58.	*Platalea leucorodia – White Spoonbill*	b
59.	*Plegadis falcinellus – Glossy Ibis*	b
60.	*Nipponia nippon – Japanese Crested Ibis*	e
61.	*Threskiornis aethiopica – Sacred Ibis*	v
62.	*T. melanocephala – Oriental Ibis*	v
63.	*Ciconia ciconia – White Stork*	b
64.	*C. boyciana – Oriental White Stork*	b
65.	*C. nigra – Black Stork*	b
66.	*Phoenicopterus ruber roseus – Greater Flamingo*	b
67.	*Branta canadensis – Canada Goose*	v
68.	*B. leucopsis – Barnacle Goose*	b
69.	*B. bernicla – Brent Goose*	b
70.	*B. nigricans – Pacific Brent Goose*	b
71.	*Rufibrenta ruficollis – Red-breasted Goose*	b
72.	*Anser anser – Greylag Goose*	b
73.	*A. albifrons – Greater White-fronted Goose*	b
74.	*A. erythropus – Lesser White-fronted Goose*	b
75.	*A. fabalis – Bean Goose*	b
76.	*A. indica – Bar-headed Goose*	b
77.	*A. cygnoides – Swan Goose*	b
78.	*Chen hyperboreus – Snow Goose*	b
79.	*C. rossi – Ross's Goose*	v
80.	*Philacte canagica – Emperor Goose*	b
81.	*Cygnus olor – Mute Swan*	b
82.	*C. cygnus – Whooper Swan*	b

83. *C. bewickii – Bewick's Swan*   b
84. *C. columbianus – Tundra Swan*   b
85. *Tadorna ferruginea – Ruddy Shelduck*   b
86. *T. tadorna – Common Shelduck*   b
87. *T. cristata – Crested Shelduck*   e
88. *Anas platyrhynchos – Mallard*   b
89. *A. poecilorhyncha – Spotbill Duck*   b
90. *A. crecca – Green-winged Teal*   b
91. *A. carolinensis – Common Teal*   v
92. *A. formosa – Baikal Teal*   b
93. *A. falcata – Falcated Teal*   b
94. *A. strepera – Gadwall*   b
95. *A. penelope – Eurasian Wigeon*   b
96. *A. americana – American Wigeon*   v
97. *A. acuta – Northern Pintail*   b
98. *A. querquedula – Garganey*   b
99. *A. clypeata – Northern Shoveller*   b
100. *A. angustirostris – Marbled Teal*   b
101. *Aix galericulata – Mandarin Duck*   b
102. *Netta rufina – Red-crested Pochard*   b
103. *Aythya americana – Redhead*   v
104. *A. ferina – Common Pochard*   b
105. *A. nyroca – Ferruginous Duck*   b
106. *A. baeri – Baer's Pochard*   b
107. *A. fuligula – Tufted Duck*   b
108. *A. marila – Greater Scaup*   b
109. *A. affinis – Lesser Scaup*   v
110. *Histrionicus histrionicus – Harlequin Duck*   b
111. *Clangula hyemalis – Long-tailed Duck*   b
112. *Bucephala clangula – Common Goldeneye*   b
113. *B. islandica – Barrow's Goldeneye*   v
114. *B. albeola – Bufflehead*   v
115. *Somateria molissima – Common Eider*   b
116. *S. spectabilis – King Eider*   b
117. *S. fischeri – Spectacled Eider*   b
118. *Polysticta stelleri – Steller's Eider*   b
119. *Melanitta nigra – Black Scoter*   b
120. *M. americana – American Scoter*   b
121. *M. perspicillata – Surf Scoter*   v
122. *M. deglandi – Pied-billed Scoter*   b
123. *M. fusca – Velvet Scoter*   b
124. *Oxyura leucocephala – White-headed Duck*   b
125. *Mergus albellus – Smew*   b
126. *M. serrator – Red-breasted Merganser*   b

230

127.	*M. squamatus – Chinese Merganser*	b
128.	*M. merganser – Goosander*	b
129.	*Pandion haliaetus – Osprey*	b
130.	*Elanus caeruleus – Black-shouldered Kite*	v
131.	*Pernis apivorus – Western Honey Buzzard*	b
132.	*P. ptilorhyncus – Crested Honey Buzzard*	b
133.	*Milvus milvus – Red Kite*	b
134.	*M. migrans – Black Kite*	b
135.	*Circus cyaneus – Hen Harrier*	b
136.	*C. macrourus – Pallid Harrier*	b
137.	*C. pygargus – Montagu's Harrier*	b
138.	*C. melanoleucus – Pied Harrier*	b
139.	*C. aeruginosus – Marsh Harrier*	b
140.	*Accipiter gentilis – Northern Goshawk*	b
141.	*A. nisus – Northern Sparrowhawk*	b
142.	*A. brevipes – Levant Sparrowhawk*	b
143.	*A. badius – Shikra Sparrowhawk*	b
144.	*A. soloensis – Horsfield's Sparrowhawk*	b
145.	*A. gularis – Besra Sparrowhawk*	b
146.	*Buteo lagopus – Rough-legged Buzzard*	b
147.	*B. hemilasius – Upland Buzzard*	b
148.	*B. rufinus – Long-legged Buzzard*	b
149.	*B. buteo – Eurasian Buzzard*	b
150.	*Butastur indicus – Grey-faced Buzzard Eagle*	b
151.	*Circaetus gallicus – Short-toed Eagle*	b
152.	*Spizaetus nipalensis – Hodgson's Hawk Eagle*	b
153.	*Hieraaetus pennatus – Booted Eagle*	b
154.	*H. fasciatus – Bonelli's Eagle*	b
155.	*Aquila rapax – Steppe Eagle*	b
156.	*A. clanga – Greater Spotted Eagle*	b
157.	*A. pomarina – Lesser Spotted Eagle*	b
158.	*A. heliaca – Imperial Eagle*	b
159.	*A. chrysaetos – Golden Eagle*	b
160.	*Haliaeetus leucoryphus – Pallas' Sea Eagle*	b
161.	*H. albicilla – White-tailed Sea Eagle*	b
162.	*H. leucocephalus – Bald Eagle*	v
163.	*H. pelagicus – Steller's Sea Eagle*	b
164.	*Gypaetus barbatus – Lammergeier*	b
165.	*Neophron percnopterus – Egyptian Vulture*	b
166.	*Aegypius monachus – Black Vulture*	b
167.	*Gyps fulvus – Griffon Vulture*	b
168.	*G. himalayensis – Himalayan Griffon Vulture*	b
169.	*Pseudogyps bengalensis – Oriental White-backed Vulture*	v
170.	*Falco rusticolus – Gyrfalcon*	b

171. *F. cherrug – Saker Falcon*   b
172. *F. jugger – Lagger Falcon*   b
173. *F. biarmicus – Lanner Falcon*   b
174. *F. pelegrinoides – Barbary Falcon*   b
175. *F. peregrinus – Peregrine Falcon*   b
176. *F. subbuteo – Northern Hobby*   b
177. *F. columbarius – Merlin*   b
178. *F. vespertinus – Western Red-footed Falcon*   b
179. *F. amurensis – Amur Red-footed Falcon*   b
180. *F. naumanni – Lesser Kestrel*   b
181. *F. tinnunculus – Common Kestrel*   b
182. *F. sparverius – American Kestrel*   v
183. *Lagopus lagopus – Willow Ptarmigan*   b
184. *L. mutus – Rock Ptarmigan*   b
185. *Lyrurus tetrix – Black Grouse*   b
186. *L. mlokosiewiczi – Caucasian Black Grouse*   b
187. *Tetrao urogallus – Western Capercaillie*   b
188. *T. parvirostris – Black-billed Capercaillie*   b
189. *Falcipennis falcipennis – Siberian Spruce Grouse*   b
190. *Tetrastes bonasia – Hazel Grouse*   b
191. *Tetraogallus caucasicus – Caucasian Snowcock*   b
192. *T. caspius – Caspian Snowcock*   b
193. *T. himalayensis – Himalayan Snowcock*   b
194. *T. tibetanus – Tibetan Snowcock*   b
195. *T. altaicus – Altai Snowcock*   b
196. *Alectoris chukar – Chuckar Partridge*   b
197. *Ammoperdix griseogularis – See-see Partridge*   b
198. *Francolinus francolinus – Black Partridge*   b
199. *Perdix perdix – Grey Partridge*   b
200. *P. dauuricae – Daurian Partridge*   b
201. *Coturnix coturnix – Common Quail*   b
202. *C. japonica – Japanese Quail*   b
203. *Phasianus colchicus – Common Pheasant*   b
204. *Turnix tanki – Yellow-legged Buttonquail*   b
205. *Grus japonensis – Manchurian Crane*   b
206. *G. leucogeranus – Siberian White Crane*   b
207. *G. grus – Common Crane*   b
208. *G. canadensis – Sandhill Crane*   b
209. *G. vipio – Japanese White-naped Crane*   b
210. *G. monacha – Hooded Crane*   b
211. *Anthropoides virgo – Demoiselle Crane*   b
212. *Rallus aquaticus – Water Rail*   b
213. *Porzana porzana – Spotted Crake*   b
214. *P. parva – Little Crake*   b

215. *P. pusilla* – Baillon's Crake — b
216. *P. fusca* – Ruddy-breasted Crake — b
217. *P. paykullii* – Band-bellied Crake — b
218. *P. exquisita* – Swinhoe's Yellow Rail — b
219. *Amaurornis phoenicurus* – White-breasted Water Hen — v
220. *Crex crex* – Corncrake — b
221. *Gallinula chloropus* – Moorhen — b
222. *Gallicrex cinerea* – Water Cock — b
223. *Porphyrio porphyrio* – Purple Gallinule — b
224. *Fulica atra* – Black Coot — b
225. *Otis tarda* – Great Bustard — b
226. *Tetrax tetrax* – Little Bustard — b
227. *Chlamydotis undulata* – Houbara Bustard — b
228. *Hydrophasianus chirurgus* – Pheasant-tailed Jacana — v
229. *Burhinus oedicnemus* – Stone Curlew — b
230. *Rostratula benghalensis* – Greater Painted Snipe — b
231. *Pluvialis squatarola* – Grey Plover — b
232. *P. fulva* – Pacific Golden Plover — b
233. *P. dominica* – American Golden Plover — v
234. *P. apricaria* – European Golden Plover — b
235. *Charadrius hiaticula* – Ringed Plover — b
236. *C. semipalmatus* – Semipalmated Plover — v
237. *C. dubius* – Little Ringed Plover — b
238. *C. placidus* – Long-billed Ringed Plover — b
239. *C. leschenaultii* – Greater Sand Plover — b
240. *C. mongolus* – Lesser Sand Plover — b
241. *C. asiaticus* – Caspian Plover — b
242. *C. veredus* – Eastern Sand Plover — b
243. *C. alexandrinus* – Kentish Plover — b
244. *Eudromias morinellus* – Eurasian Dotterel — b
245. *Chettusia gregaria* – Sociable Plover — b
246. *C. leucura* – White-tailed Plover — b
247. *Vanellus vanellus* – Northern Lapwing — b
248. *V. cinereus* – Grey-headed Lapwing — b
249. *V. spinosus* – Spur-winged Plover — v
250. *Lobivanellus indicus* – Red-wattled Lapwing — b
251. *Arenaria interpres* – Ruddy Turnstone — b
252. *A. melanocephala* – Black Turnstone — v
253. *Himantopus himantopus* – Black-winged Stilt — b
254. *Recurvirostra avosetta* – Pied Avocet — b
255. *Haematopus ostralegus* – Palaearctic Oystercatcher — b
256. *Ibidorhyncha struthersii* – Ibisbill — b
257. *Tringa ochropus* – Green Sandpiper — b
258. *T. glareola* – Wood Sandpiper — b

259. *T. nebularia* – *Common Greenshank*   b
260 . *T. guttifer* – *Spotted Greenshank*   b
261. *T. totanus* – *Common Redshank*   b
262. *T. flavipes* – *Lesser Yellowlegs*   v
263. *T. erythropus* – *Spotted Redshank*   b
264. *T. stagnatilis* – *Marsh Sandpiper*   b
265. *Heteroscelus brevipes* – *Grey-tailed Tattler*   b
266. *H. incanus* – *Wandering Tattler*   b
267. *Actitis hypoleucos* – *Common Sandpiper*   b
268. *A. macularia* – *Spotted Sandpiper*   v
269. *Xenus cinereus* – *Terek Sandpiper*   b
270. *Phalaropus fulicarius* – *Grey Phalarope*   b
271. *P. tricolor* – *Wilson's Phalarope*   v
272. *P. lobatus* – *Red-necked Phalarope*   b
273. *Philomachus pugnax* – *Ruff*   b
274. *Eurynorhynchus pygmeus* – *Spoon-billed Sandpiper*   b
275. *Calidris minuta* – *Little Stint*   b
276. *C. ruficollis* – *Red-necked Stint*   b
277. *C. subminuta* – *Long-toed Stint*   b
278. *C. minutilla* – *Least Sandpiper*   v
279. *C. temmickii* – *Temminck's Stint*   b
280. *C. bairdii* – *Baird's Sandpiper*   b
281. *C. fuscicollis* – *White-rumped Sandpiper*   v
282. *C. ferruginea* – *Curlew Sandpiper*   b
283. *C. alpina* – *Dunlin*   b
284. *C. maritima* – *Purple Sandpiper*   b
285. *C. ptilocnemys* – *Rock Sandpiper*   b
286. *C. acuminata* – *Sharp-tailed Sandpiper*   b
287. *C. melanotos* – *Pectoral Sandpiper*   b
288. *C. tenuirostris* – *Great Knot*   b
289. *C. canutus* – *Red Knot*   b
290. *C. mauri* – *Western Sandpiper*   b
291. *C. pusilla* – *Semipalmated Sandpiper*   b
292. *C. alba* – *Sanderling*   b
293. *Tryngites subruficollis* – *Buff-breasted Sandpiper*   b
294. *Limicola falcinellus* – *Broad-billed Sandpiper*   b
295. *Lymnocryptes minima* – *Jack Snipe*   b
296. *Gallinago gallinago* – *Common Snipe*   b
297. *G. hardwickii* – *Japanese Snipe*   b
298. *G. megala* – *Swinhoe's Snipe*   b
299. *G. stenura* – *Pintail Snipe*   b
300. *G. solitaria* – *Solitary Snipe*   b
301. *G. media* – *Great Snipe*   b
302. *Scolopax rusticola* – *Eurasian Woodcock*   b

303. *Numenius borealis* – *Eskimo Curlew*   e
304. *N. minutus* – *Little Curlew*   b
305. *N. tenuirostris* – *Slender-billed Curlew*   b
306. *N. arquata* – *Western Curlew*   b
307. *N. madagascariensis* – *Far Eastern Curlew*   b
308. *N. phaeopus* – *Whimbrel*   b
309. *Limosa limosa* – *Black-tailed Godwit*   b
310. *L. lapponica* – *Bar-tailed Godwit*   b
311. *Limnodromus scolopaceus* – *Long-billed Dowitcher*   b
312. *L. semipalmatus* – *Asiatic Dowitcher*   b
313. *Cursorius cursor* – *Cream-coloured Courser*   b
314. *Glareola pratincola* – *Common Pratincole*   b
315. *G. maldivarum* – *Oriental Pratincole*   b
316. *G. nordmanni* – *Black-winged Pratincole*   b
317. *Stercorarius skua* – *Great Skua*   v
318. *S. pomarinus* – *Pomarine Skua*   b
319. *S. parasiticus* – *Arctic Skua*   b
320. *S. longicaudus* – *Long-tailed Skua*   b
321. *Larus ichthyaetus* – *Great Black-headed Gull*   b
322. *L. relictus* – *Relict Gull*   b
323. *L. melanocephalus* – *Mediterranean Gull*   b
324. *L. minutus* – *Little Gull*   b
325. *L. ridibundus* – *Black-headed Gull*   b
326. *L. brunnicephalus* – *Brown-headed Gull*   b
327. *L. genei* – *Slender-billed Gull*   b
328. *L. fuscus* – *Lesser Black-backed Gull*   b
329. *L. argentatus* – *Herring Gull*   b
330. *L. heuglini*   b
331. *L. cachinnans* – *Eastern Herring Gull*   b
332. *L. schistisagus* – *Slaty-backed Gull*   b
333. *L. glaucescens* – *Glaucous-winged Gull*   b
334. *L. glaucoides* – *Iceland Gull*   v
335. *L. hyperboreus* – *Glaucous Gull*   b
336. *L. marinus* – *Great Black-backed Gull*   b
337. *L. canus* – *Common Gull*   b
338. *L. crassirostris* – *Black-tailed Gull*   b
339. *L. saundersi* – *Saunder's Gull*   v
340. *Xema sabini* – *Sabine's Gull*   b
341. *Rissa tridactyla* – *Black-legged Kittiwake*   b
342. *R. brevirostris* – *Red-legged Kittiwake*   b
343. *Rhodostethia rosea* – *Ross's Gull*   b
344. *Pagophila eburnea* – *Ivory Gull*   b
345. *Chlidonias niger* – *Black Tern*   b
346. *C. leucopterus* – *White-winged Black Tern*   b

347. *C. hybrida* – Whiskered Tern	b
348. *Gelochelidon nilotica* – Gull-billed Tern	b
349. *Hydroprogne caspia* – Caspian Tern	b
350. *Sterna sandvicensis* – Sandwich Tern	b
351. *S. hirundo* – Common Tern	b
352. *S. paradisaea* – Arctic Tern	b
353. *S. aleutica* – Aleutian Tern	b
354. *S. albifrons* – Little Tern	b
355. *Alle alle* – Little Auk	b
356. *Alca torda* – Razorbill	b
357. *Uria aalge* – Common Guillemot	b
358. *U. lomvia* – Brünnich's Guillemot	b
359. *Cepphus grylle* – Black Guillemot	b
360. *C. columba* – Pigeon Guillemot	b
361. *C. carbo* – Spectacled Guillemot	b
362. *Brachyramphus marmoratus* – Marbled Murrelet	b
363. *B. brevirostris* – Kittlitz's Murrelet	b
364. *Synthliboramphus antiquus* – Ancient Murrelet	b
365. *S. wumizusume* – Japanese Murrelet	v
366. *Ptychoramphus aleuticus* – Cassin's Auklet	v
367. *Aethia cristatella* – Crested Auklet	b
368. *A. pygmaea* – Whiskered Auklet	b
369. *A. pusilla* – Least Auklet	b
370. *Cyclorrhynchus psittacula* – Parakeet Auklet	b
371. *Cerorhinca monocerata* – Rhinoceros Auklet	b
372. *Fratercula arctica* – Atlantic Puffin	b
373. *F. corniculata* – Horned Puffin	b
374. *Lunda cirrhata* – Tufted Puffin	b
375. *Pterocles orientalis* – Black-bellied Sandgrouse	b
376. *P. alchata* – Pin-tailed Sandgrouse	b
377. *Syrrhaptes paradoxus* – Pallas's Sandgrouse	b
378. *S. tibetanus* – Tibetan Sandgrouse	b
379. *Columba janthina* – Japanese Wood Pigeon	v
380. *C. palumbus* – Wood Pigeon	b
381. *C. oenas* – Stock Dove	b
382. *C. eversmanni* – Eversmann's Dove	b
383. *C. livia* – Rock Dove	b
384. *C. rupestris* – Eastern Rock Dove	b
385. *C. leuconota* – Snow Pigeon	b
386. *Streptopelia decaocto* – Collared Dove	b
387. *S. tranquebarica* – Red-collared Dove	v
388. *S. turtur* – Turtle Dove	b
389. *S. orientalis* – Rufous Turtle Dove	b
390. *S. senegalensis* – Laughing Dove	b

391.	*Sphenurus sieboldi – Japanese Green Pigeon*	b
392.	*Hierococcyx fugax – Fugitive Hawk Cuckoo*	b
393.	*Cuculus micropterus – Indian Cuckoo*	b
394.	*C. canorus – Eurasian Cuckoo*	b
395.	*C. saturatus – Oriental Cuckoo*	b
396.	*C. poliocephalus – Little Cuckoo*	b
397.	*Clamator glandarius – Great Spotted Cuckoo*	v
398.	*Nyctea scandiaca – Snowy Owl*	b
399.	*Bubo bubo – Northern Eagle Owl*	b
400.	*Ketupa blakistoni – Blakiston's Fish Owl*	b
401.	*Asio otus – Long-eared Owl*	b
402.	*A. flammeus – Short-eared Owl*	b
403.	*Otus scops – Eurasian Scops Owl*	b
404.	*O. sunia – Indian Scops Owl*	b
405.	*O. brucei – Pallid Scops Owl*	b
406.	*O. bakkamoena – Collared Scops Owl*	b
407.	*Aegolius funereus – Tengmalm's Owl*	b
408.	*Athene noctua – Little Owl*	b
409.	*Glaucidium passerinum – Eurasian Pygmy Owl*	b
410.	*Surnia ulula – Hawk Owl*	b
411.	*Ninox scutulata – Brown Hawk Owl*	b
412.	*Strix aluco – Eurasian Tawny Owl*	b
413.	*S. uralensis – Ural Owl*	b
414.	*S. nebulosa – Great Grey Owl*	b
415.	*Tyto alba – Barn Owl*	b
416.	*Caprimulgus indicus – Jungle Nightjar*	b
417.	*C. europaeus – European Nightjar*	b
418.	*C. aegyptius – Egyptian Nightjar*	b
419.	*Hirundapus caudacuta – White-throated Needle-tailed Swift*	b
420.	*Apus affinis – House Swift*	b
421.	*A. apus – Eurasian Swift*	b
422.	*A. pacificus – Pacific Swift*	b
423.	*A. melba – Alpine Swift*	b
424.	*Selasphorus rufus – Rufous Hummingbird*	v
425.	*Coracias garrulus – European Roller*	b
426.	*Eurystomus orientalis – Eastern Broad-billed Roller*	b
427.	*Ceryle lugubris – Greater Pied Kingfisher*	b
428.	*C. rudis – Lesser Pied Kingfisher*	v
429.	*Halcyon smyrnensis – White-throated Kingfisher*	v
430.	*H. pileata – Black-capped Kingfisher*	b
431.	*H. coromanda – Ruddy Kingfisher*	v
432.	*Alcedo atthis – European Kingfisher*	b
433.	*Merops apiaster – European Bee-eater*	b
434.	*M. superciliosus – Blue-cheeked Bee-eater*	b

435. *Upupa epops – Hoopoe*　　　　　　　　　　　　b
436. *Jynx torquilla – Northern Wryneck*　　　　　　b
437. *Picus viridis – Green Woodpecker*　　　　　　　b
438. *P. squamatus – Scaly-bellied Woodpecker*　　　e
439. *P. canus – Grey-headed Woodpecker*　　　　　　b
440. *Dryocopus martius – Black Woodpecker*　　　　b
441. *Dendrocopos major – Great Spotted Woodpecker*　b
442. *D. leucopterus – White-winged Woodpecker*　　b
443. *D. syriacus – Syrian Woodpecker*　　　　　　　b
444. *D. medius – Middle Spotted Woodpecker*　　　　b
445. *D. leucotos – White-backed Woodpecker*　　　　b
446. *D. hyperythrus – Rufous-bellied Woodpecker*　　b
447. *D. minor – Lesser Spotted Woodpecker*　　　　　b
448. *D. canicapillus – Grey-headed Pygmy Woodpecker*　b
449. *D. kizuki – Japanese Pygmy Woodpecker*　　　　b
450. *Picoides tridactylus – Three-toed Woodpecker*　b
451. *Tachycineta bicolor – Tree Swallow*　　　　　　v
452. *Riparia riparia – Sand Martin*　　　　　　　　b
453. *R. paludicola – African Sand Martin*　　　　　b
454. *Ptyonoprogne rupestris – Crag Martin*　　　　　b
455. *Hirundo rustica – Barn Swallow*　　　　　　　　b
456. *H. smithii – Needle-tailed Swallow*　　　　　　b
457. *H. daurica – Red-rumped Swallow*　　　　　　　b
458. *Petrochelidon pyrrhonota – American Cliff Swallow*　v
459. *Delichon urbica – House Martin*　　　　　　　　b
460. *D. dasypus – Eastern House Martin*　　　　　　b
461. *Ammomanes deserti – Desert Lark*　　　　　　　b
462. *Galerida cristata – Crested Lark*　　　　　　　b
463. *Calandrella cinerea – Short-toed Lark*　　　　b
464. *C. acutirostris – Hume's Short-toed Lark*　　　b
465. *C. rufescens – Lesser Short-toed Lark*　　　　b
466. *C. cheleensis – Mongolian Short-toed Lark*　　b
467. *Melanocorypha calandra – Calandra Lark*　　　b
468. *M. bimaculata – Bimaculated Lark*　　　　　　b
469. *M. mongolica – Mongolian Lark*　　　　　　　　b
470. *M. leucoptera – White-winged Lark*　　　　　　b
471. *M. yeltonensis – Black Lark*　　　　　　　　　b
472. *Eremophila alpestris – Shore Lark*　　　　　　b
473. *Lullula arborea – Wood Lark*　　　　　　　　　b
474. *Alauda arvensis – Skylark*　　　　　　　　　　b
475. *A. japonica – Japanese Skylark*　　　　　　　　b
476. *A. gulgula – Oriental Skylark*　　　　　　　　b
477. *Anthus richardii – Richard's Pipit*　　　　　　b
478. *A. godlewskii – Blyth's Pipit*　　　　　　　　　b

479.	*A. campestris – Tawny Pipit*	b
480.	*A. trivialis – Tree Pipit*	b
481.	*A. hodgsoni – Olive-backed Pipit*	b
482.	*A. gustavi – Pechora Pipit*	b
483.	*A. pratensis – Meadow Pipit*	b
484.	*A. cervinus – Red-throated Pipit*	b
485.	*A. rubescens – Buff-bellied Pipit*	b
486.	*A. spinoletta – Water Pipit*	b
487.	*Motacilla flava – Yellow Wagtail*	b
488.	*M. felgedd – Black-headed Wagtail*	b
489.	*M. taivana*	b
490.	*M. lutea*	b
491.	*M. citreola – Citrine Wagtail*	b
492.	*M. cinerea – Grey Wagtail*	b
493.	*M. alba – White Wagtail*	b
494.	*M. lugens – Kamchatka Wagtail*	b
495.	*M. personata – Masked Wagtail*	b
496.	*M. grandis – Japanese Pied Wagtail*	v
497.	*Dendronanthus indicus – Forest Wagtail*	b
498.	*Lanius bucephalus – Bull-headed Shrike*	b
499.	*L. tigrinus – Tiger Shrike*	b
500.	*L. cristatus – Brown Shrike*	b
501.	*L. isabellinus – Isabelline Shrike*	b
502.	*L. collurio – Red-backed Shrike*	b
503.	*L. vittatus – Bay-backed Shrike*	b
504.	*L. nubicus – Masked Shrike*	v
505.	*L. senator – Woodchat Shrike*	b
506.	*L. schach – Long-tailed Shrike*	b
507.	*L. minor – Lesser Grey Shrike*	b
508.	*L. excubitor – Great Grey Shrike*	b
509.	*L. sphenocercus – Chinese Great Grey Shrike*	b
510.	*Oriolus oriolus – Golden Oriole*	b
511.	*O. chinensis – Black-naped Oriole*	b
512.	*Sturnia sturnina – Daurian Starling*	b
513.	*S. sinensis – Chinese Starling*	v
514.	*S. philippensis – Violet-backed Starling*	b
515.	*Sturnus cineraceus – Grey Starling*	b
516.	*S. podagorum – Black-headed Starling*	b?
517.	*S. vulgaris – European Starling*	b
518.	*S. roseus – Rose-coloured Starling*	b
519.	*Acridotheres tristis – Indian Myna*	b
520.	*Perisoreus infaustus – Siberian Jay*	b
521.	*Garrulus glandarius – Eurasian Jay*	b
522.	*Cyanopica cyana – Azure-winged Magpie*	b

523. *Pica pica* – *Black-billed Magpie*   b
524. *Podoces hendersoni* – *Henderson's Ground Jay*   b?
525. *P. panderi* – *Pander's Ground Jay*   b
526. *Nucifraga caryocatactes* – *Spotted Nutcracker*   b
527. *Pyrrhocorax pyrrhocorax* – *Red-billed Chough*   b
528. *P. graculus* – *Alpine Chough*   b
529. *Corvus monedula* – *Western Jackdaw*   b
530. *C. dauuricus* – *Daurian Jackdaw*   b
531. *C. frugilegus* – *Rook*   b
532. *C. macrorhynchos* – *Jungle Crow*   b
533. *C. corone* – *Carrion Crow*   b
534. *C. cornix* – *Hooded Crow*   b
535. *C. ruficollis* – *Desert Raven*   b
536. *C. corax* – *Common Raven*   b
537. *Bombycilla garrulus* – *Bohemian Waxwing*   b
538. *B. japonica* – *Japanese Waxwing*   b
539. *Hypocolius ampelinus* – *Grey Hypocolius*   b
540. *Pericrocotus divaricatus* – *Ashy Minivet*   b
541. *Mycroscelis amaurotis* – *Chestnut-eared Bulbul*   b
542. *Pycnonotus leucogenys* – *White-cheeked Bulbul*   v
543. *Cinclus cinclus* – *White-throated Dipper*   b
544. *C. pallasi* – *Brown Dipper*   b
545. *Troglodytes troglodytes* – *Northern Wren*   b
546. *Prunella collaris* – *Alpine Accentor*   b
547. *P. himalayana* – *Himalayan Accentor*   b
548. *P. fulvescens* – *Brown Accentor*   b
549. *P. ocularis* – *Radde's Accentor*   b
550. *P. montanella* – *Siberian Accentor*   b
551. *P. atrogullaris* – *Black-throated Accentor*   b
552. *P. modularis* – *Dunnock*   b
553. *P. rubida* – *Japanese Accentor*   b
554. *Urosphena squameiceps* – *Short-tailed Bush Warbler*   b
555. *Horeites diphone* – *Japanese Bush Warbler*   b
556. *Cettia cetti* – *Cetti's Warbler*   b
557. *Bradypterus thoracicus* – *Spotted Bush Warbler*   b
558. *B. major* – *Large-billed Bush Warbler*   v
559. *B. tacsanowskius* – *Chinese Bush Warbler*   b
560. *Megalurus pryeri* – *Japanese Marsh Warbler*   b
561. *Locustella fasciolata* – *Gray's Grasshopper Warbler*   b
562. *L. amnicola* – *Stepanyan's Grasshopper Warbler*   b
563. *L. luscinioides* – *Savi's Warbler*   b
564. *L. fluviatilis* – *River Warbler*   b
565. *L. certhiola* – *Pallas's Grasshopper Warbler*   b
566. *L. ochotensis* – *Middendorff's Grasshopper Warbler*   b

567. *L. pleskei* – *Styan's Grasshopper Warbler*   b
568. *L. naevia* – *Grasshopper Warbler*   b
569. *L. lanceolata* – *Lanceolated Warbler*   b
570. *Lusciniola melanopogon* – *Moustached Warbler*   b
571. *Acrocephalus paludicola* – *Acquatic Warbler*   b
572. *A. schoenobaenus* – *Sedge Warbler*   b
573. *A. bistrigiceps* – *Black-browed Reed Warbler*   b
574. *A. agricola* – *Paddyfield Warbler*   b
575. *A. dumetorum* – *Blyth's Reed Warbler*   b
576. *A. palustris* – *Marsh Warbler*   b
577. *A. scirpaceus* – *Reed Warbler*   b
578. *A. stentoreus* – *Clamourous Reed Warbler*   b
579. *A. arundinaceus* – *Great Reed Warbler*   b
580. *Phragmaticola aedon* – *Thick-billed Warbler*   b
581. *Hippolais icterina* – *Icterine Warbler*   b
582. *H. caligata* – *Booted Warbler*   b
583. *H. rama* – *Southern Booted Warbler*   b
584. *H. pallida* – *Olivaceous Warbler*   b
585. *H. languida* – *Upcher's Warbler*   b
586. *H. olivetorum* – *Olive-tree Warbler*   v
587. *Sylvia nisoria* – *Barred Warbler*   b
588. *S. hortensis* – *Orphean Warbler*   b
589. *S. atricapilla* – *Blackcap*   b
590. *S. borin* – *Garden Warbler*   b
591. *S. communis* – *Whitethroat*   b
592. *S. curruca* – *Lesser Whitethroat*   b
593. *S. althaea* – *Hume's Lesser Whitethroat*   b
594. *S. mystacea* – *Ménétrie's Warbler*   b
595. *Sylvia cantillans* – *Subalpine Warbler*   b?
596. *S. nana* – *Desert Warbler*   b
597. *Phylloscopus trochilus* – *Willow Warbler*   b
598. *P. collybita* – *Chiffchaff*   b
599. *P. lorenzii* – *Mountain Chiffchaff*   b
600. *P. neglectus* – *Plain Willow Warbler*   b
601. *P. bonelli* – *Bonelli's Warbler*   v
602. *P. sibilatrix* – *Wood Warbler*   b
603. *P. borealis* – *Arctic Warbler*   b
604. *P. trochiloides* – *Greenish Warbler*   b
605. *P. nitidus* – *Green Warbler*   b
606. *P. tenellipes* – *Pale-legged Leaf Warbler*   b
607. *P. occipitalis* – *Large Crowned Willow Warbler*   b
608. *P. coronatus* – *Crowned Leaf Warbler*   b
609. *P. inornatus* – *Yellow-browed Warbler*   b
610. *P. subviridis* – *Brooks's Willow Warbler*   v

611. *P. proregulus* – *Pallas's Leaf Warbler*   b
612. *P. fuscatus* – *Dusky Warbler*   b
613. *P. griseolus* – *Sulphur-bellied Warbler*   b
614. *P. schwarzii* – *Radde's Bush Warbler*   b
615. *Scotocerca inquieta* – *Streaked Scrub Warbler*   b
616. *Regulus regulus* – *Goldcrest*   b
617. *R. ignicapillus* – *Firecrest*   b
618. *R. calendula* – *Ruby-crowned Kinglet*   v
619. *Leptopoecile sophiae* – *Severtzov's Tit Warbler*   b
620. *Dicrurus macrocercus* – *Black Drongo*   v
621. *D. hottentotus* – *Hair-crested Drongo*   v
622. *Terpsiphone atrocaudata* – *Black Paradise Flycatcher*   v
623. *T. paradisi* – *Asiatic Paradise Flycatcher*   b
624. *Ficedula hypoleuca* – *Pied Flycatcher*   b
625. *F. albicollis* – *White-collared Flycatcher*   b
626. *F. zanthopygia* – *Yellow-rumped Flycatcher*   b
627. *F. narcissina* – *Narcissus Flycatcher*   b
628. *F. mugimaki* – *Mugimaki Flycatcher*   b
629. *F. parva* – *Red-breasted Flycatcher*   b
630. *Cyanoptila cyanomelana* – *Blue-and-White Flycatcher*   b
631. *Muscicapa striata* – *Spotted Flycatcher*   b
632. *M. sibirica* – *Siberian Flycatcher*   b
633. *M. griseisticta* – *Grey-streaked Flycatcher*   b
634. *M. latirostris* – *Brown Flycatcher*   b
635. *M. ruficauda* – *Rufous-tailed Flycatcher*   b
636. *Saxicola rubetra* – *Whinchat*   b
637. *S. torquata* – *Stonechat*   b
638. *S. insignis* – *Hodgson's Bushchat*   b
639. *S. caprata* – *Pied Stonechat*   b
640. *Oenanthe oenanthe* – *Northern Wheatear*   b
641. *O. pleschanka* – *Pied Wheatear*   b
642. *O. hispanica* – *Black-eared Wheatear*   b
643. *O. picata* – *Variable Wheatear*   b
644. *O. finschii* – *Finsch's Wheatear*   b
645. *O. deserti* – *Desert Wheatear*   b
646. *O. xanthoprymna* – *Red-tailed Wheatear*   b
647. *O. isabellina* – *Isabelline Wheatear*   b
648. *Cercotrichas galactotes* – *Rufous Bush Chat*   b
649. *Monticola saxatilis* – *Rock Thrush*   b
650. *M. solitarius* – *Blue Rock Thrush*   b
651. *Petrophila gularis* – *White-throated Rock Thrush*   b
652. *Phoenicurus caeruleocephalus* – *Blue-headed Redstart*   b
653. *P. phoenicurus* – *Common Redstart*   b
654. *P. ochruros* – *Black Redstart*   b

655. *P. erythronotus – Eversmann's Redstart*   b
656. *P. auroreus – Daurian Redstart*   b
657. *P. erythrogaster – Güldenstädt's Redstart*   b
658. *Chaimarrornis leucocephalus – River Chat*   b
659. *Rhyacornis fuliginosus – Plumbeous Water Redstart*   v
660. *Erithacus rubecula – European Robin*   b
661. *Luscinia akahige – Japanese Robin*   b
662. *L. megarhynchos – Nightingale*   b
663. *L. luscinia – Thrush Nightingale*   b
664. *L. calliope – Siberian Rubythroat*   b
665. *L. pectoralis – Himalayan Rubythroat*   b
666. *L. svecica – Bluethroat*   b
667. *L. cyane – Siberian Blue Robin*   b
668. *L. sibilans – Swinhoe's Robin*   b
669. *Tarsiger cyanurus – Red-flanked Bluetail*   b
670. *Irania gutturalis – White-throated Robin*   b
671. *Catharus minimus Grey-cheeked Thrush*   b
672. *C. ustulatus – Swainson's Thrush*   v
673. *Ixoreus naevius – Varied Thrush*   v
674. *Turdus pallidus – Pale Thrush*   b
675. *T. chrysolaus – Red-billed Thrush*   b
676. *T. obscurus – Eye-browed Thrush*   b
677. *T. hortulorum – Grey-backed Thrush*   b
678. *T. ruficollis – Red-throated Thrush*   b
679. *T. atrogullaris – Black-throated Thrush*   b
680. *T. naumanni – Naumann's Thrush*   b
681. *T. eunomus – Dusky Thrush*   b
682. *T. pilaris – Fieldfare*   b
683. *T. torquatus – Ring Ouzel*   b
684. *T. merula – Blackbird*   b
685. *T. cardis – Japanese Grey Thrush*   v
686. *T. iliacus – Redwing*   b
687. *T. philomelos – Song Thrush*   b
688. *T. viscivorus – Mistle Thrush*   b
689. *Zoothera sibirica – Siberian Ground Thrush*   b
690. *Z. dauma – White's Thrush*   b
691. *Myiophoneus caeruleus – Blue Whistling Thrush*   b
692. *Microcichla scouleri – Little Forktail*   b
693. *Garrulax lineatus – Himalayan Streaked Laughing Thrush*   b
694. *Paradoxornis polivanovi – Polivanov's Parrotbill*   b
695. *Suthora webbiana – Vinous-throated Parrotbill*   b
696. *Panurus biarmicus – Bearded Tit*   b
697. *Aegithalos caudatus – Long-tailed Tit*   b
698. *Remiz pendulinus – Penduline Tit*   b

699.	R. *macronyx* – Reed Penduline Tit	b
700.	Parus *palustris* – Marsh Tit	b
701.	P. *montanus* – Willow Tit	b
702.	P. *songarus* – Songar Tit	b
703.	P. *lugubris* – Sombre Tit	b
704.	P. *hyrcanus* – Iranian Sombre Tit	b
705.	P. *cinctus* – Siberian Tit	b
706.	P. *cristatus* – Crested Tit	b
707.	P. *ater* – Coal Tit	b
708.	P. *rufonuchalis* – Rufous-naped Tit	b
709.	P. *varius* – Varied Tit	b
710.	P. *caeruleus* – Blue Tit	b
711.	P. *flavipectus* – Yellow-breasted Azure Tit	b
712.	P. *cyanus* – Azure Tit	b
713.	P. *major* – Great Tit	b
714.	P. *minor*	b
715.	P. *cinereus* – Grey Tit	b
716.	P. *bokharensis* – Turkestan Tit	b
717.	Sitta *europaea* – Eurasian Nuthatch	b
718.	S. *neumayer* – Rock Nuthatch	b
719.	S. *tephronota* – Eastern Rock Nuthatch	b
720.	S. *villosa* – Chinese Nuthatch	b
721.	S. *kruperi* – Krüper's Nuthatch	b
722.	Tichodroma *muraria* – Wallcreeper	b
723.	Certhia *familiaris* – Common Treecreeper	b
724.	C. *brachydactyla* – Short-toed Treecreeper	b
725.	C. *himalayana* – Himalayan Treecreeper	b
726.	Zosterops *japonica* – Japanese White-eye	b
727.	Z. *erythropleura* – Chestnut-flanked White-eye	b
728.	Dendroica *coronata* – Yellow Rumped Warbler	v
729.	Seiurus *novoeboracensis* – Northern Waterthrush	v
730.	Passer *domesticus* – House Sparrow	b
731.	P. *indicus* – Indian Sparrow	b
732.	P. *hispaniolensis* – Spanish Sparrow	b
733.	P. *ammodendri* – Saxaul Sparrow	b
734.	P. *montanus* – Tree Sparrow	b
735.	P. *rutilans* – Cinnamon Sparrow	b
736.	P. *simplex* – Desert Sparrow	b
737.	Petronia *petronia* – Streaked Rock Sparrow	b
738.	P. *brachydactyla* – Pale Rock Sparrow	b?
739.	Montifringilla *nivalis* – White-winged Snow Finch	b
740.	M. *theresae* – Meinertzhagen's Snow Finch	v
741.	Pyrgilauda *davidiana* – Pierre David's Sparrow	b
742.	Euphagus *carolinus* – Rusty Blackbird	v

743.	*Fringilla coelebs – Chaffinch*	b
744.	*F. montifringilla – Brambling*	b
745.	*Serinus pusillus – Red-fronted Serin*	b
746.	*S. serinus – European Serin*	b
747.	*Chloris chloris – Western Greenfinch*	b
748.	*C. sinica – Chinese Greenfinch*	b
749.	*Spinus spinus – Siskin*	b
750.	*Carduelis carduelis – European Goldfinch*	b
751.	*C. caniceps – Grey-headed Goldfinch*	b
752.	*Acanthis cannabina – Linnet*	b
753.	*A. flavirostris – Twite*	b
754.	*A. flammea – Redpoll*	b
755.	*A. hornemanni – Arctic Redpoll*	b
756.	*Leucosticte nemoricola – Hodgson's Rosy Finch*	b
757.	*L. brandtii – Brandt's Rosy Finch*	b
758.	*L. arctoa – Rosy Finch*	b
759.	*L. tephrocotis – American Rosy Finch*	b
760.	*Rhodopechys sanguinea – Crimson-winged Finch*	b
761.	*Bucanetes githagineus – Trumpeter Finch*	b
762.	*B. mongolicus – Mongolian Trumpeter Finch*	b
763.	*Rhodospiza obsoleta – Black-billed Desert Finch*	b
764.	*Carpodacus erythrinus – Scarlet Rosefinch*	b
765.	*C. roseus – Pallas's Rosefinch*	b
766.	*C. rhodochlamys – Red-mantled Rosefinch*	b
767.	*C. grandis – Himalayan Red-mantled Rosefinch*	b
768.	*C. rubicilla – Great Rosefinch*	b
769.	*Pyrrospiza punicea – Red-breasted Rosefinch*	b
770.	*Uragus sibiricus – Long-tailed Rosefinch*	b
771.	*Pinicola enucleator – Pine Grosbeak*	b
772.	*Loxia pytyopsittacus – Parrot Crossbill*	b
773.	*L. curvirostra – Red Crossbill*	b
774.	*L. leucoptera – White-winged Crossbill*	b
775.	*Pyrrhula pyrrhula – Northern Bullfinch*	b
776.	*P. griseiventris*	b
777.	*P. cineracea – Grey Bullfinch*	b
778.	*Eophona migratoria – Chinese Grosbeak*	b
779.	*E. personata – Japanese Grosbeak*	b
780.	*Coccothraustes coccothraustes – Hawfinch*	b
781.	*Mycerobas carnipes – White-winged Grosbeak*	b
782.	*Paserella iliaca – Fox Sparrow*	v
783.	*Zonotrichia atriacapilla – Golden-crowned Sparrow*	v
784.	*Z. leucophrys – White-crowned Sparrow*	v
785.	*Passerculus sandwichensis – Savannah Sparrow*	b
786.	*Spizella arborea – American Tree Sparrow*	v

787. *Junco hyemalis – Dark-eyed Junco*   v
788. *Emberiza calandra – Corn Bunting*   b
789. *E. variabilis – Japanese Grey Bunting*   b
790. *E. citrinella – Yellowhammer*   b
791. *E. leucocephala – Pine Bunting*   b
792. *E. cirlus – Cirl Bunting*   v
793. *E. stewarti – White-capped Bunting*   b
794. *E. cia – Rock Bunting*   b
795. *E. godlewskii – Godlewski's Bunting*   b
796. *E. cioides – Long-tailed Bunting*   b
797. *E. jankowskii – Jankowski's Bunting*   b
798. *E. fucata – Grey-hooded Bunting*   b
799. *E. schoeniclus – Reed Bunting*   b
800. *E. pallasi – Pallas's Bunting*   b
801. *E. yessoensis – Japanese Reed Bunting*   b
802. *E. elegans – Yellow-throated Bunting*   b
803. *E. chrysophrys – Yellow-browed Bunting*   b
804. *E. tristrami – Tristram's Bunting*   b
805. *E. rustica – Rustic Bunting*   b
806. *E. pusilla – Little Bunting*   b
807. *E. spodocephala – Black-faced Bunting*   b
808. *E. aureola – Yellow-breasted Bunting*   b
809. *E. rutila – Chestnut Bunting*   b
810. *E. hortulana – Ortolan Bunting*   b
811. *E. buchanani – Grey-necked Bunting*   b
812 . *E. caesia – Cretzschmar's Bunting*   v
813. *E. melanocephala – Black-headed Bunting*   b
814. *E. bruniceps – Red-headed Bunting*   b
815. *Calcarius lapponicus – Lapland Bunting*   b
816. *Plectrophenax nivalis – Snow Bunting*   b

BIBLIOGRAPHY

Bannikov, A. G (1969) *Nature Reserves of the USSR*. (In English). Israel Program for Scientific Translations, Jerusalem. (Originally published in Russian, 1966, by Mysl', Moscow, who have also published, in 1974, a 2nd, revised edition).

Borodin, A. M. (1984-5) *Krasnaya Kniga SSSR 1-2* (Red Data Book of USSR Vols. 1-2). (In Russian.) Second revised and enlarged edition. Lesnaya promyshlennost', Moscow

Borodin, A. M. & Syroechkovsiy, E. E. (Eds.) (1983) *Zapovedniki SSSR Spravochnik*. (Nature Reserves of the USSR. A Guide.) (In Russian.) Lesnaya promyshlennost', Moscow

Delin, H. & Svensson, L. (1988) *Photographic Guide to the Birds of Britain & Europe*. (In English). Hamlyn, London

Dementiev, G. P. & Gladkov, N.A. (1966-70) *The Birds of the Soviet Union*. In 6 vols. (In English.) Israel Program for Scientific Translations, Jerusalem. (Originally published in Russian, 1951-4, by Sovetskaya Nauka.)

Dolgushin, I. A., Korelov, M. N., Kuz'mina, M. A. *et al* (1960-74) *Pitsy Kazakhstana* (The Birds of Kazakhstan). (In Russian.) In 5 vols. Nauka Kazakh SSr, Alma Ata, Kazakhstan

Durrell, G. & Durrell, L. (1986) *Durrell in Russia*. (In English.) Macdonald, London

Flint, V.E., Boehme, R.L., Kostin, Y.V. & Kuznetsov, A. A. (1984) *A Field Guide to Birds of the USSR*. (In English.) Princeton University Press, Princeton, N.J., USA. (Originally published in Russian, 1968, Mysl', Moscow

Ilychev, V.D. & Flint, V. E. (Eds.) (1982) *Plitsy SSSR 1* (The birds of the USSR, Vol. 1); 12 vols. are planned; Vols 2 & 3 have also been published. (In Russian.) Nauka, Moscow

Knystautas, A. (1987) *The Natural History of the USSR*. (In English.) Century, London

Knystautas, A. (1987) *Nature of the Soviet Union*, Mokslas Publishers, Vilnius, Lithuania

Knystautas, A. & Ivashenko, A. (1987) *Aksu-Dzabagly*. On the Oldest Nature Reserve in Kazakhstan, Kainar, Alma-Ata, Kazakhstan

Knystautas, A. & Liutkus, A. (1982) *In the World of Birds*. (In Lithuanian, Russian & English.) Mokslas Publishers, Vilnius, Lithuania

Knystautas, A. & Shibnev, Yu. (1987) *Die Vogelwelt Ussuriens* (The Bird World of Ussuriland). (In German.) Paul Parey Verlag, Hamburg und Berlin, Germany

Kumari, E. (1981) *An Ornithological Journey through the Estonian SSR*. (In English.) Valgus, Tallinn, Estonia

Kumari, E. Maemets, A. & Renno, O. (1974) *Estonian Wetlands and their Life*. (In English). Valgus, Tallinn, Estonia

Perrins, C. (Consultant in Chief) (1990) *The Illustrated Encyclopaedia of Birds*. (In English.) Headline, London

Pride, P. R. (1972) *Conservation in the Soviet Union*. (In English). Cambridge University Press, Cambridge

Pukinski, J. (1983). *In der Ussuri-Taiga*. (In the Ussuri Taiga.) (In German: a translation of the original 1975 Russian title Po Taezhnoy reke Bikin - along the Bikin, River of the Taiga.) VEB F. A Brockhaus Verlag, Leipzig, Germany and Progress Publsihers, Moscow

Pukinskiy, Yu. B. (1984) *Pitsy Ussuriyskoy Taygi* (The Birds of the Ussuri Taiga). (In Russian.) Khabarovsk Book Publishers, Khabarovsk

Pukinskiy, Yu. B. (1985) *Bird Sounds of the Ussuri Taiga*: Melodiya 92 46559 009. (In Russian.) A 17cm 33.3 r.p.m mono disc, designed to accompany Pukinskiy's 1984 book (see above). Melodiya, Moscow

St. George, G. (1974). *Soviet Deserts & Mountains* (The World's Wild Place series. (In English.) Time-Life Books, Amsterdam

Stepanyan, L. S. (1975-8) *Sostav i Raspredelenie Ptits Fauny SSSR* (Composition and Distribution of the USSR's Bird Fauna.) In 2 vols. (In Russian.) Nauka, Moscow

Stepanyan, L. S. (1990) *Survey of the ornithological fauna of the USSR*. (In Russian.) Nauka, Moscow

Vorobiev, K. A. (1963) *Ptitsy Yakutii* (The Birds of Yakutiya). (In Russian.) Nauka, Moscow

INDEX